Electrical Engineering Probability

Electrical Engineering Probability

Richard H. Williams, Sc. D.
University of New Mexico

WEST PUBLISHING COMPANY

St. Paul ◆ New York ◆ Los Angeles ◆ San Francisco

Copyeditor	Loretta Palagi
Interior Design	Katherine Townes
Artwork	Scientific Illustrators
Composition	Progressive Typographers, Inc.

Copyright ©1991　By West Publishing Company
50 W. Kellogg Boulevard
P.O. Box 64526
St. Paul, MN 55164-0526

Library of Congress Cataloging-in-Publication Data

Williams, Richard H., 1931–
Electrical engineering probability / Richard H. Williams.
　　p.　cm.
Includes bibliographical references and index.
ISBN 0-314-79980-X
　　1. Electric engineering—Mathematics.　　2. Probabilities.
3. Stochastic processes.　　I. Title.
TX153.W57　　1991
621.3—dc20　　　　　　90-13111
　　　　　　　　　　CIP　∞

This textbook is dedicated to the memory of Richard Jr.

Contents

APPENDICES

INDEX   381

Preface

◆ ◆

Probabilistic methods have steadily increased in their importance for electrical engineering applications. Consider, for example, the importance of probability theory for communication systems, random signal analysis, characterization of noise, spectral estimation, physical electronics, queuing processes, statistics, robust design, reliability, quality in manufacturing, and decision processes. After teaching probabilistic methods a few times to electrical engineering students, I decided that the available textbooks fell short in making today's electrical engineering applications meaningful and accessible to undergraduate students. Discussing this conclusion with other electrical engineers, both in industry and in academe, I found that many were in strong agreement. I therefore began to write "supplements" to fill in the perceived gaps in the existing textbooks. After several years of this, the "supplements" became substantial, and this textbook began to come together.

The major improvements in this textbook, as far as an undergraduate electrical engineering student is concerned, are (a) the integration of computer examples and exercises within the entire text, (b) the chapter on reliability, and (c) the chapter on counting processes (which deals with the Poisson random variable).

The level at which this textbook is written is also one of its strengths. Most undergraduate students want and need physical intuition and applications ahead of rigor when they are being introduced to probabilistic methods. This textbook therefore stresses physical intuition and applications. Mathematical developments are done carefully, but rigor *per se* is not stressed.

Prerequisites

Electrical Engineering Probability is a textbook designed for contemporary undergraduate electrical engineering students. It may, of course, be well used by others, such as computer engineers, who share similar technical prerequisites: calculus through several variables, ordinary differential equations, the linear operational transforms of Fourier or Laplace, and the ability to program a digital computer for technical work in FORTRAN, C, Pascal, or BASIC. Students are expected to be familiar with the Dirac-delta function as it is typically employed in an introductory circuits course. In Chapter 8, students are expected to be knowledgeable about frequency domain descriptions of signals and systems.

How To Use This Book

There is more material in this textbook than can be covered in one semester. Instructors therefore have options as they match their institutional requirements to the forthcoming changes in electrical engineering practice.

A traditional course in probabilistic methods would use Chapters 2, 3, 4, and 8 along with a part of Chapter 5. A glance at the topics in the Contents shows that Chapters 2, 3, and 4, deal with essential probabilistic concepts and methods ranging from the axioms through multiple random variables. In any case, these three chapters must be the core material in *any* probabilistic methods course for electrical engineers. (The essential portion of Chapter 5 that was mentioned brings in the binomial and the Poisson discrete random variables.) Chapter 8 describes wide-sense stationary random processes, and directly supports signal processing and communication theory.

The last four chapters, Chapters 5, 6, 7, and 8, are independent and may be taken in any order. Also, each of the last four chapters could take approximately five semester-weeks if used fully.

Descriptive Statistics

Students coming into a probability course have a great variability in their skills for handling even a modest amount of data. The quality of the course is increased if this variability is reduced. To do this, I suggest starting the semester with approximately one week of lectures from Chapter 1, including the topics of sample mean, sample variance, sample correlation, frequency plots, and cumulative frequency plots. Students should be encouraged to write their own computer code for these descriptive statistics. Time spent here is repaid later in a richer student comprehension when computer-based exercises are used to illustrate specific models of random behavior.

The Counting Processes

The material in Chapter 5 on binomial, Poisson and (to a lesser extent) hypergeometric counting processes is essential for any modern electrical engineering undergraduate student. The only question is where to draw the line if the entire chapter cannot be covered. Continuity correction techniques, Section 5.4, is admittedly a numerical topic, but it reinforces the central limit theorem concept and the generality of the Gaussian random variable. Reviewers were quite mixed in their recommendations on whether to include queues, Section 5.5, in this textbook. After some debate, my editor, Michael Slaughter, and I decided that the variability of reviewer opinion suggested that times are changing, and that queues should be included in order to leave that option open to our electrical engineering colleagues. At the very least, when a student runs into some reference to "Little's formula", or the "M/M/1" notation, then the textbook may be a resource.

Statistical Estimation

The material in Chapter 6 was suggested by the many and increasing number of times an engineer runs into statistical confidence: confidence levels, confidence limits, and confidence intervals. In practice, engineers frequently make decisions based on "estimates." The major purpose of Chapter 6 is, therefore, to point out that an estimate without a statement of statistical confidence, i.e. without some description of its potential error, is not complete. What we do in Chapter 6 makes a reasonably tidy set of topics, and brings in the chi-square and Student's t random variables.

Reliability and Quality

A major issue facing undergraduate electrical engineering education today is the relation between design and manufacturing. Frequently, electrical engineering students feel that design and manufacturing are at arm's length from each other. Faculty leadership cannot let this dichotomy between design and manufacturing continue. This concern motivated the introductory comments on control charts and reliability in this textbook.

Process control charts are mentioned in two places in *Electrical Engineering Probability*. In Chapter 1, control charts for quantitative data are introduced in Section 1.6 as an application of sample statistics. In Section 5.6 control charts for attribute data are introduced as an application of the binomial counting process. Some instructors might enjoy introducing these techniques, and students then might become more aware of some powerful tools used in the engineering and fabrication of quality products.

There is a driving necessity to introduce "reliability" concurrently with "function" in modern electrical engineering design. Reliability must not be left as an afterthought to a design when it is supposedly done. This is true for high-tech VLSI chips, for competitive consumer products, for effective military systems, and so on to include all products and services used by any customer. Reliability is based directly on probability theory and therefore has a place in a course on probabilistic methods. Chapter 7 introduces three major areas in reliability: Section 7.2 — failure rates, Section 7.3 — system reliability, and Sections 7.4 through 7.6 — failure rate estimation techniques using Weibull and lognormal models.

Exercises

There is a wide variety of exercises at the end of each chapter in this textbook. In many cases an exercise is repeated three times with only some of its numbers changed. This may be helpful to instructors because they can use the exercises for three semesters before "the answer" repeats. Answers to selected exercises are given in Appendix H. An answer book is available for instructors.

Acknowledgments

I'm grateful to the many people who made a difference as work on this textbook progressed: the chair of the EECE Department at the University of New Mexico—first Russell H. Seacat, Jr. and now Nasir Ahmed; Jerry Soden at Sandia National Laboratories; Bert Kortegaard at Los Alamos National Laboratories; David Penasa at BPLW—Architects and Engineers, Inc.; and George Brown, M.D. at the Los Lunas Hospital and Training School. Thanks to Nancy Roth, my production editor, for her cheerful disposition as well as her quality work. I'm especially grateful to the several reviewers of this textbook, for having the benefit of their insight and wisdom:

Alan C. Bovik, University of Texas, Austin;

A. W. Drake, Massachusetts Institute of Technology;

Terrence L. Fine, Cornell University;

Firman D. King, University of South Florida;

Ditlev Monrad, University of Illinois, Urbana-Champaign;

Paul J. Nahin, University of New Hampshire;

James A. Ritcey, University of Washington;

John J. Shynk, University of California, Santa Barbara;

Venkatarana Krishnan, University of Lowell;

Guy Sohie, General Electric Corporate Research and Development

All these reviewers were helpful and challenging, but a special thank you goes to Alan Bovik.

I also have expressions of gratitude and appreciation to the following people: the innumerable students for their learning and their questions; Michael Slaughter, my editor, for helping me to be at the right place at the right time; Charles F. Hawkins, my colleague in the EECE Department, for friendship as well as first-rate mentoring; and Dorothy, my wife, along with Lynn, Lois, Mark, Paul, and Jon.

Richard H. Williams

Electrical Engineering Probability

1

Techniques for Summarizing and Simulating Data

• •

Those who have the habit of correctness and precision can do things by design; those who don't usually have to depend upon luck.

Richard Mitchell in *Less Than Words Can Say,* Little, Brown and Company, 1979

Introduction   In practice, engineers frequently have to arrange data containing random fluctuations into forms that are easier to analyze and interpret. The several topics within **descriptive statistics**[1-7] assist engineers in these "data reduction" tasks. Descriptive statistics also just happens to provide excellent insights on why probability theory is the way it is. As a foundation for a study of probability theory, we therefore include selected topics from descriptive statistics: the average (the sample mean), the variability (the sample variance), and the correlation between two sets of sample data. Graphical techniques (frequency and cumulative frequency plots) illustrating the variable nature of data are also presented. An example of the use of descriptive statistics in engineering practice is given at the end of this chapter in a very brief introduction to statistical process control.

The reader doesn't have to use a computer to understand the gist of this chapter. Facility in using a computer is, however, a virtue, and this chapter is written from that point of view. The reader is encouraged to obtain a computer algorithm that will generate a sequence of random numbers uniformly distributed between zero and one. We make frequent use of such an algorithm to simulate the variability of data. In particular, we illustrate a computer technique, called **Monte Carlo,** that is used for simulating the statistical variations in relatively complicated systems.

Section 1.1   THE SAMPLE MEAN, VARIANCE, AND STANDARD DEVIATION

• • • • •

Measured data, such as those in Table 1.1, are a sample taken from the larger collection (the **population**) of all possible data. If another set of independent measurements is obtained from the same population, different sample data will be recorded. Computations based on different sample data produce different results. When we speak of a **sample computation** we are giving recognition to this fact.

If there are n data in a sample, and if the data are ordered in some sequence x_i, $i = 1, 2, 3, \ldots, n$, which is usally the order in which the data were measured, then a **sample mean** $\bar{x}$ of the data x_i is computed using

$$\bar{x} = \frac{1}{n} \sum_{i=1}^{n} x_i \qquad (1.1a)$$

If there is no ambiguity regarding the index of summation in (1.1a), the following notation is useful:

$$\bar{x} = \frac{1}{n} \sum x_i \qquad (1.1b)$$

Example 1.1   Suppose that 100 integrated circuit chips are fabricated in an experimental process, and that each chip is analyzed to find the number of defects. Data for the $n = 100$ chips are given in Table 1.1. If these data are added, then $\sum x_i = 243$, and the sample average is $\bar{x} = 2.43$. If data are measured from a different group of 100 chips produced by the same process—i.e., from the same population—then, sample means slightly different from $\bar{x} = 2.43$ will be found.

• • • • •

The sample mean, which is the arithmetic average of the data in a specific sample, is interpreted as the point about which the sample data fluctuate. The difference d_i between a sample datum and the sample mean is called a **residual:**

$$d_i = x_i - \bar{x} \qquad (1.2)$$

Table 1.1 Number of Defects per Chip for 100 64k X 1 RAM Chips

1	7	1	0	5
0	0	2	4	2
0	4	8	2	2
0	2	3	1	0
0	1	4	1	0
3	5	4	0	3
14	0	1	3	2
1	4	4	0	1
7	2	0	4	3
4	4	0	1	0
2	1	3	3	0
8	5	3	2	8
5	3	5	1	1
1	3	2	5	3
4	1	0	0	2
2	0	1	0	4
0	1	0	3	1
0	4	10	0	0
2	4	6	1	1
0	0	2	1	9

If all the residuals are summed, the result is zero. This can be seen by modifying (1.1b):

$$\sum x_i - n\bar{x} = 0$$
$$\sum (x_i - \bar{x}) = 0$$
$$\sum d_i = 0 \tag{1.3}$$

The second statement in (1.3) uses the fact that if the constant $\bar{x}$ is summed n times the result is $n\bar{x}$. The last statement uses (1.2). It follows from (1.3) that the average of the residuals in (1.2) cannot be used as a measure of how much the data fluctuate about their sample mean. Also, (1.3) shows that only $n - 1$ of the residuals are independent: given $n - 1$ values of d_i, the last value can be calculated using (1.3).

If the residuals are squared before they are averaged, the result is not zero unless every residual is zero. This calculation is quite useful to us and is defined as the **sample variance**:

$$s_x^2 = \frac{1}{n-1}\sum (x_i - \bar{x})^2 \tag{1.4}$$

We choose $n - 1$ as the denominator of (1.4) because only $n - 1$ of the residuals in the sum (1.3) are independent. (Another reason is given in Section 6.4.)

Expanding the right side of (1.4):

$$\sum (x_i - \bar{x})^2 = \sum (x_i^2 - 2\bar{x}x_i + \bar{x}^2)$$
$$= \sum x_i^2 - 2\bar{x} \sum x_i + n\bar{x}^2$$

Using (1.1b), this becomes

$$\sum (x_i - \bar{x})^2 = \sum x_i^2 - \frac{2}{n}\left(\sum x_i\right)^2 + \frac{1}{n}\left(\sum x_i\right)^2$$

$$= \sum x_i^2 - \frac{1}{n}\left(\sum x_i\right)^2$$

Therefore, an alternative expression for the sample variance in (1.4) is

$$s_x^2 = \frac{n\sum x_i^2 - (\sum x_i)^2}{n(n-1)} \tag{1.5}$$

The sample variance is a measure of how far data fluctuate from their sample mean. Another measure is the positive square root of the variance called the **sample standard deviation,**

$$s_x = \sqrt{\frac{n\sum x_i^2 - (\sum x_i)^2}{n(n-1)}} \tag{1.6}$$

The sample standard deviation has the same dimensions (units) as the data.

Example 1.2   If the data for the $n = 100$ integrated circuit chips in Table 1.1 are examined, then $\Sigma x_i = 243$ and $\Sigma x_i^2 = 1245$. By using (1.5) and (1.6), we find that $s_x^2 = 6.61$ and the sample standard deviation is $s_x = 2.57$.

◆ ◆ ◆ ◆ ◆

The expressions for calculating the sample variance in (1.4) and (1.5) are mathematically equal. Computationally, however, each has an advantage and a disadvantage. The sample variance in (1.4) requires the data to be manipulated twice, once to calculate the sample mean, and then once again to calculate the sample variance. On the other hand, (1.5) requires the data to be manipulated only one time when both sums in (1.5) are calculated. This means that (1.5) is more attractive for use in a computer algorithm because one pass through the data will suffice. However, the expression in (1.5) is computationally unstable; its numerator may be the difference between two large numbers, and significant computational errors can occur. The sample variance in (1.4) does not have this computational instability.

The sample mean and standard deviation in measurements are related to accuracy and precision as follows. First, we assume that a measurement is an attempt to find the true value τ of some characteristic of interest. Next, we must admit that the true value τ, which we seek, is unknown and actually unknowable. However, we can conceptualize the errors in a measurement process with

$$\text{error} = x_i - \tau \tag{1.7}$$

where the values of x_i correspond to the n measurements. Note that the error is different from the residual (1.2): τ is unknown, but $\bar{x}$ is calculated from data. If the error (1.7) is averaged, we find the **systematic error:**

$$\text{systematic error} = \bar{x} - \tau \tag{1.8}$$

This is illustrated in Figure 1.1 on page 6: Measurements in (a) have less systematic error than those in (c). Similarly, measurements in (b) have less systematic error than those in (d).

The **precision** of a measurement describes how well sample data tend to agree with each other. **Imprecision,** on the other hand, describes the dispersion or variability of data. A sample standard deviation (or a "sample variance"), therefore, describes the imprecision of a measurement process. A small sample standard deviation characterizes good precision. This is also illustrated in Figure 1.1. Measurements in (a) are more precise than those in (b). Similarly, measurements in (c) are more precise than those in (d).

The **accuracy**[a] of a measurement process describes how close the measurement is to the truth τ. Therefore, accuracy includes both the concept of systematic error and precision. In Figure 1.1, the measurements in (a) are more accurate than the measurements in (c).

Section 1.2   THE SAMPLE COVARIANCE AND CORRELATION COEFFICIENT

◆ ◆ ◆ ◆ ◆

When random data occur in pairs (x_i, y_i) they are called **bivariate** data. Typically, when this happens, we want to find some relation between x and y, a relation that may not be obvious because of the fluctuations of the data. For example, in Figure 1.2 we plot the (x_i, y_i) data presented in Table 1.2. Examining the plot, we do not find any simple relation between x and y. In fact, with data such as these, perhaps the best we can do is to note a tendency for the data to occur in the vicinity of a straight line with a positive slope.

Suppose we specify a straight line

$$y = \alpha x + \beta \tag{1.9}$$

---

[a] Some writers equate accuracy with systematic error. We do not do that; we consider accuracy to be a broader term. Considerably more can be said on this subject, and we refer the interested reader to Eisenhart's treatise.[8]

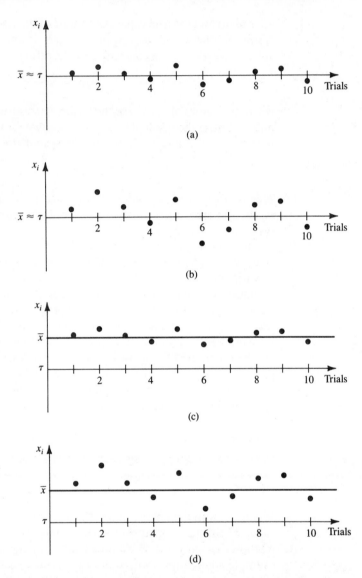

Figure 1.1   Illustrating systematic errors, precision, and accuracy in sequences of measured data.

and then try to determine the constants α and β such that the line best fits a collection of bivariate data. We need to agree on a criterion for a **best** fit; we use the definition of sample variance in (1.4) as a guide. Define ϵ as the average of the squared difference between a datum y_i and the linear approximation to the datum using (1.9):

$$\epsilon = \frac{1}{n-1} \sum (y_i - \alpha x_i - \beta)^2$$

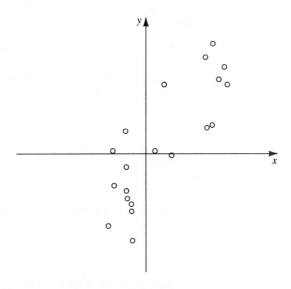

Figure 1.2   A plot of the 20 data (x_i, y_i) recorded in Table 1.2. The data x_i are inputs to a communication system at selected times t_i. Each datum y_i is supposed to be a specific response to input x_i. However, the relation between x_i and y_i is not straightforward because of some undesired and unspecified noise.

• •

Next, we solve for the constants α and β such that ϵ is made as small as possible. Differentiating ϵ with respect to α and setting the result equal to zero to find a minimum, we have

$$\frac{\partial \epsilon}{\partial \alpha} = \frac{-2}{n-1}\sum (y_i - \alpha x_i - \beta)x_i = 0$$

Table 1.2 $n = 20$ Measured Pairs of Data

i	x_i	y_i	i	x_i	y_i
1	−19.8	−18.9	11	−12.3	−7.9
2	15.6	−0.9	12	−12.8	13.5
3	44.8	44.5	13	40.7	17.2
4	−20.6	1.7	14	−9.2	−30.1
5	5.6	1.7	15	36.5	57.7
6	−12.3	−22.0	16	−23.4	−43.1
7	48.2	51.8	17	−9.0	−34.3
8	−11.7	−26.7	18	41.1	65.8
9	50.0	41.4	19	−8.5	−51.9
10	37.4	15.5	20	11.2	41.4

This simplifies to

$$\sum x_i^2 \alpha + \sum x_i \beta = \sum x_i y_i \qquad (1.10)$$

Differentiating ϵ with respect to β, and again setting the result equal to zero to find a minimum, we have

$$\frac{\partial \epsilon}{\partial \beta} = \frac{-2}{n-1} \sum (y_i - \alpha x_i - \beta) = 0$$

This simplifies to

$$\sum x_i \alpha + n\beta = \sum y_i \qquad (1.11)$$

The two simultaneous equations in (1.10) and (1.11) have a determinant of

$$\Delta = n \sum x_i^2 - \left(\sum x_i \right)^2$$

which, using (1.5), can be expressed as

$$\Delta = n(n-1)s_x^2$$

If the sample variance for x is not zero, then the determinant is not zero, and a solution for α and β can be found. Solving (1.10) and (1.11) simultaneously, we find

$$\alpha = \frac{n\Sigma x_i y_i - \Sigma x_i \Sigma y_i}{n(n-1)s_x^2}$$

$$\beta = \bar{y} - \alpha \bar{x}$$

where the sample means are defined by (1.1b).

Now, we define a **sample covariance** c_{xy}:

$$c_{xy} = \frac{1}{n-1} \sum (x_i - \bar{x})(y_i - \bar{y}) \qquad (1.12)$$

By expanding the product, it follows that an equivalent expression for the sample covariance is

$$c_{xy} = \frac{n\Sigma x_i y_i - \Sigma x_i \Sigma y_i}{n(n-1)} \qquad (1.13)$$

Therefore, using the sample covariance, the constant α can be expressed as

$$\alpha = c_{xy}/s_x^2$$

Then, if we combine the constants α and β with the equation for a straight line (1.9), we obtain

$$y = (c_{xy}/s_x^2)x + \bar{y} - (c_{xy}/s_x^2)\bar{x} \qquad (1.14)$$

The statistical technique we used to obtain (1.14) is called a **regression technique,** and the straight line in (1.14) is called a **regression line.**

Another expression for the regression line (1.14) is

$$(y - \bar{y}) = (c_{xy}/s_x^2)(x - \bar{x})$$

If we define a **sample correlation coefficient** r_{xy} to be

$$r_{xy} = c_{xy}/s_x s_y \tag{1.15}$$

then the regression line can be expressed in normalized form as

$$\frac{y - \bar{y}}{s_y} = r_{xy} \frac{x - \bar{x}}{s_x} \tag{1.16}$$

If $r_{xy} = 0$, the regression line vanishes, and we say that the sample bivariate data are **uncorrelated.** As another extreme case, assume that the data x_i and y_i are linearly related:

$$y_i = mx_i + b$$

We can then show that

$$\bar{y} = m\bar{x} + b \tag{1.17}$$

$$s_y^2 = \frac{1}{n-1} \sum (y_i - \bar{y})^2 = m^2 s_x^2 \tag{1.18}$$

$$c_{xy} = \frac{1}{n-1} \sum (x_i - \bar{x})(y_i - \bar{y}) = m s_x^2 \tag{1.19}$$

Using (1.18) and (1.19) in (1.15), we see in this case that the sample correlation coefficient is:

$$r_{xy} = m/\sqrt{m^2} = \pm 1$$

Its magnitude is unity, and its sign is the sign of m.

The sample correlation coefficient is useful for analyzing sample bivariate data. The magnitude of r_{xy} is bounded by zero and one. To demonstrate this, we start with the following inequality:

$$\frac{1}{n-1} \sum \left\{ \frac{x_i - \bar{x}}{s_x} \pm \frac{y_i - \bar{y}}{s_y} \right\}^2 \geq 0$$

While this inequality looks complicated, we can derive some useful results from it. These results are valid because, as the inequality says, the left side can never be negative, even when the square is expanded:

$$\frac{1}{n-1} \sum \left\{ \frac{(x_i - \bar{x})^2}{s_x^2} \pm 2 \frac{(x_i - \bar{x})(y_i - \bar{y})}{s_x s_y} + \frac{(y_i - \bar{y})^2}{s_y^2} \right\} \geq 0$$

Then, using (1.4) and (1.12),

$$1 \pm 2 \frac{c_{xy}}{s_x s_y} + 1 \geq 0$$

Finally, using (1.15),

$$0 \leq |r_{xy}| \leq 1 \qquad\qquad (1.20)$$

Here, **zero** means that the data are uncorrelated; **one** means a precisely linear correspondence exists between the data x_i and y_i. Magnitudes of the sample correlation coefficient that are between one and zero describe a **statistical relation** between x_i and y_i, by which we mean that the straight line (1.14) or (1.16) has significance **on the average.** We say that x_i and y_i are more correlated when $|r_{xy}|$ is larger (nearer one), and less correlated when it is smaller (nearer zero). A positive correlation occurs when a dependent variable is related with an independent variable **on the average** with a positive slope. A negative correlation means the same except that the slope of the average relation is negative. An extensive discussion of correlation is available in Spiegel's outline.[7]

Example 1.3   Referring again to the sampled communication data in Table 1.2, we calculate the following:

$$\sum x_i = 191.50 \qquad\qquad \sum x_i^2 = 15{,}512.31$$
$$\sum y_i = 116.40 \qquad\qquad \sum y_i^2 = 24{,}725.50$$
$$\sum x_i y_i = 15{,}991.56 \qquad\qquad n = 20$$

Therefore, for this example,

$$\bar{x} = 9.58 \qquad\qquad \bar{y} = 5.82$$
$$s_x^2 = 719.93 \qquad\qquad s_y^2 = 1265.69$$
$$c_{xy} = 783.00 \qquad\qquad r_{xy} = 0.82$$

Figure 1.3 shows the same bivariate data that are in Figure 1.2 but, in addition, we plot the regression line (1.14) determined by the data in this example. The sample bivariate data have a positive correlation $r_{xy} = 0.82 > 0$. The statistical techniques presented allow us to be quantitative and to say that the sample correlation coefficient for the communication data in Table 1.2 is $+0.82$.

◆ ◆ ◆ ◆ ◆

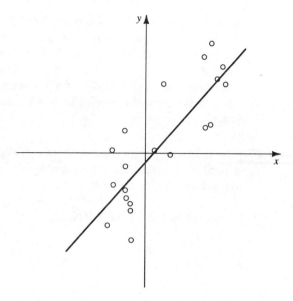

Figure 1.3   A plot of the 20 data (x_i, y_i) recorded in Table 1.2 with a plot of the data's regression line.

• •

Section 1.3   SIMULATING UNIFORM RANDOM NUMBERS

• • • • • •

As the examples in this section begin to show, we need to have available a **uniform random number** generator algorithm with the following features:

1. To start the algorithm, we need to give it an initializing integer I_0 called a **seed.**

2. Repeated use of the algorithm after initializing will result in a sequence of numbers:

$$x_1, x_2, x_3, \ldots$$

Different seeds will result in different sequences.

3. The numbers x_i will be uniformly (evenly) distributed between zero and one.

4. Any number x_i will be uncorrelated with any other number x_j, where $x_i \neq x_j$.

Practical algorithms merely approximate these criteria and therefore may be referred to as uniform **pseudorandom** number generators.

Almost every computing facility has available a uniform random number generator. Alternatively, in Appendix A, we give the code for a portable uni-

form random number generator. While this algorithm is written in FOR-
TRAN, its code may easily be translated into other computer languages. Frequently we ask the reader to use a uniform random number generator; when we
do, the reader may use the algorithm in Appendix A or some other algorithm.
Therefore, we use "URNG" (for Uniform Random Number Generator) to
refer to the algorithm preferred **by the reader;** we intend "URNG" to be a
generic designation.

Example 1.4   The following pseudocode describes an algorithm that operates a URNG for
a total of 10 times. The algorithm was coded and run; a listing of typical
output follows the algorithm.

```
Set the SEED for the URNG
For I = 1 to 10
    x = URNG
    Print I, x
Endfor
```

1	0.67379	6	0.08815
2	0.89466	7	0.26290
3	0.56994	8	0.63122
4	0.53041	9	0.84852
5	0.69002	10	0.22982

Notice that each datum in the output is a number between zero and one. As
a collection, the 10 numbers are fairly uniformly distributed between zero
and one. The seed used for this algorithm was an integer arbitrarily chosen,
such as the last four digits in a social security number. If the algorithm is
run again, the same 10 numbers will occur. If the FOR loop is extended from
10 to, say 20, then another 10 numbers uniformly distributed between zero
and one will be listed following the first 10 illustrated in this example. If a
different seed is selected, and the algorithm run again, an altogether different
sequence of ten numbers will appear, such as:

1	0.30228	6	0.10981
2	0.15177	7	0.55145
3	0.37086	8	0.70504
4	0.41086	9	0.80871
5	0.19908	10	0.80435

◆ ◆ ◆ ◆ ◆

Example 1.5   The output of URNG, which is uniformly distributed within the range of
zero to one may be changed to another range with a shifting and scaling
transformation. For example, if x is between zero and one then $2x - 1$
is between ± 1. We may use this transformation to produce numbers y that
are uniformly random between $\pm \pi$:

$$y = \pi(2x - 1)$$

Incorporating this into an algorithm,

> Set the SEED for the URNG
> For I = 1 to 10
>   x = URNG
>   y = $\pi(2x - 1)$
>   Print I, y
> Endfor

Output data y using the first 10 data x in Example 1.4 are:

1	1.09195	6	−2.58773
2	2.47972	7	−1.48974
3	0.43945	8	0.82448
4	0.19107	9	2.18982
5	1.19393	10	−1.69759

◆ ◆ ◆ ◆ ◆

Example 1.6 We can use a URNG to simulate the flip of an honest coin. If x is uniformly random between zero and one, then $x < 0.5$ will occur half of the time, and $x \geq 0.5$ will occur the other half of the time. We can generalize this if we compare x to other values. For example, the following If-Then-Else statement will produce "1" one-third of the time and "0" two-thirds of the time:

$$\text{If } x < 1/3 \text{ Then } y = 1 \text{ Else } y = 0$$

Incorporating this into an algorithm, the following pseudocode lists zeros and ones; the ones occur approximately one-third of the time, and the zeros occur approximately two-thirds of the time.

> Set the SEED for the URNG
> For I = 1 to 10
>   x = URNG
>   If x < 1/3 Then y = 1 Else y = 0
>   Print I, y
> Endfor

Output data using the first 10 data in Example 1.4 are:

1	0	6	1
2	0	7	1
3	0	8	0
4	0	9	0
5	0	10	1

◆ ◆ ◆ ◆ ◆

Example 1.7   The output of a URNG can be used to generate integers when we use the integer function. Here, $[y]$ is the largest integer less than or equal to y. For example, $[6.74] = 6$. Our URNG produces values uniformly random between zero and one, **but it cannot produce either exactly[b] zero or exactly one.** Therefore, if x is a number from our URNG, and if $y = [10x]$, then y will take integer values from zero through nine. If $y = [10x] + 1$, then y will take integer values from 1 through 10. The following pseudocode produces integers uniformly distributed between 1 and 10:

```
Set the SEED for the URNG
For I = 1 to 10
    x = URNG
    y = [10x] + 1
    Print I, y
Endfor
```

If x has the values of the first 10 data in Example 1.4, the output will be as follows:

1	7	6	1
2	9	7	3
3	6	8	7
4	6	9	9
5	7	10	3

◆ ◆ ◆ ◆ ◆

Section 1.4   FREQUENCY AND CUMULATIVE FREQUENCY

◆ ◆ ◆ ◆ ◆

Refer again to Table 1.1; the data are listed in the order in which they were recorded. As such, these data are difficult to interpret. To help characterize them, we calculated their sample mean and standard deviation in Examples 1.1 and 1.2. However, we can better interpret the data if we know the **frequency** at which they occur. Table 1.3 presents the same data as Table 1.1, but in Table 1.3, the data are listed according to their frequency of occurrence n_k. For example, we see that 26 of the chips had zero defects, 20 had exactly one defect,

---

[b] There are occasions in which we compute $\ln(x)$ or $\ln(1 - x)$ where x is obtained from URNG. Because x is not exactly zero or exactly one, we avoid the difficulty of asking a computer to produce $\ln(0)$. In this situation, the probabilities $P(x = 0)$ and $P(x = 1)$ are of negligible significance.

Table 1.3   A Summary of the Measured Data shown in Table 1.1

k	Data $\tilde{x}_k$	Frequency n_k	Cumulative Frequency N_k	$n_k\tilde{x}_k$	$n_k\tilde{x}_k^2$
1	0	26	26	0	0
2	1	20	46	20	20
3	2	14	60	28	56
4	3	12	72	36	108
5	4	13	85	52	208
6	5	6	91	30	150
7	6	1	92	6	36
8	7	2	94	14	98
9	8	3	97	24	192
10	9	1	98	9	81
11	10	1	99	10	100
12	11	0	99	0	0
13	12	0	99	0	0
14	13	0	99	0	0
15	14	1	100	14	196
				243	1245

14 had exactly two defects, etc. Also shown in Table 1.3 is N_k, the **cumulative frequency** of the data:

$$N_k = \sum_{i=1}^{k} n_i \tag{1.21}$$

Figure 1.4 shows plots of the frequency and the cumulative frequency in Table 1.3. The frequency plot—also known as a **histogram**—has traditionally been used to display data distributions. The cumulative frequency plot is an alternative way of presenting the data.

The index k in (1.21) varies from 1 to k_M, the maximum index useful with the frequency and cumulative frequency plots. The following equalities apply to the integer data in Table 1.3:

$$\sum_{i=1}^{n} x_i = \sum_{k=1}^{k_M} n_k\tilde{x}_k \tag{1.22}$$

$$\sum_{i=1}^{n} x_i^2 = \sum_{k=1}^{k_M} n_k\tilde{x}_k^2 \tag{1.23}$$

where we use the tilde, $\sim$, to denote the value of x used in the interval k. This helps us to avoid possible confusion between the two different sums in (1.22) and (1.23).

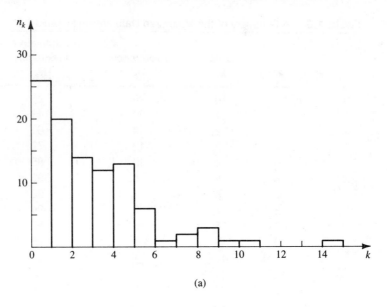

(a)

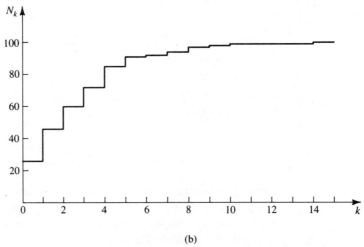

(b)

Figure 1.4   Plots of (a) frequency and (b) cumulative frequency. The abscissa is the number of failures per chip for 64k $\times$ 8 RAM chips. Data for these plots are in Table 1.3.

◆ ◆

Example 1.8   Using (1.22) and (1.23) with the data in Table 1.3,

$$\sum_{i=1}^{n} x_i = \sum_{k=1}^{k_M} n_k \tilde{x}_k = 243$$

$$\sum_{i=1}^{n} x_i^2 = \sum_{k=1}^{k_M} n_k \tilde{x}_k^2 = 1245$$

These are the same values obtained in Examples 1.1 and 1.2. Hence, the same sample mean and variance are calculated using the relative frequency data as are calculated with the sums in (1.1b) and (1.5).

◆ ◆ ◆ ◆ ◆

The data in Table 1.3 are integer and are, therefore, easily adapted to the frequency and cumulative frequency plots in Figure 1.4. A different and somewhat more difficult problem occurs if the data are continuous valued rather than integer valued. Consider the data produced by a uniform random number generator. We are interested in finding out how uniformly the data actually distribute over the interval from zero to one. To do so, we could generate a large number of data and divide the abscissa into, say, 10 **cells** (intervals):

Cell 1 $0 \leq x < 0.1$
Cell 2 $0.1 \leq x < 0.2$

           .   .

           .   .

           .   .

Cell 10 $0.9 \leq x < 1.0$ **(1.24)**

Approximately one-tenth of the data should occur in each of these 10 cells if the data are generated uniformly. Note that in this example we are not interested in finding out what the data are. Our only interest is in counting the number of data occurring in each of the 10 cells indicated in (1.24). A variety of methods could be used to count data in a study such as this. The method we use follows.

Example 1.9   Suppose we calculate an integer k for each of 1000 data from a URNG algorithm according to

$$k = [x/0.1] + 1 \tag{1.25}$$

If a datum occurs in the interval of the first cell, then k in (1.25) calculates to be one; if it occurs in the second cell, $k = 2$; etc. The maximum value of k in this example is $k_M = 10$. Therefore, each of the $n = 1000$ data is used in (1.25) to calculate an integer $1 \leq k \leq 10$ that designates the proper cell into which it should be sorted. Next, we employ an array, say, freq(k), which has a dimension equal to the number of cells (a dimension of 10 in this example). Every entry in the array is initialized to zero. Then, as each integer k is calculated in (1.25), the appropriate entry in the array is used as a counter[c]:

$$\text{freq}(k) = \text{freq}(k) + 1 \tag{1.26}$$

---

[c] Please note that the "=" in (1.26) is actually the FORTRAN assignment symbol; it is *not* an equals sign. Individuals familiar with other notations should translate this accordingly here and in other places where this occurs.

After (1.25) and (1.26) have been used with all n data, the integers remaining in the array are n_k, the frequency data:

$$\text{freq}(k) = n_k, \quad k = 1, 2, 3, \ldots, 10$$

$$\sum \text{freq}(k) = \sum n_k = n$$

We illustrate this in Table 1.4. Here, data were obtained from the URNG algorithm in Appendix A using a seed of 7524. In Table 1.4 we see the following:

1. Each cell is identified with an integer k. Also shown is each cell's lower boundary x_l, upper boundary x_u, and center $\tilde{x}_k$ (also called the **cell mark**). The lower boundary is included in a cell while the upper is not. That is, the interval or cell k is

$$x_{l(k)} \leq x < x_{u(k)}$$

2. The frequency at which data occur in each cell is n_k. Frequency data are plotted in Figure 1.5(a).

3. Cumulative frequency data N_k are the sum of all n_k in cell k and lower. Cumulative frequency data are plotted in Figure 1.5(b).

4. All data occurring in cell k are approximated by the value at the center of cell $\tilde{x}_k$. An **approximate** sum of all individual data in cell k is $n_k\tilde{x}_k$. We then employ (1.22) to write

$$\sum_{i=1}^{n} x_i \approx \sum_{k=1}^{k_M} n_k\tilde{x}_k = 499.40$$

This value is obtained from the column that is second from the right in Table 1.4. Similarly, from (1.23),

Table 1.4 Data Obtained from a Uniform Random Number Generator Algorithm, URNG

k	x_l	x_u	$\tilde{x}_k$	n_k	N_k	$n_k\tilde{x}_k$	$n_k\tilde{x}_k^2$
1	0.0	0.1	0.05	111	111	5.55	0.2775
2	0.1	0.2	0.15	90	201	13.50	2.0250
3	0.2	0.3	0.25	99	300	24.75	6.1875
4	0.3	0.4	0.35	96	396	33.60	11.7600
5	0.4	0.5	0.45	100	496	45.00	20.2500
6	0.5	0.6	0.55	104	600	57.20	31.4600
7	0.6	0.7	0.65	99	699	64.35	41.8275
8	0.7	0.8	0.75	105	804	78.75	59.0625
9	0.8	0.9	0.85	95	899	80.75	68.6375
10	0.9	1.0	0.95	101	1000	95.95	91.1525
						499.40	332.6400

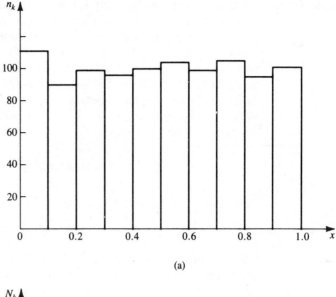

(a)

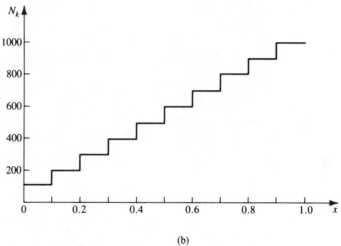

(b)

Figure 1.5   Plots of (a) frequency and (b) cumulative frequency. The data are from a uniform random number generator algorithm, URNG, and are listed in Table 1.4.

• •

$$\sum_{i=1}^{n} x_i^2 \approx \sum_{k=1}^{k_M} n_k \tilde{x}_k^2 = 332.640$$

This value is obtained using the column on the far right in Table 1.4. These values are used in (1.1b) and (1.6) to calculate the sample mean $\bar{x} = 0.4994$ and the sample standard deviation $s_x = 0.2887$.

• • • • • •

Example 1.10   If we look at the data in Table 1.5, we are faced with a new problem. The data are listed in the order in which they were measured, but they do not suggest any straightforward scheme for choosing cells, so a histogram can be constructed. Recall that the integer data in Table 1.1 guided us into constructing a histogram with cells that have a unit width. With the data obtained from the URNG in Table 1.4, we made an arbitrary but reasonable choice to divide the interval between zero and one into 10 cells. How might we be guided to choose cells for the data in Table 1.5? First, we use the $n = 100$ data in Table 1.5 to compute

$$\sum_{i=1}^{n} x_i = 156{,}600 \quad \text{and} \quad \sum_{i=1}^{n} x_i^2 = 246{,}746{,}000$$

Then, using (1.1b) and (1.6), we find

$$\bar{x} = 1566 \quad \text{and} \quad s_x = 123.5$$

The value of n in this example is 100, which is not very large. Therefore, we do not want too many cells because too few data will be collected in each of them. We arbitrarily decide there will be five cells. In another arbitrary but convenient choice, we position the five cells to be between $\bar{x} \pm 2s_x$. In making this choice we use the sample mean to guide us to the center of the cells, and we use the sample standard deviation to guide how far the cells should extend on either side of the sample mean. We proceed to use these arbitrary choices in a study of the data in Table 1.5. (Other data may suggest choices other than the ones we made here. Also, after making arbitrary choices, we may find information that causes us to change our choices and to begin anew.)

The lower boundary of the first cell is

$$x_{l(1)} = \bar{x} - 2s_x = 1319 \ \Omega$$

The upper boundary of the last cell k_M is

$$x_{u(5)} = \bar{x} + 2s_x = 1813 \ \Omega$$

The width w of each of the cells is

$$w = \frac{x_{u(5)} - x_{l(1)}}{k_M}$$

$$w = \frac{\bar{x} + 2s_x - (\bar{x} - 2s_x)}{k_M}$$

$$w = 4s_x / k_M$$

In this example $s_x = 123.5$ and $k_M = 5$, therefore $w = 98.80 \ \Omega$.

Each datum x_i may be assigned to a cell $k = 1$ through k_M using a relation similar to (1.25):

$$k = [(x_i - x_{l(1)})/w] + 1$$

$$k = [(x_i - 1319)/98.8] + 1$$

Table 1.5   100 Measured Values of Resistance*

1531.0	1506.3	1594.7	1734.9	1527.3
1554.0	1530.9	1627.7	1543.7	1564.1
1371.7	1631.3	1745.2	1437.5	1546.1
1646.8	1504.8	1471.3	1559.2	1575.1
1383.5	1830.4	1707.8	1449.3	1414.3
1623.9	1365.0	1566.3	1366.2	1544.8
1487.9	1695.3	1668.2	1362.0	1581.4
1737.0	1693.4	1636.6	1414.4	1460.7
1342.6	1609.5	1548.1	1691.2	1309.0
1577.8	1619.4	1669.5	1625.5	1706.4
1397.3	1692.7	1533.1	1632.5	1574.8
1529.8	1328.7	1520.8	1392.9	1741.7
1573.5	1536.6	1412.7	1701.5	1508.5
1712.7	1667.0	1442.2	1562.5	1818.1
1529.0	1656.7	1636.6	1489.9	1823.5
1454.0	1631.8	1421.1	1659.7	1659.3
1317.2	1644.6	1466.5	1777.3	1649.6
1797.5	1672.9	1445.3	1474.2	1516.8
1651.9	1356.1	1483.9	1495.4	1568.5
1542.8	1579.7	1634.4	1719.7	1642.3

*These data are in ohms, and were measured from $n = 100$ "identical" resistive components. The design target value of the resistance is 1600 Ω.

These choices allow us to process the measured data in Table 1.5 and to obtain the corresponding frequency and cumulative frequency data in Table 1.6. These tabular data are plotted in Figure 1.6. Note that in selecting the five cells to be located within the interval $\bar{x} \pm 2s_x$, we have no guarantee that all the data in Table 1.5 will fall in this interval. Table 1.6 therefore introduces cells 0 and 6 to collect all data that occur to the left of cell 1 and to the right of cell 5, respectively. Doing this on a computer requires that we write the following code:

$$\text{If } k < 0 \text{ then } k = 0$$

$$\text{If } k > 6 \text{ then } k = 6$$

The cell marks of cells 0 and 6 are not defined.

◆ ◆ ◆ ◆ ◆

Example 1.11   In this example, we introduce the situation in which the available measured data are few and little advantage is gained by constructing a frequency plot. A cumulative frequency plot, however, may still be estimated using a few sample data.

Table 1.6   A Summary of the Measured Data shown in Table 1.5

Cell k	Boundaries x_l	x_u	Mark $\tilde{x}_k$	Frequency n_k	Cumulative Frequency N_k
0	$-\infty$	1319.00	—	2	2
1	1319.00	1417.80	1368.40	13	15
2	1417.80	1516.60	1467.20	17	32
3	1516.60	1615.40	1566.00	28	60
4	1615.40	1714.20	1664.80	30	90
5	1714.20	1813.00	1763.60	7	97
6	1813.00	$+\infty$	—	3	100

Twelve measurements are presented in Table 1.7(a) in the order in which they were obtained. The 12 data are too few to attempt to construct a meaningful frequency plot. Typically, we would like at least 20 data *per cell* in a histogram, but here *total* data number less than that. The distinctive feature of a cumulative frequency plot is that it sums the number of data at, and less than, each abscissa value. In the previous examples using cumulative frequency, we increased the sums cell by cell. In the technique we are now introducing, we increase the sum by one unit whenever a datum occurs. We use

$$N_k = \frac{kn}{n+1} \qquad (1.27)$$

as a formula to express this idea. Here, n is the total number of data. If we apply (1.27), which is called the **mean ranking** technique, to the data in Table 1.7(a) we will obtain the results in Table 1.7(b). The first column lists the rank; the second column presents the same data as in Table 1.7(a), but rank-ordered from the smallest value to the largest; and the third column lists values for (1.27) when $n = 12$. A plot of N_k for this example is shown in Figure 1.7. As this plot shows, the mean ranking technique is an approximation technique for a plot that would, as n becomes large, blend smoothly to an ordinate of zero on the left and a maximum ordinate of n on the right.

◆ ◆ ◆ ◆ ◆

It will take us too far afield to discuss it in any detail, but a relatively new collection of statistical techniques known as **exploratory data analysis** has come into use. Sometimes practical data are distributed in a way that, if calculated by a computer without human oversight, makes sample mean and sample variance difficult or misleading to interpret. Suffice it to say that exploratory data analysis reduces these potential difficulties and misinterpretations. Interested readers are encouraged to study Tukey's book[9] on this subject. An introduction to exploratory data analysis is also presented by Koopmans.[1]

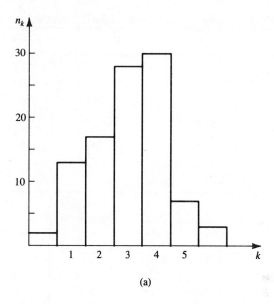

(a)

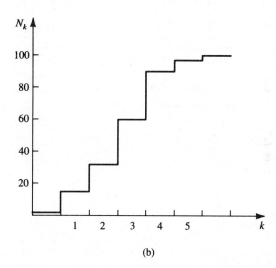

(b)

Figure 1.6   Plots of (a) frequency and (b) cumulative frequency for the data in Table 1.6.

Table 1.7   Twelve Measurements Used to Illustrate the Mean Ranking Technique*

(a)

481.4	584.4
493.2	590.4
552.9	539.0
531.8	437.7
530.3	356.6
531.4	461.6

(b)

Rank k	Data x_k	Cumulative Frequency N_k	Rank k	Data x_k	Cumulative Frequency N_k
1	356.6	0.9	7	531.4	6.5
2	437.7	1.8	8	531.8	7.4
3	461.6	2.8	9	539.0	8.3
4	481.4	3.7	10	552.9	9.2
5	493.2	4.6	11	584.4	10.2
6	530.3	5.5	12	590.4	11.1

*There are 12 measurements in part (a) which are listed in the order in which they were recorded. These data are in microns and they correspond to a measured distance within an integrated circuit. In part (b), these data are rank-ordered, and mean rank values approximating cumulative frequency are listed.

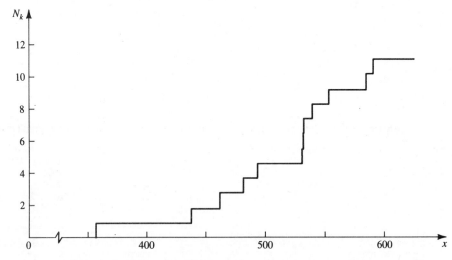

Figure 1.7   The plot of the mean ranked cumulative frequency data in Table 1.7(b).

Section 1.5   SIMULATION: MONTE CARLO

♦ ♦ ♦ ♦ ♦

Suppose we have a known function of several variables:

$$y = g(x_1, x_2, \ldots, x_n) \tag{1.28}$$

It is straightforward to calculate a value for y given any set of x_i. However, suppose the x_i are not know exactly, but are only specified to be within some region of tolerance. Presumably, values of x_i can be found that will make y a minimum: y_{MIN}. Another group of values can be found that will make y a maximum: y_{MAX}. These, then, bound values of y for any other set of x_i:

$$y_{MIN} \leq y \leq y_{MAX}$$

y_{MAX} and y_{MIN} are valuable because they provide **worst-case** information. Nevertheless, more can be learned if we simulate (1.28) on a computer. To do this, we let a random number generator, such as URNG, choose a value for x_1, then choose another value for x_2, and still another for x_3, and so forth until all the required x_i have a value. When this is done, (1.28) is used to calculate a sample value for y. The process can be repeated to obtain another value for y. Finally, after many values for y have been simulated, we can graph frequency and cumulative frequency plots for y and then analyze the behavior of the relatively complicated system suggested by (1.28).

Simulation techniques such as this are called **Monte Carlo,** or **synthetic sampling** techniques. Their virtue is that, if (1.28) is known, useful insight can be obtained when a theoretical analysis is intransigent. Their weakness is that we need to repeat the entire numerical process to study the effect of one parameter change in (1.28). We illustrate this simulation technique with an example.

Example 1.12   The resonant frequency of a series inductance and capacitance is

$$f = \frac{1}{2\pi\sqrt{LC}} \tag{1.29}$$

If components are selected with the values of $L = 1$ mH and $C = 2\ \mu$F, the resonant frequency is $f_r = 3558.81$ Hz.

Practical components cannot be expected to be at their exact specified values. In practice, we must place a tolerance on the value of components. For example, with the components mentioned above, we place a $\pm 20\%$ tolerance on the 1 mH inductance and $\pm 10\%$ tolerance on the 2 μF capacitance. This selection (which is arbitrary in this example) means that the values that actually determine the resonant frequency in (1.29) are

$$0.8 < L < 1.2 \text{ mH} \tag{1.30}$$

$$1.8 < C < 2.2\ \ \mu\text{F} \tag{1.31}$$

We assume that inductances and capacitances occur uniformly in their allowed intervals. Further, we assume that the variations in L are independent of those in C. Given these assumed random variations in L and C, the resonant frequency will vary randomly in the vicinity of f_r.

A worst-case analysis shows that the smallest resonant frequency, $f_L = 3097.55$ Hz, occurs when both L and C have their largest possible values, and that the highest resonant frequency, $f_H = 4194.10$ Hz, occurs when both L and C have their smallest possible values.

A worst-case analysis may be satisfactory for some purposes. However, worst-case situations rarely occur. Realistically, we may be more interested in determining how the resonant frequency varies with random selections of the inductance and capacitance. Thus, we simulate (1.29): Suppose we use URNG to obtain a random number x_i, and then we compute a value within the range of (1.30) for the inductance:

$$L_i = (0.8 + 0.4x_i) \times 10^{-3} \text{ H} \tag{1.32}$$

Here, if x_i is obtained from URNG, its minimum and maximum values of zero and one will give the minimum and maximum values of inductance in (1.30). Other values of inductance (1.32) are equally likely in the interval shown by (1.30) because x_i is equally likely between zero and one.

We use URNG again to obtain a second random number y_i, independent of x_i. This can be used to obtain a value for the capacitance within the range of (1.31):

$$C_i = (1.8 + 0.4y_i) \times 10^{-6} \text{ F} \tag{1.33}$$

If y_i is obtained from URNG, values of capacitance in (1.33) are equally likely to be obtained in the interval given by (1.31). Thus, independent random numbers from separate cells from URNG can be used to calculate a sample resonant frequency f_i from (1.29).

We repeat this simulation until we have $n = 1000$ data for f_i. To determine how these data distribute into frequency and cumulative frequency plots, we select (arbitrarily) the number of cells $k_M = 7$. Then, the cell width is

$$w = (f_H - f_L)/k_M$$
$$w = 156.857 \text{ Hz}$$

The cell number for each datum f_i is

$$k_i = [(f_i - f_L)/w] + 1 \tag{1.34}$$

Table 1.8(a) shows the data we computed after processing all $n = 1000$ values for i. We also graph the frequency and cumulative frequency plots in Figure 1.8, which show how the resonant frequencies f_i distribute between the worst-cast limits of f_L and f_H. The data in Table 1.8(a) are used again, as shown in Table 1.8(b), to calculate

Table 1.8   (a) A Summary of 1000 Resonant Frequencies f_i (in Hertz)

| Cell | Boundaries | | Mark | Frequency | Cumulative Frequency |
k	f_l	f_u	$\tilde{f}_k$	n_k	N_k
1	3097.0	3253.9	3175.4	72	72
2	3253.9	3410.7	3332.3	203	275
3	3410.7	3567.6	3489.1	243	518
4	3567.6	3724.4	3646.0	198	716
5	3724.4	3881.3	3802.9	177	893
6	3881.3	4038.1	3959.7	88	981
7	4038.1	4195.0	4116.6	19	1000

(b) Illustrating the Calculation of Σf_i and Σf_i^2 for the Data in (a)

Cell k	Mark $\tilde{f}_k$	Frequency n_k	$n_k \tilde{f}_k$	$n_k \tilde{f}_k^2$ (10^6)
1	3175.4	72	228,628.8	725.988
2	3332.3	203	676,456.9	2,254.157
3	3489.1	243	847,851.3	2,958.238
4	3646.0	198	721,908.0	2,632.077
5	3802.9	177	673,113.3	2,559.783
6	3959.7	88	348,453.6	1,379.772
7	4116.6	19	78,215.4	321.982
			3,574,627.3	12,831.997

$$\sum_{i=1}^{n} f_i \approx \sum_{k=1}^{k_M} n_k \tilde{f}_k = 3{,}574{,}627.3$$

$$\sum_{i=1}^{n} f_i^2 \approx \sum_{k=1}^{k_M} n_k \tilde{f}_k^2 = 12{,}831.997 \times 10^6$$

Here, the relations in (1.22) and (1.23) are used. We then use these values in (1.1b) and (1.6) to calculate the sample mean and standard deviation:

$$\bar{f} = 3574.6 \text{ Hz}$$

$$s_f = 232.6 \text{ Hz}$$

This simulation demonstrates that a worst-case analysis can be very conservative: The worst case may not be very likely at all. In fact, in our simulation, the maximum simulated resonant frequency was 4184.8 Hz; the minimum, 3115.9 Hz. These are close to, but within, the worst-case limits of 4194.10 and 3097.55 Hz, respectively. However, the frequency and cumulative frequency plots in Figure 1.8 provide us with a real sense of the practical variations for the resonant frequency.

◆ ◆ ◆ ◆ ◆

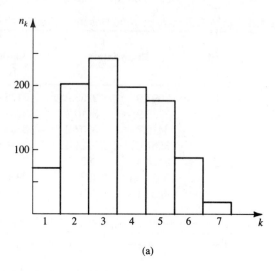

(a)

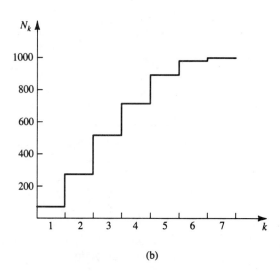

(b)

Figure 1.8   Plots of (a) frequency and (b) cumulative frequency for the data in Table 1.8(a).

◆ ◆

Section 1.6   STATISTICAL PROCESS CONTROL

◆ ◆ ◆ ◆ ◆

We can use the sample mean and the sample variance to introduce a few of the ideas in **statistical process control** (SPC). SPC is one of the major tools in use today to improve the quality of a process. In very practical terms, SPC may be used whenever a process produces either a product or a service and undesired variations are present in that process. We assume the process is not changing, but that conditions beyond our control cause undesired variations in the output of the process. These undesired variations might be in the materials used in the process, people implementing the process, ambient temperature changes, etc.

The process we are considering is quite general; it may be manufacturing a product in a factory, or providing a service, such as processing insurance forms. A measurement of the process must be found that is important for its success. For example, a manufactured product might have a critical spacing between mounting holes, or the time it takes to process an insurance claim might be important for customer satisfaction. We illustrate SPC with an example.

Example 1.13   The resistance data in Table 1.5 were recorded in the order in which they were measured starting in the upper left (1531.0 Ω), and ending at the lower right (1642.3 Ω). We average the data in Table 1.5 using relatively small lots, say $n = 5$. The average of the first five resistance values is 1497.4 Ω. The average of the next five resistance values is 1553.8 Ω. Continuing in this way, we arrive at the data in Table 1.9. The 20 data in Table 1.9 are plotted in sequence in Figure 1.9.

An inspection of Table 1.9 or Figure 1.9 shows that the sequence of $\bar{x}$ values fluctuates. The SPC technique proceeds to find the sample mean and the sample standard deviation of the data in Table 1.9. We find

$$n = 20, \quad \sum \bar{x} = 31{,}367.7, \quad \sum \bar{x}^2 = 49{,}260{,}815.3$$

Then, using (1.1b),

$$\bar{\bar{x}} = \frac{1}{n} \sum \bar{x} = 1568.4 \ \Omega \tag{1.35}$$

Table 1.9   Values of the Sample Mean $\bar{x}$ (in ohms) of Lots of Five Resistive Devices*

Lot of Five	$\bar{x}$	Lot of Five	$\bar{x}$
1	1497.4	11	1509.1
2	1553.8	12	1490.2
3	1548.5	13	1544.9
4	1552.7	14	1491.9
5	1600.7	15	1555.9
6	1596.5	16	1625.3
7	1576.3	17	1525.4
8	1577.0	18	1520.4
9	1683.3	19	1693.3
10	1617.7	20	1607.3

*Lot values are taken from Table 1.5 starting from the beginning.

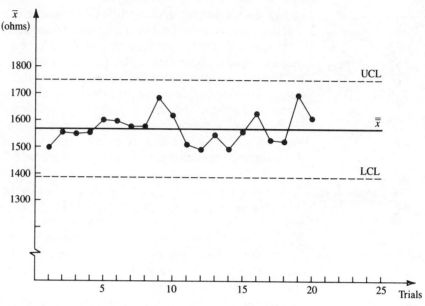

Figure 1.9   A control chart for the data in Table 1.9.

• •

The convention in SPC is to use the two overbars to signify the sample mean of a group of sample means obtained from small lots. Using (1.6)

$$s_{\bar{x}} = 58.1 \; \Omega$$

A line corresponding to $\bar{\bar{x}}$ is drawn in Figure 1.9. It is also conventional in SPC to place an **upper control limit** (UCL) and a **lower control limit** (LCL) on the SPC chart. By convention, these control limits are

$$\text{UCL} = \bar{\bar{x}} + 3s_{\bar{x}} \qquad (1.36)$$

$$\text{LCL} = \bar{\bar{x}} - 3s_{\bar{x}} \qquad (1.37)$$

The UCL and the LCL are also shown in Figure 1.9.

Figure 1.9 shows the start of a control chart with 20 sample lots of five resistance elements. We have also placed on the control chart the control limits UCL and LCL. In the future, as resistance elements are manufactured, lots of five are selected randomly, and their value of $\bar{x}$ is calculated and plotted in sequence following the data in Figure 1.9. If future $\bar{x}$ data stay between the UCL and the LCL, and stay centered about $\bar{\bar{x}}$, then the process making the resistance element is said to be under control. If not, the process is not under control, and the reason must be found and remedied.

• • • • •

Much more can be said about SPC charts than is illustrated in this brief example. Control charts are finding wide application as companies and government agencies become increasingly concerned about quality products and services. References 10 and 11 present more information on statistical process control for the interested reader.

Exercises

◆　◆　◆　◆　◆

1. Given below are 10 data recorded in the order in which they were measured in an experiment. Calculate the sample mean and the sample standard deviation for these data by first calculating Σx_i and Σx_i^2.

3643.8	4449.6
4002.4	3902.4
3745.2	4291.1
3852.0	3720.2
3877.5	3669.6

2. Given below are 10 data recorded in the order in which they were measured in an experiment. Calculate the sample mean and the sample standard deviation for these data by first calculating Σx_i and Σx_i^2.

3874.3	3511.6
2310.9	1473.0
1892.0	1152.8
2088.5	2625.4
1002.4	2468.7

3. Given below are 10 data recorded in the order in which they were measured in an experiment. Calculate the sample mean and the sample standard deviation for these data by first calculating Σx_i and Σx_i^2.

−24.2	−38.8
96.3	−26.4
−24.3	32.9
−4.7	−118.4
102.3	−79.5

4. Given the following bivariate data, find the regression line, $y = \alpha x + \beta$, and the correlation coefficient:

i	x_i	y_i
1	30.2	4.13
2	65.6	−6.42
3	94.8	−9.02
4	29.4	8.60
5	55.6	−1.89
6	37.7	0.51
7	98.2	−8.94
8	38.3	0.65
9	100.0	−11.70
10	87.4	−11.88

5. Given the following bivariate data, find the regression line, $y = \alpha x + \beta$, and the correlation coefficient:

i	x_i	y_i
1	86.9	−3.59
2	86.1	−7.14
3	8.6	5.14
4	15.5	7.16
5	52.8	−0.85
6	70.8	−8.62
7	47.1	−6.92
8	27.9	3.59
9	8.4	11.84
10	84.2	−5.45

6. Given the following bivariate data, find the regression line, $y = \alpha x + \beta$, and the correlation coefficient:

i	x_i	y_i
1	66.3	2.12
2	92.7	3.37
3	67.7	4.44
4	29.3	−3.68
5	16.9	−3.31
6	8.2	−11.38
7	32.9	−2.98
8	9.9	−6.44
9	34.5	−9.53
10	28.4	−0.29

7. Use a uniform random number generator $x = $ URNG(seed) to write an algorithm that will generate observations of the following:

   a. integers uniformly distributed from 0 through 100 inclusive

   b. numbers uniformly distributed over the interval $5100 \pm 10\%$

   c. a one occurs 35% of the time; a zero otherwise.

8. Use a uniform random number generator $x = $ URNG(seed) to write an algorithm that will generate observations of the following:

   a. integers uniformly distributed from 0 through 12 inclusive

   b. numbers uniformly distributed over the interval $6400 \pm 10\%$

   c. a one occurs 40% of the time; a zero otherwise.

9. Use a uniform random number generator $x = $ URNG(seed) to write an algorithm that will generate observations of the following:

   a. integers uniformly distributed from 0 through 75 inclusive

   b. numbers uniformly distributed over the interval $7200 \pm 10\%$

   c. a one occurs 45% of the time; a zero otherwise.

10. The following sums were obtained from $n = 100$ data:

$$\sum x_i = 29{,}980.4 \text{ and } \sum x_i^2 = 8{,}998{,}184$$

Calculate the sample mean and the sample standard deviation. Classify the data into $k_M = 7$ cells within the range of $x = \bar{x} \pm 2s_x$. Find the upper and lower boundaries for each cell and the cell marks. Write an algorithm in pseudocode for sorting the data into their cells. Do not assume that all data are within the range of $x = \bar{x} \pm 2s_x$.

11. Repeat Exercise 10 for the case in which $k_M = 8$.

12. Repeat Exercise 10 for the case in which $k_M = 9$.

13. Given the data in the table below:

Cell	Boundaries		Mark	Frequency
k	x_l	x_u	$\tilde{x}_k$	n_k
1	12.20	12.54	12.371	58
2	12.54	12.89	12.714	132
3	12.89	13.23	13.057	186
4	13.23	13.57	13.400	221
5	13.57	13.91	13.743	208
6	13.91	14.26	14.086	110
7	14.26	14.60	14.429	48

a. Sketch the frequency and the cumulative frequency plots.

b. Calculate the sample mean and the sample variance for the data.

14. Give the data in the table below:

Cell	Boundaries		Mark	Frequency
k	x_l	x_u	$\tilde{x}_k$	n_k
1	250.4	256.3	253.34	73
2	256.3	262.2	259.23	111
3	262.2	268.1	265.11	190
4	268.1	273.9	271.00	238
5	273.9	279.8	276.89	194
6	279.8	285.7	282.77	100
7	285.7	291.6	288.66	54

a. Sketch the frequency and the cumulative frequency plots.

b. Calculate the sample mean and the sample variance for the data.

15. Given the data in the table below:

Cell	Boundaries		Mark	Frequency
k	x_l	x_u	$\tilde{x}_k$	n_k
1	628.8	675.7	652.26	62
2	675.7	722.6	699.17	138
3	722.6	769.5	746.09	175
4	769.5	816.5	793.00	210
5	816.5	863.4	839.91	199
6	863.4	910.3	886.83	107
7	910.3	957.2	933.74	68

a. Sketch the frequency and the cumulative frequency plots.

b. Calculate the sample mean and the sample variance for the data.

16. In Example 1.9 we showed a method for analyzing the statistical quality of a uniform random number generator algorithm (URNG). Repeat Example 1.9 for the uniform random number generator algorithm of your choice.

17. Estimate the cumulative frequency for the following data using the mean ranking technique.

0.278	0.576
0.469	0.836
0.140	0.175
0.121	0.371
0.071	0.717

18. Estimate the cumulative frequency for the following data using the mean ranking technique.

1.76	0.21
9.07	5.70
8.21	3.46
0.52	9.10
5.32	8.80

19. Estimate the cumulative frequency for the following data using the mean ranking technique.

36.9	94.0
29.6	16.8
6.4	20.1
1.4	71.1
34.5	93.4

20. Modify the algorithm in (1.34) to simulate the following problem: Ohm's law may be written as

$$I = V/R$$

where I is current, the voltage V is 28 volts $\pm 10\%$ and the resistance R is 1300 ohms $\pm 20\%$. Assume that values of V and R are uniformly distributed within their respective tolerance ranges. Find frequency and cumulative frequency tables and plots for I using $n = 1000$ trials. Calculate a sample mean and variance for I using the frequency data. Let $k_m = 8$.

21. Modify the algorithm in (1.34) to simulate the following problem: The equivalent resistance of two parallel resistors is

$$R = \frac{R_1 R_2}{R_1 + R_2}$$

Let $R_1 = 1100$ ohms $\pm 10\%$ and $R_2 = 910$ ohms $\pm 10\%$. Assume that values of R_1 and R_2 are uniformly distributed within their respective tolerance ranges. Find frequency and cumulative frequency tables and plots for R using $n = 1000$ trials. Calculate a sample mean and variance for R using the frequency data. Let $k_M = 8$.

22. Modify the algorithm in (1.34) to simulate the following problem: Let

$$V = \sqrt{V_1^2 + V_2^2}$$

where $V_1 = 10$ volts $\pm 15\%$ and $V_2 = 20$ volts $\pm 25\%$. Assume that values of V_1 and V_2 are uniformly distributed within their respective tolerance ranges. Find frequency and cumulative frequency tables and plots for V using $n = 1000$ trials. Calculate a sample mean and variance for V using the frequency data. Let $k_M = 8$.

23. Use the data in Table 1.5 to plot a control chart, as was done in Example 1.13, but using $n = 6$ instead of $n = 5$. (Ignore the last four data in Table 1.5 so that only 16 values of $\bar{x}$ are calculated.) Plot values of $\bar{x}$, and show $\bar{\bar{x}}$, UCL, and LCL.

References

◆ ◆ ◆ ◆ ◆

1. Koopmans, Lambert H. *Introduction to Contemporary Statistical Methods.* 2d ed. Boston: Duxbury Press, 1987.

2. Kennedy, John B., and Adam M. Neville. *Basic Statistical Methods for Engineers and Scientists.* 3d ed. New York: Harper and Row, Publishers, 1986.

3. Lapin, Lawrence L. *Probability and Statistics for Modern Engineering.* Monterey, Calif.: Brooks/Cole Engineering Division, 1983.

4. McCuen, Richard H. *Statistical Methods for Engineers.* Englewood Cliffs, N.J.: Prentice-Hall, Inc., 1985.

5. Milton, J. S., and Jessie C. Arnold. *Probability and Statistics in the Engineering and Computing Sciences.* New York: McGraw-Hill Book Company, 1986.

6. Walpole, Ronald E., and Raymond H. Myers. *Probability and Statistics for Engineers and Scientists.* 3d ed. New York: Macmillan Publishing Company, 1985.

7. Spiegel, Murray R. *Probability and Statistics (Schaum's Outline Series).* New York: McGraw-Hill Book Company, 1975.

8. Eisenhart, Churchill. *Realistic Evaluation of the Precision and Accuracy of Instrument Calibration Systems,* pp. 21–47 in *Precision Measurement and Calibration: Selected NBS Papers on Statistical Concepts and Procedures,* Harry Ku, Ed. NBS Special Publication 300, Volume 1, U.S. Department of Commerce, February 1969.

9. Tukey, J. W. *Exploratory Data Analysis.* Reading, Mass.: Addison-Wesley Publishing Company, 1977.

10. Grant, Eugene L., and Richard S. Leavenworth, *Statistical Quality Control.* 6th ed. New York: McGraw-Hill Book Company, 1988.

11. Montgomery, Douglas C. *Introduction to Statistical Quality Control.* 2d ed. New York: John Wiley and Sons, 1985.

2 Probability and Its Properties

* *

The debate concerning [probability] *will, I am sure, go on forever. In the meantime, do not for one moment forget one massive fact about probability theory — it works.*

Warren Weaver, in *Lady Luck,* Dover Publications, 1963

Introduction   Statistics are but one technique we use to manage variability in our everyday lives: If some matter of experience does not submit to the rigor of certainty, we describe its behavior on the average. A carefully framed concept of probability is not needed to discuss statistics, at least as far as the descriptive statistics we presented in Chapter 1 are concerned. Rather, statistical experience serves to guide the thought behind a theory of probability.

We begin with the concept of a **random experiment:** We conceptualize the experience of doing some physical process several times the same way and finding that the results are not the same — they vary in a way we term "random." We do not discard the results of random experiments simply because they are variable. We study the nature of variability — the randomness — so we can better understand it. This, then, is the origin of a **theory of probability.**

Section 2.1   **EQUALLY LIKELY EVENTS**

◆ ◆ ◆ ◆ ◆

An important step in understanding randomness occurred during the Renaissance when games of chance were studied seriously. In that historical context, a random experiment in a game of chance is called a **play,** and typically involves a limited number of events that occur randomly. For example, a coin when tossed will present only one of two sides, or a die, when rolled, will come to rest with only one of six faces showing.

We, of course, are not interested in games of chance here. However, some rather specific applications of equally likely events do occur in engineering, mostly in sampling processes. After all, if we need to select one sample from a group of N items, our concept of honest sampling requires that each of the N items is as equally likely to be selected as any other.

Generalizing, suppose we have N distinct items A_i, $i = 1, 2, \ldots, N$. The collection of all items A_i is called a **sample space** S:

$$S = \{A_1, A_2, \ldots, A_N\} \tag{2.1}$$

Probability *per se* enters when we agree to use a number between zero and one as a measure of the certainty that an event will occur. We denote the probability of an event A by $P(A)$:

$$0 \le P(A) \le 1 \tag{2.2}$$

We agree that if an event is impossible, its probability is zero. If an event is certain, its probability is unity. A method for obtaining specific values for probabilities is introduced when we agree that each event A_i in (2.1) is equally likely, and it has a probability of $1/N$:

$$P(A_i) = 1/N, \, i = 1, 2, \ldots, N \tag{2.3}$$

If an event A is a collection of the events A_i, then the probability of A is determined by n_A, the number of distinct events A_i contained in A:

$$P(A) = n_A/N \tag{2.4}$$

Example 2.1   Twenty-five items, which are supposed to be identical, are placed on a tray as they are manufactured. An inspector selects one item at random. (It is common usage to use the phrase "at random" meaning the assumption of equally likely events.) This means that each item on the tray is equally likely to be selected. Using (2.3), each item on the tray may be selected with a probability of 1/25.

If 3 of the items on the tray happen to be defective, and the other 22 are not, then, using (2.4), the probability of the inspector selecting a defective item is 3/25.

◆ ◆ ◆ ◆ ◆

Section 2.2   RANDOM SAMPLING

◆ ◆ ◆ ◆ ◆

When a sample is randomly selected, we must take special precautions to assure that there is no question of either an inadvertent or an overt bias. Evidence indicates that if humans select items presumedly at random, according to their intuition or convenience, a bias of some sort enters the process, and selection of the items is not equally likely. Good practice dictates that we use a table of random numbers, or some equivalent unbiased assistance. We first assign a number to each item in the population, beginning at one and continuing through N. Next, we search through the table of random numbers until we find one of the numbers 1 through N. We take as a sample the item which was assigned that number. Specific details on how this is done follow.

Table 2.1 is a table of random numbers constructed using URNG. Each entry in the table is one of the integers 0 through 9. They appear equally likely throughout the table, and the integers are not correlated so that particular patterns of intergers are not favored over others. We may enter the table anywhere and then move across the table in any direction developing a sequence of integers as we go; in any sequence each integer 0 through 9 will occur equally likely.

If we take a sequence of single integers we find 0 through 9. If we take the sequence in pairs, we find 00 through 99. If we do not need a full decade range, we use only as many integers as we need and ignore the rest. Those we use are still equally likely.

Example 2.2   Suppose we have 63 items, and we want to select 5 of them at random. Identify each of the items with a number from 1 through 63. Then, going to the table of random numbers (Table 2.1), we start at, say, the sixth row of numbers in the first column. There we find 83143, 51036, 83681, 66794,. . . . Taking this sequence in pairs, we have

83 ignore
14 choose item #14
35 choose item #35
10 choose item #10
36 choose item #36
83 ignore
68 ignore
16 choose item #16

Thus, the five randomly selected items are those numbered

10, 14, 16, 35, 36

Table 2.1   A Table of Random Numbers

02103	27753	43751	27802	44115	44209	32858	54679
15550	11061	64509	49254	17030	76116	51324	71734
29768	24365	00712	83714	66599	28040	59472	97865
26776	80689	73432	43550	97017	21484	09732	06857
59220	48098	70312	97577	49745	48322	89851	34869
83143	51036	83681	66794	61911	39352	77096	66120
33991	52429	57859	42980	90470	35281	81574	98769
62543	72857	50537	62382	87888	56211	89596	63985
20244	39564	47076	87964	55995	27606	60624	73048
37053	46382	36529	52115	84674	11083	00202	32399
08164	95954	89966	83823	97771	31323	51203	03203
51728	73304	63089	11226	24659	08742	09984	90140
52489	15468	30061	18867	00214	00627	10901	56291
43883	68075	12580	91480	08067	27134	70161	00709
58649	32581	02046	86757	52211	99738	27978	17647
47104	86987	54502	41583	68719	07323	23409	82661
78245	37133	61214	96682	61532	11884	48959	30939
71079	93160	37079	67274	02697	02270	26150	31616
72660	09324	44822	55434	07994	51280	56931	06614
57218	35743	27794	52665	19383	07700	66134	47769
52581	15304	32636	89639	09441	44962	28441	74768
47405	62096	33210	66620	84684	75628	42460	46001
37587	36489	39928	57421	94529	45807	81807	06179
74812	72746	10760	41151	89103	41580	68994	41804
02803	23796	29634	86787	43908	59512	18162	98858
02786	03143	69775	21785	76363	36865	67756	28293
00285	53451	24469	80576	96646	03232	40528	76353
24128	83945	35561	71673	83923	25269	53922	51442
97872	10028	14748	70856	83976	68668	82503	84212
82845	73838	71290	65423	47374	47113	83009	75821
44564	77281	78009	42412	58784	18055	46860	66974
89393	66251	11173	77225	46898	82405	85816	53553
23808	86690	37618	24282	78197	55505	91450	13292
12447	92869	91709	00949	26313	02692	56139	55572
55138	85524	30296	73972	20329	83287	36699	96433
60228	38574	25097	98632	21058	09595	13524	91085
84237	58120	77321	59194	98827	33065	32537	08755
53862	54661	63002	40818	43099	66707	87363	35321
44513	70873	74928	98579	83683	62782	91188	90209
84945	04481	51791	95131	36732	76162	75758	95608

If we entered Table 2.1 at a different place we would have found a different random sample. A repetition of a number previously selected is ignored.

◆ ◆ ◆ ◆ ◆

Example 2.3   We have seven items— a, b, c, d, e, f, g— which we want to arrange in a random order. First, assign integers to the items:

$(1,a)\ (2,b)\ (3,c)\ (4,d)\ (5,e)\ (6,f)\ (7,g)$

Then, enter Table 2.1 at, say, the seventh group of 5 in the sixth column. We find . . . 18055. . . . Proceeding from right to left, we have

5 choose e
5 ignore
0 ignore
8 ignore
1 choose a
4 choose d
8 ignore

Continuing in this way, the randomized order of the seven items is:

e, a, d, g, b, f, c

◆ ◆ ◆ ◆ ◆

Section 2.3   **RELATIVE FREQUENCY**

◆ ◆ ◆ ◆ ◆

Another approach to a theory of probability, which also started during the Renaissance, was developed by actuaries. They used observations, not intuition, to provide data for their insurance businesses. Suppose, for example, that they insured merchant ships against loss at sea, denoting the event of a ship lost at sea as A. The actuaries would then gather data on the frequency n_A of ships being lost. If these losses occurred from a total of n voyages, the **relative frequency** of loss would be n_A/n. This was then used to estimate the probability of a merchant ship being lost:

$$P(A) = n_A/n \qquad (2.5)$$

Of course, as with all actuarial data, the larger the base of the data n, the more confidence can be invested in the thought that a relative frequency (2.5) is a useful probability for insurance purposes.

Relative frequency applied to probabilities has been a very attractive concept for engineers. On the one hand, the data used to determine $P(A)$ are measured, not obtained *a priori*, as is the case with equally likely events. Further, the relative frequency approach to probabilities is not limited to sample spaces, which are finite and discrete as in (2.1). For example, an event A in (2.5) could be defined as the voltage of a power supply occurring within some tolerance range. In fact, relative frequency allows probability to be used with any experimental situation that is repeatable and in which the outcomes of random experiments can be measured or counted. Relative frequency can therefore be used as an empirical check on the assumption of equally likely events!

But on the other hand, we note that the relative frequency probability (2.5) is actually a descriptive statistic called a sample mean (1.1). As such, then, this probability is dependent on the sample used. We attempt to eliminate the difficulties of sample statistics by letting the sample size n be as large as needed:

$$P(A) = \lim_{n \to \infty} n_A/n \qquad (2.6)$$

Example 2.4   Suppose integrated circuit chips on a wafer are tested, and each chip either passes or fails. The following data are obtained:

a. 5 chips pass the test when 10 are tested.

b. 63 chips pass when 100 are tested.

c. 589 chips pass when 1000 are tested.

d. 6008 chips pass when 10,000 are tested.

Using (2.5), the probability of a chip passing the test is approximately 0.6. The limiting relation (2.6) can, of course, never be implemented with rigor, but the approximate relation (2.5) may serve us adequately when n is large.

♦ ♦ ♦ ♦ ♦

Section 2.4   ABSTRACT PROBABILITY

♦ ♦ ♦ ♦ ♦

Sometimes, in practice, the limiting process in (2.6) can be usefully approximated. However, at other times, it cannot because either we simply do not have enough data or because the repeated random experiments cannot be made independent of each other. We want to be able to use probabilities even when we cannot assume equally likely events or when the limiting process of relative frequency is nonsense. We want to be able to use probabilities in an abstract theoretical sense. In short, we want to use probability as a concept, as an entity with specific properties, without having to say how we will obtain its values.

These properties, which all probabilities must have, are summarized in some axioms, or *postulates*. They are the conceptual foundation for all that follows. Events in probability are **sets**. Therefore, readers desiring a brief review of set operations will find the following section helpful. Others should proceed directly to Sec. 2.6, Axioms and Properties of Probability.

Other textbooks that may assist the reader are available in Refs. 1 through 5.

Section 2.5   REVIEW OF SET OPERATIONS

◆ ◆ ◆ ◆ ◆

A **set** is a collection of **elements** gathered according to some useful rule. The concept here is quite general; we can speak of a set of numbers, a set of specific physical objects, a set of signals, etc. Sets are denoted by uppercase italic letters such as A. Elements, or members, of a set may be denoted by lowercase italic letters such as a. The statement

$$a \in A$$

is read "a is an element of set A." Alternatively, elements may be specified by some prescription within braces, such as

$$\{0 \le x < 10\}$$

Here, the elements are the real numbers between 0 and 10 inclusive of zero.

If every element of A is also an element of B, then A is said to be contained in B, or A is a **subset** of B. We denote this by the statement

$$A \subset B$$

Equality for two sets A and B is established if every element of A is also an element of B, and vice versa. The equality of the two sets is denoted by

$$A = B$$

Whenever sets are introduced we specify a special set, called the **universal set**, denoted by S. The universal set has the feature that all other sets, $A, B, C, \ldots,$ are subsets of it.

$$A \subset S$$
$$B \subset S$$
$$C \subset S, \text{ etc.}$$

Relationships among sets are often expressed pictorially with the use of diagrams such as the one shown in Figure 2.1. These pictorial expressions are called **Venn diagrams**.

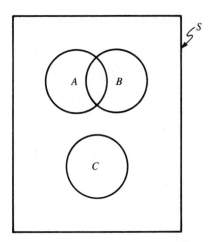

Figure 2.1   An example of a Venn diagram illustrating the universal set S, and some subsets A, B, and C.

• •

Another special set is the **null,** or **empty,** set denoted by $\emptyset$. The null set is the set that contains no elements; it is a subset of every set.

The **union** of two sets A and B is denoted by $A \cup B$. By definition, $A \cup B$ is a set whose elements are either members of A, or members of B, or both. Figure 2.2(a) illustrates the Venn diagram for $A \cup B$.

• •

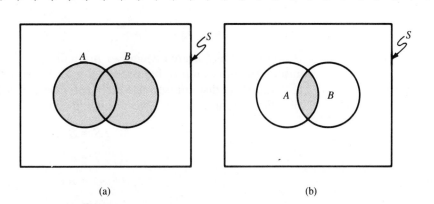

(a)   (b)

Figure 2.2   Venn diagrams illustrating with shading (a) the union of two sets A and B and (b) the intersection of A and B.

Example 2.5   Examples of the operation of union are:

1.   If $A = \{-10 < x \leq 10\}$
and $B = \{0 < x < \infty\}$
then $A \cup B = \{-10 < x < \infty\}$

2.   If $A = \{-10 < x < 0\}$
and $B = \{10 \leq x < \infty\}$
then $A \cup B = \{-10 < x < 0; 10 \leq x < \infty\}$

♦   ♦   ♦   ♦   ♦

The **intersection** of two sets A and B is denoted by $A \cap B$. By definition, $A \cap B$ is a set whose elements are members of both A and B, and its Venn diagram is shown in Figure 2.2(b).

Example 2.6   Examples of operation of intersection are:

1.   If $A = \{-10 < x \leq 10\}$
and $B = \{0 < x < \infty\}$
then $A \cap B = \{0 < x \leq 10\}$

2.   If $A = \{-10 < x < 0\}$
and $B = \{10 \leq x < \infty\}$
then $A \cap B = \emptyset$

♦   ♦   ♦   ♦   ♦

If the sets A and B are **disjoint,** or mutually exclusive, then no element is common to both A and B; hence, $A \cap B = \emptyset$. In the second case in Example 2.6, A and B are disjoint (see also the Venn diagram in Figure 2.3).

It follows from the definitions given above that

$$A \cup S = S \qquad (2.7a)$$

$$A \cap S = A \qquad (2.7b)$$

$$A \cup \emptyset = A \qquad (2.7c)$$

$$A \cap \emptyset = \emptyset \qquad (2.7d)$$

The commutative, associative, and distributive relations given below are also consequenes of the above definitions.

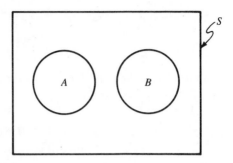

Figure 2.3   A Venn diagram illustrating the disjoint sets A and B.

Commutative relations:

$$A \cup B = B \cup A \qquad\qquad\qquad \textbf{(2.8a)}$$

$$A \cap B = B \cap A \qquad\qquad\qquad \textbf{(2.8b)}$$

Associative relations:

$$A \cup (B \cup C) = (A \cup B) \cup C = A \cup B \cup C \qquad \textbf{(2.9a)}$$

$$A \cap (B \cap C) = (A \cap B) \cap C = A \cap B \cap C \qquad \textbf{(2.9b)}$$

Distributive relations:

$$A \cup (B \cap C) = (A \cup B) \cap (A \cup C) \qquad \textbf{(2.10a)}$$

$$A \cap (B \cup C) = (A \cap B) \cup (A \cap C) \qquad \textbf{(2.10b)}$$

The **complement** of set A, denoted $\overline{A}$, is defined to be all of the elements in the universe S that are not in A. The complement of set A is illustrated in the Venn diagram in Figure 2.4. From this definition it follows that

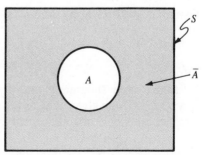

Figure 2.4   A Venn diagram illustrating a set A and its complement $\overline{A}$.

$$A \cup \bar{A} = S \qquad\qquad \text{(2.11a)}$$

$$A \cap \bar{A} = \varnothing \qquad\qquad \text{(2.11b)}$$

Example 2.7   Examples of the complement operation are:

1.   If $S = \{-\infty < x < \infty\}$
and $A = \{0 \le x < \infty\}$
then $\bar{A} = \{-\infty < x < 0\}$

2.   If $S = \{0 \le x < \infty\}$
and $B = \{10 < x < 20\}$
then $\bar{B} = \{0 \le x \le 10;\ 20 \le x < \infty\}$

◆ ◆ ◆ ◆ ◆

The theorems of **DeMorgan** are:

$$\overline{A \cup B} = \bar{A} \cap \bar{B} \qquad\qquad \text{(2.12a)}$$

$$\overline{A \cap B} = \bar{A} \cup \bar{B} \qquad\qquad \text{(2.12b)}$$

Repeated unions and intersections may be indicated using the following notations:

$$A_1 \cup A_2 \cup \ldots \cup A_N = \bigcup_{i=1}^{N} A_j \qquad\qquad \text{(2.13a)}$$

$$A_1 \cap A_2 \cap \ldots \cap A_N = \bigcap_{i=1}^{N} A_i \qquad\qquad \text{(2.13b)}$$

The notation in (2.13a) may be combined with the distributive relations (2.10b) as follows:

$$B \cap \left(\bigcup_{i=1}^{N} A_i \right) = \bigcup_{i=1}^{N} B \cap A_i \qquad\qquad \text{(2.14a)}$$

An analogous relation combining (2.13b) and (2.10a) is:

$$B \cup \left(\bigcap_{i=1}^{N} A_i \right) = \bigcap_{i=1}^{N} B \cup A_i \qquad\qquad \text{(2.14b)}$$

Many other statements and properties related to set operations could be presented. Those given here, however, are adequate for our work in establishing the concepts of probability theory.

Section 2.6   AXIOMS AND PROPERTIES OF PROBABILITY

◆ ◆ ◆ ◆ ◆

Within the context of probability theory, a random experiment is an action that produces variable outcomes. For example, a random experiment might be: Send a voice message over a telephone system. An outcome would then be one of many possible conversations. We designate the collection of all possible outcomes from a random experiment as the **sample space** S. Each **outcome** s is therefore an element of S.

We group outcomes within a sample space into various **events,** $A, B, C, \ldots$; $A \subset S, B \subset S, C \subset S, \ldots$. The nature of a given random experiment and the reasons for our interest in it determine how this is done. For example, if a sample space consists of all possible voice conversations transmitted over a telephone system, and if we are interested in the acoustic characteristics of these conversations, it may suit our purposes to define the following events:

$$A = \{\text{All conversations by adult males}\}$$

$$B = \{\text{All conversations by adult females}\}$$

$$C = \{\text{All conversations by children}\}$$

We assign probabilities to events; a **probability** is a real number bounded by zero and one; $0 \le P(A) \le 1$. The notation $P(A)$ is read "the probability of event A." A sample space can be thought of as the **certain event** because it includes all possible outcomes: $P(S) = 1$. The **impossible event,** the event that contains no outcomes, is denoted by $\varnothing$: $P(\varnothing) = 0$. Probabilities $P(A)$ with values between zero and one may be determined by a variety of methods: equally likely events, relative frequency, or other methods guided by the theory in this book.

We summarize the essential properties of probability theory in the following three axioms. We accept these axioms as the conventional wisdom of probability theory. Other important properties of probability are derived from them. A fourth axiom, related to infinite sums, is also introduced at the end of this section.

Axiom I ◆ If S is the sample space for an experiment, then

$$P(S) = 1$$

Axiom II ◆ If A is an event contained in the sample space, then

$$P(A) \ge 0$$

Axiom III ◆ If A and B are both contained in the sample space, and if A and B are disjoint events (i.e., $A \cap B = \varnothing$), then

$$P(A \cup B) = P(A) + P(B)$$

A variety of properties of probabilities follows directly from these axioms. Using Axiom III and (2.11b),

$$P(A \cup \overline{A}) = P(A) + P(\overline{A})$$

Then, using Axiom I and (2.11a),

$$P(\overline{A}) = 1 - P(A) \tag{2.15}$$

A special case of (2.15) occurs when A is S. The complement of the sample space is the impossible event, $\overline{S} = \varnothing$, and

$$P(\varnothing) = 1 - P(S)$$

It then follows, using Axiom I, that

$$P(\varnothing) = 0 \tag{2.16}$$

We note from (2.15) that when either $P(A)$ or $P(\overline{A})$ is zero the other has a value of one. Axiom II and (2.15) lead to the generalization

$$P(A) \leq 1 \tag{2.17}$$

It frequently happens that events A and B are not disjoint: $A \cap B \neq \varnothing$ [see Figure 2.5(a)]. Axiom III may be applied if $A \cup B$ is decomposed into events that are disjoint, as shown in Figure 2.5(b). In this case we use the events A and $B \cap \overline{A}$. Using the associative relation (2.9b),

$$A \cap (B \cap \overline{A}) = B \cap (A \cap \overline{A}) = \varnothing$$

Also, using the distributive relation (2.10a),

$$A \cup (B \cap \overline{A}) = (A \cup B) \cap (A \cup \overline{A}) = A \cup B$$

Then, using these results with Axiom III,

$$P(A \cup B) = P(A) + P(B \cap \overline{A}) \tag{2.18}$$

The probability of an event which is the intersection of other events, e.g., $P(B \cap \overline{A})$, may be called a **joint probability.**

A process similar to that used to obtain (2.18) can also be used with the events $B \cap A$ and $B \cap \overline{A}$ to show that

$$(B \cap A) \cap (B \cap \overline{A}) = \varnothing$$

and

$$(B \cap A) \cup (B \cap \overline{A}) = B$$

A glance at the Venn diagrams in Figure 2.5 may assist in verifying these. Then, using Axiom III,

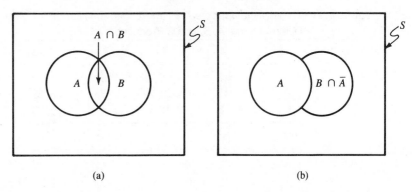

Figure 2.5   Venn diagrams illustrating (a) events A and B that are not disjoint and (b) events A and $B \cap \bar{A}$ that are disjoint.

$$P(B \cap A) + P(B \cap \bar{A}) = P(B) \tag{2.19}$$

Finally, combining (2.18) with (2.19) yields another relation for $P(A \cup B)$,

$$P(A \cup B) = P(A) + P(B) - P(A \cap B) \tag{2.20}$$

Both (2.18) and (2.20) reduce to Axiom III if A and B are disjoint.

The principle expressed in Axiom III may be generalized. Assume there are n disjoint events A_i, $i = 1, 2, \ldots, n$, in the sample space S. Then the generalized Axiom III is

$$P\left(\bigcup_{i=1}^{n} A_i\right) = \sum_{i=1}^{n} P(A_i) \tag{2.21}$$

where $A_i \cap A_j = \varnothing$, all i and j, $i \neq j$. The notation of repeated unions in (2.21) is defined in (2.13a).

Example 2.8   Let the events X, Y, and Z represent three different manufacturers, each of whom produces items A, B, and C. Table 2.2 lists the number of items produced by each manufacturer. In this example each one of the 107 items identified in Table 2.2 is equally likely to be selected. Therefore, using (2.3), each item in Table 2.2 has the probability of 1/107 of being selected. Further, if there are 15 items in the event $B \cap X$, the probability of selecting one item and having it jointly be a B, and manufactured by X is, by (2.4), $P(B \cap X) = 15/107$. Other examples involving joint probabilities are

$$P(B) = P(B \cap X) + P(B \cap Y) + P(B \cap Z)$$
$$= 15/107 + 21/107 + 3/107$$
$$= 39/107 = 0.364$$

Table 2.2   Three Manufacturers X, Y, and Z, and the Number of Different Items A, B, and C Produced by Them

	X	Y	Z	Total
A	13	6	19	38
B	15	21	3	39
C	8	18	4	30
Total	36	45	26	107

$$P(X) = P(X \cap A) + P(X \cap B) + P(X \cap C)$$
$$= 13/107 + 15/107 + 8/107$$
$$= 36/107 = 0.336$$

To calculate the probability of $B \cup X$, we may use (2.20):

$$P(B \cup X) = P(B) + P(X) - P(B \cap X)$$
$$= 39/107 + 36/107 - 15/107$$
$$= 60/107 = 0.561$$

Or we may use (2.18):

$$P(B \cup X) = P(B) + P(\overline{B} \cap X)$$
$$= P(B) + P(A \cap X) + P(C \cap X)$$
$$= 39/107 + 13/107 + 8/107$$
$$= 60/107 = 0.561$$

Probabilities of other events selected from Table 2.2 using the assumption of equally likely events are calculated similarly.

◆ ◆ ◆ ◆ ◆

The case of **infinite additivity** occurs if the number of disjoint events A_i becomes countably infinite. This special case would require consideration of convergence in (2.21) as $n \rightarrow \infty$, and is therefore separated out and given the rank of a fourth axiom:

Axiom IV ◆   Infinite additivity

$$P\left(\bigcup_{i=1}^{\infty} A_i\right) = \sum_{i=1}^{\infty} P(A_i)$$

Section 2.7   **CONDITIONAL PROBABILITY**

◆ ◆ ◆ ◆ ◆

That the probability of an event, say A, depends on, or is conditioned by, the occurrence of another event, say B, arises quite naturally and inevitably in the study of random experiments. For example, the probability that a device will fail in some interval of time may depend on the device's operating temperature. Or the probability of making an error when detecting a signal in the presence of noise is influenced by the power of the noise.

The notation used to denote a conditional probability is $P(A|B)$. This notation is read "the probability of the event A on the condition that B has occurred" or "the probability of A given B."

Conditional probability is defined as follows:

$$P(A|B) = \frac{P(A \cap B)}{P(B)}, \; P(B) \neq 0 \qquad (2.22)$$

One way of viewing the conditional probability $P(A|B)$ is that it is a probability based on random experiments that have the event B as their sample space: $S_B = B$.

1. The event $A \cap B$ in the definition (2.22) represents that part of A which is contained in B [see Figure 2.5(a) again]:

$$0 \leq \frac{P(A \cap B)}{P(B)} \leq 1$$

2. If A is a subset of B, $A \cap B = A$, and the conditional probability $P(A|B)$ is the ratio $P(A)/P(B)$.

3. If B is a subset of A, $A \cap B = B$, and the occurrence of B guarantees the occurrence of A: $P(A|B) = 1$.

4. Finally, if A and B are disjoint, the occurrence of either A or B precludes the occurrence of the other. Therefore, if B is given, A is an impossible event:

$$A \cap B = \varnothing \quad \text{and} \quad P(A|B) = 0.$$

The definition of conditional probability (2.22) satisfies the probability axioms I, II and III:

I. Because B is always a subevent of S, it follows, using (2.22), that $P(S|B) = 1$.

II. The numerator and the denominator of (2.22) are non-negative. Hence, $P(A|B) \geq 0$.

III. Finally, if A_1 and A_2 are disjoint, then it is also true that $A_1 \cap B$ and $A_2 \cap B$ are disjoint. Using (2.22),

$$P[(A_1 \cup A_2)|B] = \frac{P[(A_1 \cup A_2) \cap B]}{P(B)}$$

Using the distributive relation (2.10b),

$$P[(A_1 \cup A_2)|B] = \frac{P[(A_1 \cap B) \cup (A_2 \cap B)]}{P(B)}$$

Using Axiom III,

$$P[(A_1 \cup A_2)|B] = \frac{P(A_1 \cap B)}{P(B)} + \frac{P(A_2 \cap B)}{P(B)}$$

Then, using (2.22) again,

$$P[(A_1 \cup A_2)|B] = P(A_1| B) + P(A_2|B)$$

A *partition with respect to S* is a set of events A_i, $i = 1, 2, \ldots, n$, such that the events are disjoint

$$A_i \cap A_j = \emptyset, i \neq j \tag{2.23}$$

and such that

$$\bigcup_{i=1}^{n} A_i = S \tag{2.24}$$

A partition with respect to S where $n = 3$ is illustrated in Figure 2.6.

Using (2.23) and (2.24), the events $B \cap A_i$ are a partition with respect to B, which is also illustrated in Figure 2.6:

$$(B \cap A_i) \cap (B \cap A_j) = B \cap (A_i \cap A_j) = B \cap \emptyset = \emptyset, i \neq j \tag{2.25}$$

$$\bigcup_{i=1}^{n} B \cap A_i = B \cap \left(\bigcup_{i=1}^{n} A_i \right) = B \cap S = B \tag{2.26}$$

We use the partition with respect to B in (2.25) and (2.26) with the expression (2.21) to write a form of the **total probability theorem:**

$$P(B) = \sum_{i=1}^{n} P(B \cap A_i) \tag{2.27}$$

Then, using the definition of conditional probability (2.22), we obtain the second form of the total probability theorem:

$$P(B) = \sum_{i=1}^{n} P(B|A_i)P(A_i) \tag{2.28}$$

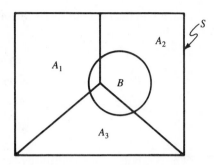

Figure 2.6   A Venn diagram illustrating events A_1, A_2, and A_3 that are a partition with respect to S.

• •

Either form of the total probability theorem is valid if and only if the A_i are a partition as described in (2.23) and (2.24). The usefulness of the total probability theorem is illustrated in the following example.

Example 2.9   We look at the data in Table 2.2 from a point of view different from that used in Example 2.8. There we applied the assumption of equally likely events to the entire collection of 107 items. In this example we first choose one of the three manufacturers; suppose we have data which say that the probabilities of our selecting each manufacturer are

$$P(X) = 0.47 \quad P(Y) = 0.31 \quad P(Z) = 0.22$$

Given that we have selected a manufacturer, the assumption of equally likely events and the data in Table 2.2 are used to calculate the conditional probabilities

$$P(B|X) = 15/36 \quad P(B|Y) = 21/45 \quad P(B|Z) = 3/26$$

We then use the total probability theorem in (2.28) to calculate $P(B)$:

$$P(B) = P(B|X)P(X) + P(B|Y)P(Y) + P(B|Z)P(Z)$$
$$= (15/36)(0.47) + (21/45)(0.31) + (3/26)(0.22)$$
$$= 0.366$$

Similar computations will yield $P(A) = 0.372$ and $P(C) = 0.262$. Note that the sum of $P(A)$, $P(B)$, and $P(C)$ is one, as it should be. To calculate the joint probability of B and X, we must use (2.22):

$$P(B \cap X) = P(B|X)P(X)$$
$$= (15/36)(0.47)$$
$$= 0.196$$

To calculate the probability of the union of the events B and X, we use (2.20):

$$P(B \cup X) = P(B) + P(X) - P(B \cap X)$$
$$= 0.366 + 0.47 - 0.196$$
$$= 0.640$$

$\bullet \quad \bullet \quad \bullet \quad \bullet \quad \bullet$

The symbols in the definition of conditional probability (2.22) may be interchanged with the result

$$P(B|A) = \frac{P(B \cap A)}{P(A)}, \; P(A) \neq 0 \tag{2.29}$$

Using the commutative relation (2.8b) it then follows that (2.22) and (2.29) may be combined to express **Bayes' theorem:**

$$P(B|A)P(A) = P(A|B)P(B) \tag{2.30}$$

Applying Bayes' theorem (2.30) to any event A_i in a partition with respect to B, we have

$$P(A_i|B) = P(B|A_i)P(A_i)/P(B) \tag{2.31}$$

This can then be combined with the total probability theorem (2.28) to yield a second form of *Bayes' theorem:*

$$P(A_j|B) = \frac{P(B|A_1)P(A_1)}{\sum\limits_{i=1}^{n} P(B|A_i)P(A_i)} \tag{2.32}$$

When applications of Bayes' theorem are expressed as in (2.32), then the probabilities $P(A_i)$ are called **prior** *(a priori)* probabilities. The probabilities conditioned by the event B: $P(A_i|B)$, are called **posterior** *(a posteriori)* probabilities; and the conditional probabilities $P(B|A_i)$ are called **transition** probabilities.

The idea expressed here is that prior information contained in $P(A_i)$ can be combined with a random experiment, which yields new information associated with the event B. Then, given the new information derived from B, posterior probabilities $P(A_i|B)$ are considered to be a new description of the probability of the events A_i.

Example 2.10 Consider the problem of testing a device for defects as it is manufactured. If a defect D is identified, the test should fail F the device. Correspondingly, the process should pass (or, not fail) $\overline{F}$ a device with no defects $\overline{D}$. The testing process itself makes errors: A **type I error** occurs when a device has no defect, but fails the test. And a **type II error** occurs when a device has a defect, but passes the test.

Assume that the prior probability of a device not being defective is 0.99. Also, assume that the probability of the test failing a device when it has a defect is 0.95, and that the probability of the test accepting a device when it has no defect is 0.98. These assumptions may be expressed as

$$P(\overline{D}) = 0.99, \qquad P(D) = 0.01$$
$$P(F|D) = 0.95, \qquad P(\overline{F}|D) = 0.05$$
$$P(F|\overline{D}) = 0.02, \qquad P(\overline{F}|\overline{D}) = 0.98$$

Note that the probability of type II error is 0.05, and a type I error is 0.02. Using the total probability theorem (2.28) we calculate the probability of a device passing (i.e., not failing) the test following its manufacture:

$$\begin{aligned} P(\overline{F}) &= P(\overline{F}|D)P(D) + P(\overline{F}|\overline{D})P(\overline{D}) \\ &= (0.05)(0.01) + (0.98)(0.99) \\ &= 0.9707 \end{aligned}$$

This probability is less than the prior probability of no defect $[P(\overline{D}) = 0.99]$ because the testing process makes errors. When a manufactured device fails its test, the probability that it is defective is, using Bayes' theorem (2.30),

$$\begin{aligned} P(D|F) &= P(F|D)P(D)/P(F) \\ &= (0.95)(0.01)/(1 - 0.9707) \\ &= 0.3242 \end{aligned}$$

Therefore, $P(\overline{D}|F) = 1 - 0.3242 = 0.6758$.

We also use Bayes' theorem (2.30) to calculate the posterior probability $P(\overline{D}|\overline{F})$, which is the probability of no defect given that a device passes the test:

$$\begin{aligned} P(\overline{D}|\overline{F}) &= P(\overline{F}|\overline{D})P(\overline{D})/P(\overline{F}) \\ &= (0.98)(0.99)/(0.9707) \\ &= 0.9995 \end{aligned}$$

This shows that even with the errors, something is accomplished by the test: Before the test, we expect 1 out of 100 devices to be defective $[P(D) = 0.01]$ but, of those which pass the test, 1 out of 2000 devices is defective: $[P(\overline{D}|\overline{F}) = 0.9995]$. Of course, the price for achieving this improvement is $P(\overline{D}|F) = 0.6758$, as shown above. Approximately two out of every three devices that fail the test are **not defective**. To improve this, a better test process that makes fewer errors would have to be designed.

◆ ◆ ◆ ◆ ◆

Section 2.8   INDEPENDENT RANDOM EVENTS

♦ ♦ ♦ ♦ ♦

Our interest here is in describing the effect on probabilities when two events are independent. Suppose, for example, that a signal is composed of two parts: a desired message A and an undesired noise B. Often (but not always!) the nature of the system containing the signal is such that the message and the noise exist independently of each other. That is, the noise could be present if the message were not, and vice versa. And, there is no interaction between the noise and signal when both are present. As another example, the events A and B could be independent of each other even when they refer to the same signal but at different times. Or A could refer to a signal at the input to a network, while B refers to a different signal at the network's output.

In general, the condition of event A being **independent** of event B is defined using conditional probability:

$$P(A|B) = P(A) \tag{2.33}$$

Any conditioning by the event B has no effect on the probability of A if A is independent of B. If we combine (2.33) with (2.22),

$$P(A|B) = P(A) = P(A \cap B)/P(B)$$

or

$$P(A \cap B) = P(A)P(B) \tag{2.34}$$

The two statements (2.33) and (2.34) are equivalent expressions of independence. Because (2.34) is symmetrical with respect to A and B, it follows that if A is independent of B, then B is also independent of A, and we may then refer to A and B as independent.

For three events A, B, and C to be independent requires that (2.34) be extended into the following four equations:

$$P(A \cap B) = P(A)P(B) \tag{2.35a}$$

$$P(A \cap C) = P(A)P(C) \tag{2.35b}$$

$$P(B \cap C) = P(B)P(C) \tag{2.35c}$$

$$P(A \cap B \cap C) = P(A)P(B)P(C) \tag{2.35d}$$

Independence of events A, B, and C requires the independence of arbitrary combinations of the three events. The definitions in (2.35) satisfy this requirement. For example, consider the event $A \cap (B \cup C)$:

$$P[A \cap (B \cup C)] = P[(A \cap B) \cup (A \cap C)]$$
$$= P(A \cap B) + P(A \cap C) - P(A \cap B \cap C)$$

We used (2.20) to obtain this expression. Then, using (2.35) [in particular note that it is necessary to use (2.35d), which involves each of the three events]:

$$P[A \cap (B \cup C)] = P(A)P(B) + P(A)P(C) - P(A)P(B)P(C)$$
$$= P(A)[P(B) + P(C) - P(B)P(C)]$$
$$= P(A)P(B \cup C)$$

This shows how all four statements in (2.35) are needed if arbitrary combinations of the three events A, B, and C are to be independent.

If we consider the independence of four or more random events, the system of equations (2.35) must be extended to include all possible pairs of events, all possible triplets of events, all possible quadruples of events, etc. We will not dwell on that extension except to point out the following necessary but not sufficient condition. If it is known that the n events A_i, $i = 1, 2, \ldots, n$, are independent, then (2.35d) extends to

$$P\left(\bigcap_{i=1}^{n} A_i\right) = \prod_{i=1}^{n} P(A_i) \tag{2.36}$$

Some applications of this important relation follow.

Suppose a system consists of n components, all of which must operate properly if the system is to work. In a sense, all the components are competing with each other; the first single component to fail causes the entire system to fail. This situation can be modeled by the n switches in Figure 2.7. Each switch represents a component, and the entire assembly of switches represents the system. A closed switch represents a working component. All switches in series represents the necessity for all components to work if the system is to work.

Let A_i be the event that the i'th component in Figure 2.7 functions properly, and let B be the event that the entire system works:

$$B = \bigcap_{i=1}^{n} A_i$$

If we assume the components are independent we can use (2.36):

$$P(B) = \prod_{i=1}^{n} P(A_i) \tag{2.37}$$

Because each $P(A_i)$ in (2.37) is less than one, the probability of the system working is less than the smallest $P(A_i)$.

Example 2.11 Suppose a system has three independent components, each of which must work if the system is to work. The probabilities for successful operation of the components are

$$P(A_1) = P(A_2) = 0.9, \quad P(A_3) = 0.85$$

Because successful operation of the system requires successful operation of all its components, as in Figure 2.7 when $n = 3$, the probability that the system will work is, using (2.37),

$$P(B) = (0.9)(0.9)(0.85) = 0.689$$

◆　◆　◆　◆　◆

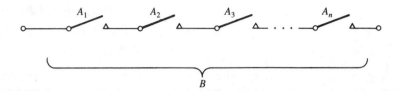

Figure 2.7 A model of a system of n components, all of which must function properly if the system is to work.

This same model can be used with a single component if within the component there are several physical mechanisms competing such that the first to fail will cause the component to fail.

Consider the case in which there are n redundant components; the system will work if at least one of the components operates properly. Again, proper operation of a component is indicated by a switch closure. Therefore, a system of n redundant components can be represented by n switches in parallel, as in Figure 2.8. Let A_i be the event the i'th component is operating properly, and B the event the system works. Then, using the complement of B, the event of system failure is

$$\bar{B} = \bigcap_{i=1}^{n} \bar{A}_i$$

That is, for the system to fail, all redundant components must fail. Using (2.15) and (2.36), and assuming the components are independent, the probability that the system works is

$$P(B) = 1 - \prod_{i=1}^{n} P(\bar{A}_i)$$

$$P(B) = 1 - \prod_{i=1}^{n} [1 - P(A_i)] \tag{2.38}$$

With redundant components, the probability that the system will work is greater than the probability of any single component.

Example 2.12 A system consists of three redundant and independent components. The probabilities of successful operation of the components are

$$P(A_1) = P(A_2) = 0.9, \quad P(A_3) = 0.85$$

Because the three components are independent as well as redundant, (2.38) applies, and the probability of the system working is

$$P(B) = 1 - (1 - 0.9)(1 - 0.9)(1 - 0.85) = 0.9985$$

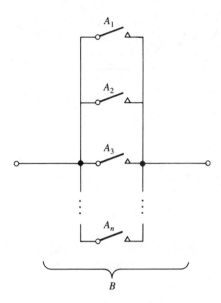

Figure 2.8   A model of a system of n redundant components, all of which must fail if the system is to fail.

♦ ♦

If there are only two independent redundant components, then

$$B = A_1 \cup A_2$$

Also, using (2.20),

$$P(B) = P(A_1) + P(A_2) - P(A_1)P(A_2) \qquad (2.39)$$

Example 2.13   Figure 2.9 shows a model for a system with both series and parallel components. Assume the components are independent. The probabilities of successful operation of the components are

$$P(A_1) = P(A_2) = 0.9, \quad P(A_3) = 0.85$$

Using (2.39), components A_1 and A_2 can be combined into an equivalent
component, $A_1 \cup A_2$, and its probability of successful operation is

$$P(A_1 \cup A_2) = 0.9 + 0.9 - (0.9)^2 = 0.99$$

This equivalent component is in series with A_3. Therefore, the probability
the system works is

$$P(B) = [(A_1 \cup A_2) \cap A_3]$$
$$= (0.99)(0.85) = 0.842$$

♦ ♦ ♦ ♦ ♦

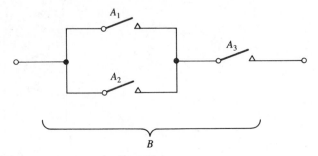

Figure 2.9   A model of a system containing both redundant components and components competing for failure.

◆ ◆ ◆ ◆ ◆ ◆ ◆

Section 2.9   SEQUENCES OF RANDOM EXPERIMENTS

◆ ◆ ◆ ◆ ◆

Typically, we use a sequence of trials, or repetitions, of the same random experiment to obtain enough data to draw some valid conclusions. We can repeat a random experiment as many times as we wish, and, if the trials are independent, the result of any trial has no effect on any other trial. On the other hand, there are situations in which independence among the trials cannot be assumed. For example, in expensive experiments, such as manned space shuttles, there is certainly no intention to perform many *identical* launches simply to obtain better relative frequency data. On the contrary, every bit of information learned on one launch is incorporated into the next launch in order to make it better and safer. In this sense, each experiment of launching a manned space shuttle is conditioned by all preceding experiments.

We use A_i, $i = 1, 2, \ldots, n$, to denote the i'th event in a sequence. The possibility that A_i is conditioned by outcomes from earlier trials is described using conditional probability. To show how this is done, let $A = A_n$, and B be the intersection of all the events A_i except the event A_n. That is, let

$$B = A_1 \cap A_2 \cap \ldots \cap A_{n-1} = \bigcap_{i=1}^{n-1} A_i$$

Then, using (2.22),

$$P\left(\bigcap_{i=1}^{n} A_i\right) = P\left(A_n \Big| \bigcap_{i=1}^{n-1} A_i\right) P\left(\bigcap_{n-1}^{i=1} A_i\right) \tag{2.40}$$

The joint probabilities on the left and right sides of (2.40) differ by one in the number of intersections they contain. By using (2.22), the joint probability on the right side of (2.40) can be combined with another conditional probability to form the following:

$$P\left(\bigcap_{i=1}^{n} A_i\right) = P\left(A_n \Big| \bigcap_{i=1}^{n-1} A_i\right) P\left(A_{n-1} \Big| \bigcap_{i=1}^{n-2} A_i\right) P\left(\bigcap_{i=1}^{n-2} A_i\right)$$

This process continues until we reach the first random experiment, which has the probability $P(A_1)$:

$$P\left(\bigcap_{i=1}^{n} A_i\right) = P(A_1)P(A_2|A_1)P(A_3|A_1 \cap A_2) \ldots P\left(A_n \Big| \bigcap_{i=1}^{n-1} A_{n-1}\right) \quad (2.41)$$

This is a general statement that allows for the possibility of the i'th event A_i to be conditioned by the outcomes of all preceding trials.

A special case of (2.41) occurs when each event A_i is conditioned only by its preceding event A_{i-1}. This special case is called a **Markov chain,** and (2.41) is written as

$$P\left(\bigcap_{i=1}^{n} A_i\right) = P(A_1)P(A_2|A_1)P(A_3|A_2) \ldots P(A_n|A_{n-1}) \quad (2.42)$$

Another way of thinking about a Markov chain is that it is a system with a memory that extends only to the immediately preceding trial.

Example 2.14   Figure 2.10 shows a diagram of two disjoint events, designated A and $\overline{A}$, which are called **states.** As a specific example, suppose we are discussing a radar set. We let A be the state that the radar is working, and $\overline{A}$ be the state that the radar is not working and needs repairs. The arrows in this figure represent conditional probabilities associated with changing from one state to the other. In our radar example, the arrow going from $\overline{A}$ to A represents the conditional probability of repair, and the arrow going from A to $\overline{A}$ represents the conditional probability of a radar failure. These conditional probabilities are therefore called **transition probabilities.**

To distinguish between a present state and the last state, we use subscripts **pr** and **last.** Then, using data in the figure,

$$P(A_{pr}|A_{last}) = 0.50$$

This is read "given that the last state was A, the transition probability of the present state becoming A is 0.50." Similarly,

$$P(\overline{A}_{pr}|A_{last}) = 0.50$$
$$P(A_{pr}|\overline{A}_{last}) = 0.30$$
$$P(\overline{A}_{pr}|\overline{A}_{last}) = 0.70$$

Figure 2.10 therefore depicts a Markov chain involving two states (events). The total probability that the present state will be A is, using (2.28),

$$P(A_{pr}) = P(A_{pr}|A_{last})P(A_{last}) + P(A_{pr}|\overline{A}_{last})P(\overline{A}_{last})$$

A steady-state condition occurs when the two probabilities $P(A_{pr})$ and $P(A_{last})$ are equal:

$$P(A_{pr}) = P(A_{last}) = P(A)$$

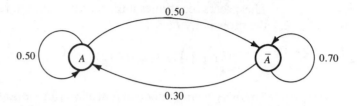

Figure 2.10   A state diagram for two disjoint events showing the transition probabilities used in Example 2.14.

• •

A similar relation holds for $P(\overline{A})$. Therefore, in the steady state,

$$P(A) = (0.50)P(A) + (0.30)P(\overline{A})$$

Using (2.15), we can solve for $P(A)$ and $P(\overline{A})$:

$$P(A) = 0.30/0.80 = 0.375$$
$$P(\overline{A}) = 0.625$$

Referring to our radar set again, this says that it needs repair 63% of the time!

The following sequence of 50 one and zero events is a specific realization of a Markov chain obtained from a computer simulation. Here, 1 represents an outcome of A, and 0 represents an outcome of $\overline{A}$:

$$\ldots 00011001011000011000101111000000000010000010100011 \ldots$$

Out of these 50 experiments, A occurred 17 times, and using relative frequency, the probability of A is approximately

$$P(A) \approx 17/50 = 0.34$$

• • • • •

If a system has **zero-memory**, the conditional probabilities in (2.41) all simplify:

$$P\left(\bigcap_{i=1}^{n} A_i\right) = P(A_1)P(A_2)P(A_3)\ldots P(A_n) = \prod_{i=1}^{n} P(A_i) \qquad \textbf{(2.43)}$$

From (2.43), a sequence of zero-memory random experiments is another way of describing a sequence of independent events. This result is the same as (2.36), but was obtained from a different point of view. An important application of zero-memory random experiments is discussed next.

A **Bernoulli trial** describes a random experiment that is binary in nature. It models a variety of two-state events such as: *accept* or *reject, on* or *off, hit* or *miss,* etc. Therefore, its sample space is partitioned into two events, A and $\overline{A}$:

$$A \cup \overline{A} = S \quad \text{and} \quad A \cap \overline{A} = \varnothing$$

Let the probability of events A and $\overline{A}$ be p and q, respectively,

$$P(A) = p, \qquad P(\overline{A}) = q, \quad p + q = 1 \qquad (2.44)$$

Now, assume the same Bernoulli experiment is repeated *independently n* times:

$$A_i = A \cup \overline{A} = S, \quad i = 1, 2, \ldots, n$$

This is read "the event A_i is certain to be either A or $\overline{A}$." From (2.43),

$$P\left(\bigcap_{i=1}^{n} A_i\right) = \prod_{i=1}^{n} P(A_i)$$

$$= \prod_{i=1}^{n} P(A \cup \overline{A})$$

Because A and $\overline{A}$ are disjoint, we can use Axiom III, and

$$P(A \cup \overline{A}) = P(A) + P(\overline{A}) = p + q = 1$$

and

$$P\left(\bigcap_{i=1}^{n} A_i\right) = (p + q)^n = 1 \qquad (2.45)$$

We combine the **binomial theorem** (B.7) with (2.45) as follows:

$$(p + q)^n = \sum_{k=0}^{n} \binom{n}{k} p^k q^{n-k} = 1 \qquad (2.46)$$

where $\binom{n}{k}$ is the combination of n things taken k at a time; see (B.2). The sum in (2.46) totals to one because it contains all possible sequences of n independent Bernoulli trials. The experiment implied by (2.46), which is a combination of n independent Bernoulli random experiments, is called a **binomial experiment**. Each term in (2.46) is a probability, and is denoted by

$$P_n(k) = \binom{n}{k} p^k q^{n-k} \qquad (2.47)$$

With the notation in (2.47), (2.46) can be expressed as

$$\sum_{k=0}^{n} P_n(k) = 1 \qquad (2.48)$$

Example 2.15   Suppose a computer pod contains $n = 10$ terminals, which may be connected to three different computers: A, B, and C via a network. Further, suppose that people enter the pod independently of each other and seek to use the computers with probabilities

$$P(A) = 0.25, \quad P(B) = 0.25, \quad P(C) = 0.50$$

Table 2.3   Values of $P_{10}(k)$ Used in Example 2.15

k	$P_{10}(k)$	$\sum_{l=0}^{k} P_{10}(l)$
0	0.0563	0.0563
1	0.1877	0.2440
2	0.2816	0.5256
3	0.2503	0.7759
4	0.1460	0.9219
5	0.0584	0.9803
6	0.0162	0.9965
7	0.0031	0.9996
8	0.0004	1.0000
9	0.0000	1.0000
10	0.0000	1.0000

We focus our interest on computer A:

$$P(A) = p = 0.25, \quad P(\overline{A}) = q = 0.75, \quad p + q = 1$$

Finally, we want to know how many ports on computer A should be allocated to the network connecting it to the pod. A person in the pod should have a probability of at least 90% of finding an open port to computer A.

We use (2.47) to calculate values in Table 2.3. These values show, for example, when $k = 4$, the probability of exactly four terminals being occupied and connected to computer A is

$$P(k = 4) = P_{10}(4) = 0.1460$$

The probability of no more than four terminals being occupied and connected to computer A is

$$P(k \le 4) = P_{10}(0) + P_{10}(1) + P_{10}(2) + P_{10}(3) + P_{10}(4)$$
$$= 0.9219$$

It therefore follows, using the data in Table 2.3 and using the interpretation of these data as described in this example, that only four ports on computer A need to be allocated to the pod.

This result is valid provided each person who attempts to use the pod is working independently of all others. Of course, if there happens to be a classroom next to the pod, and if a class meeting in the room is assigned computer A for doing homework problems, then the assumption of independence for this binomial experiment can be questioned. The assumption of *independent* Bernoulli trials must always be examined carefully in practical applications of binomial experiments.

◆   ◆   ◆   ◆   ◆

Exercises

♦ ♦ ♦ ♦ ♦

1. Do Example 2.3 again, but this time use Table 2.1 as follows: In the last row of numbers, the third group of five ends with 51791 — start at the 5 and proceed upward to select a sequence of random numbers.

2. You have 45 items and want to choose four of them randomly, without replacement. To find pairs of random numbers use Table 2.1 as follows: In the top row of numbers, the fourth group of five starts with 27802 — start at the 27 and proceed down to select a sequence of pairs of numbers. What items are selected?

3. A pointer is spun on a circular dial; it will come to rest equally likely in any direction. The dial is divided into 12 equal segments labeled a_1, $a_2, \ldots, a_{12}$.

   a. Define $A = \{a_1, a_3, a_5, a_7\}$, $B = \{a_4, a_5, a_6, a_7, a_8\}$, and $C = \{a_6, a_8, a_{10}, a_{12}\}$.

   b. Find probabilities for the following events:

   $$A, B, C, A \cap B, A \cup B, B \cap C, B \cup C, C \cap A, C \cup A$$

4. Write an algorithm, using URNG, having as its equally likely outcomes the integers 1 through 12. Operate the algorithm $n = 1000$ times, and use relative frequency to approximate the following:

   $$P\{x = 1\} \quad \text{and} \quad P\{x = 3, 4, 5, 6, 7, \text{ or } 8\}$$

   What is the relation between these results and $P(A \cup B)$ in Exercise 3?

5. A pointer is spun on a circular dial, and it will come to rest equally likely in any direction. The dial is not segmented, but is marked like a clock; it therefore represents all the real numbers $0 < x \leq 12$.

   a. Define $A = \{0 < x \leq 7\}$, $B = \{7 \leq x < 8\}$, and $C = \{6 < x < 12\}$.

   b. Find probabilities for the following events:

   $$A, B, C, A \cap B, A \cup B, B \cap C, B \cup C, C \cap A, C \cup A$$

6. Write an algorithm, using URNG, having as its outcomes the real numbers $0 < x < 12$. Operate the algorithm $n = 1000$ times, and use relative frequency to approximate the following:

   $$P\{x = 7\}, P\{7 < x < 8\}$$

   What is the relation between these results and $P(B)$ in Exercise 5?

7. A table of joint probabilities is given below. The events A, B, C, and D are a partition as are the events W, X, Y, and Z. Find:

     a. $P(C \cap X)$

     b. $P(C)$

     c. $P(X)$

     d. $P(C \cup X)$

     e. $P(W \cup X \cup B)$

     f. $P(W \cap X \cap B)$

     g. $P[(W \cup X) \cap B]$

     h. $P[W \cup (X \cap B)]$

	A	B	C	D
W	0.0588	0.1084	0.0309	0.0453
X	0.0182	0.0830	0.0508	0.1228
Y	0.0618	0.0868	0.0381	0.0423
Z	0.0931	0.0275	0.0593	0.0729

8. A table of joint probabilites is given below. The events W, X, Y, and Z are a partition as are the events A, B, C, and D. Find:

     a. $P(C \cap Y)$

     b. $P(C)$

     c. $P(Y)$

     d. $P(C \cup Y)$

     e. $P(B \cup C \cup Y)$

     f. $P(B \cap C \cap Y)$

     g. $P[(B \cup C) \cap Y]$

     h. $P[B \cup (C \cap Y)]$

	W	X	Y	Z
A	0.0391	0.0868	0.0644	0.0509
B	0.0509	0.1222	0.1426	0.0611
C	0.0153	0.0407	0.0204	0.0815
D	0.0306	0.0815	0.0713	0.0407

9. A collection of items may be classified by the partitions A, B, or C, and U, V, or W, as shown by the table of joint probabilities below. Find:

a. $P(B)$

b. $P(V)$

c. $P(B \cup V)$

d. $P(B \cup V \cup W)$

e. $P(B \cap V \cap W)$

f. $P[B \cap (V \cup W)]$

g. $P[(B \cap V) \cup W]$

	A	B	C
U	0.0916	0.1988	0.0585
V	0.1774	0.1170	0.0526
W	0.0370	0.1033	0.1638

10. Given the events A, B, and C in the sample space S, show that, in general,

$$P(A \cap B|C) = P(B|C)P(A|B \cap C)$$

11. Assume all the items in the table below are equally likely to be selected.

   a. Find $P(B \cap V)$ and $P(B \cup V)$.   c. Are A and U independent?

   b. Find $P(B|V)$ and $P(V|B)$.

	A	B	C	Total
U	47	102	30	
V	91	60	27	
W	19	53	84	
Total				513

12. An item is selected from the table below using this process: (1) First select U, V, or W; $P(U) = P(V) = P(W) = 1/3$. (2) The items A, B, and C within the selection of part (1) are now equally likely; one of those items is selected.

   a. Find $P(B \cap V)$ and $P(B \cup V)$.

   b. If the item selected is a B, what is the probability it came from V?

	A	B	C	Total
U	47	102	30	
V	91	60	27	
W	19	53	84	
Total				513

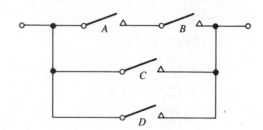

Figure 2.11   Diagram for Exercise 2.14.

• •

13. An item is selected from the table below using this process: (1) First
    select A, B, or C; $P(A) = P(B) = P(C) = 1/3$. (2) The items U, V, and
    W within the selection of part (1) are now equally likely; one of those
    items is selected.

    a. Find $P(B \cap V)$ and $P(B \cup V)$.

    b. If the item selected is a V, what is the probability it came from B?

	A	B	C	Total
U	47	102	30	
V	91	60	27	
W	19	53	84	
Total				513

14. In the network shown in Figure 2.11, each switch has a probability of
    closure of 0.80 and is independent of all the other switches. Find the
    probability of a circuit through the network.

15. In the network shown in Figure 2.12, the switches are independent.
    Switches A, C, and D have a probability of closure of 0.80, and switches
    B and E have a probability of closure of 0.90. Find the probability of a
    circuit through the network.

• •

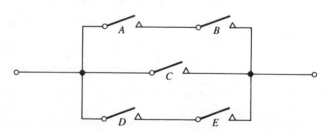

Figure 2.12   Diagram for Exercise 2.15.

16. These data are given:

$P(D) = 0.35$	$P(A|D) = 0.4$
$P(E) = 0.55$	$P(A|E) = 0.2$
$P(F) = 0.10$	$P(A|F) = 0.3$

What are the following?:

a. $P(A)$

b. $P(F|A)$

c. $P(\overline{A}|E)$

17. An error in a system can be made in three disjoint events designated A, B, and C. Let E designate the error event, and let

$$P(E|A) = 0.02, \quad P(E|B) = 0.04, \quad P(E|C) = 0.06$$

Also,

$$P(A) = 0.4, \quad P(B) = 0.4, \quad P(C) = 0.2$$

It is given that an error occurred. What is the probability that the error is associated with C?

18. A certain device may be bought from maufacturer A, B, or C. The probability manufacturer A is selected is 10%. Similarly for B, 30%, and C, 60%. It turns out that devices from A are defective 10% of the time; B, 5% of the time; and C, 2% of the time. Given that a defective device is obtained, what is the probability it came from manufacturer B?

19. A data transmission system is designed to transmit only three symbols. Its inputs are X_1, X_2, and X_3, and they are equally likely. Its outputs are Y_1, Y_2, and Y_3. The transmission system is noisy:

$$P(Y_i|X_j) = 0.98 \text{ if } i = j \text{ and}$$
$$= 0.01 \text{ if } i \neq j$$

If a Y_2 is received, what is the probability that X_2 was sent?

20. A Markov chain has a state diagram similar to that shown in Figure 2.10. However, the transition probabilities are

$$P(A|\overline{A}) = 0.20 \quad P(\overline{A}|A) = 0.45$$

What is the steady-state $P(A)$?

21. An experiment involves six independent Bernoulli trials for which the probability of an event A is $p = 0.36$. Calculate the following probabilities:

    a. P(exactly one occurrence of A).

    b. P(at least one occurrence of A).

    c. P(three or more occurrences of A).

22. Twenty items are selected independently, and randomly, for inspection. The probability of an item passing inspection is 0.78. Calculate the probability that exactly three items fail inspection.

23. If 25% of the bolts produced by a specific machine are defective, find the probability that out of four bolts chosen at random, 0, 1, and less than two bolts will be defective.

24. Suppose only two-thirds of all drivers use their seat belts. Find the probability that at least four of five drivers chosen at random will be using their seat belts.

References

• • • • •

1. Cooper, George R., and Clare D. McGillem. *Probabilistic Methods of Signal and System Analysis.* 2d ed. New York: Holt, Rinehart and Winston, 1986.

2. Peebles, Peyton Z., Jr. *Probability, Random Variables, and Random Signal Principles.* 2d ed. New York: McGraw-Hill Book Company, 1987.

3. Helstrom, Carl W. *Probability and Stochastic Processes for Engineers.* New York: Macmillan Publishing Company, 1984.

4. Larson, Harold J., and Bruno O. Shubert. *Probabilistic Models in Engineering Sciences, Volume I: Random Variables and Stochastic Processes.* New York: John Wiley and Sons, 1979.

5. Leon-Garcia, Alberto. *Probability and Random Processes for Electrical Engineering.* Reading, Mass.: Addison-Wesley Publishing Company, 1989.

Additional Reading

• • • • •

Klir, George J., and Tina A. Folger. *Fuzzy Sets, Uncertainty, and Information.* Englewood Cliffs, N.J.: Prentice Hall, 1988.

3

The Single Random Variable: Theory and Models

◆ ◆

An ounce of expectation is worth a pound of chance.

Anonymous

Introduction The world of engineering is a world of measurements; measurements connect the abstractness of theory with the reality of practice. The task before us therefore is to develop a systematic method for incorporating measurements into the theory of probability.

Heretofore, the events we discussed have been physical events, i.e., some specific collection of physical occurrences: spoken messages, manufactured parts, users of a computer, etc. The assumption we made is that, for each event A, we have some method for obtaining a value for the probability $P(A)$, such as the method of equally likely events or the method of relative frequency.

When we perform a **measurement** we obtain a number—the measured value. Examples of measured values are an average acoustic power of a spoken message, a distance measured on a manufactured part, a number of people using a computer, etc. We denote the measurement of an outcome with

$$X(a) = x_a \qquad (3.1)$$

where X is a function; its domain contains all physical outcomes a in the sample space S, and its range S_x is a set of numbers. The value x_a is called an **observation.** As shown in Figure 3.1, each event A in the sample space S is mapped using (3.1) into a set of numbers S_A. In general, however, the function X is many-to-one. Therefore, it is not possible to make a general relation between $P(A)$ and $P(S_A)$. Nevertheless, we do require

$$P(S) = P(S_X) = 1 \qquad (3.2)$$

Further, we assume observations produced by X have a **statistical consistency** such that we may speak of the probability of collections of observations (measured values). How this is done is the subject of the next section. A measurement of a random experiment, that is, the function X, is called a **random variable.** Usually, by convention, random variables are denoted by uppercase letters near the end of the alphabet: $U, V, \ldots , Z$.

To review quickly, an uppercase letter (e.g., X) refers to a random variable —a function; a lowercase letter (e.g., x) refers to an observation—a value obtained from a function.

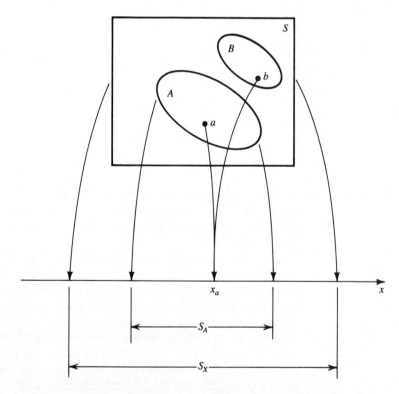

Figure 3.1   A random variable X maps outcomes from a sample space S to the real line; $X(a) = x_a$. A random variable is, in general, a many-to-one function. It is possible that some other outcome b also has x_a as an observation; $X(b) = x_a$.

Section 3.1   DISTRIBUTION AND DENSITY FUNCTIONS

◆ ◆ ◆ ◆ ◆

Frequency and cumulative frequency plots were introduced in Chapter 1 because of their utility in organizing data for study and interpretation. Examples of these plots are shown in Figure 3.2(a) where each value of n_k is the number of data occurring in a cell (an interval), and N_k is the cumulative effect of the n_k as shown in (1.21).

Suppose we normalize the frequency and cumulative frequency plots by dividing each n_k by n:

$$f_k = n_k/n \qquad (3.3)$$

$$F_k = N_k/n = \sum_{i=1}^{k} f_i \qquad (3.4)$$

The relations (3.3) and (3.4) are called **relative frequency** and the **cumulative relative frequency,** respectively. Normalizing changes the scale of the ordinate, but not the essential shape of the plots, as illustrated by comparing Figure 3.2(b) with Figure 3.2(a).

Of course, the exact shapes of relative frequency and cumulative relative frequency plots are always dependent on which sample data are used to construct them. However, if we let $n \to \infty$, and the cell widths become arbitrarily small, then the relative frequency plot becomes a **density function** $f_X(x)$, as illustrated in Figure 3.2(c):

$$f_k \to f_X(x)dx$$

Further, as is also illustrated in Figure 3.2(c), the sum in (3.4) becomes a **cumulative distribution function** $F_X(x)$:

$$F_k \to F_X(x)$$

where, guided by (3.4),

$$F_X(x) = \int_{-\infty}^{x} f_X(\alpha)d\alpha \qquad (3.5)$$

The cumulative distribution function (cdf) is a probability:

$$F_X(x) = P[a : X(a) \le x] \qquad (3.6a)$$

The right side of (3.6a) is read "the probability of outcome a such that observations obtained using random variable X are less than or equal to the independent variable x." Usually, we use the shorter notation

$$F_X(X) = P(X \le x) \qquad (3.6b)$$

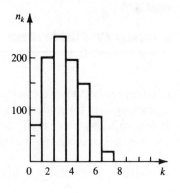
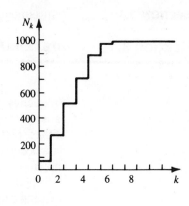

(a)

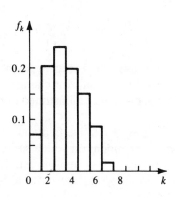
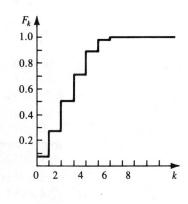

(b)

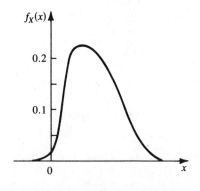
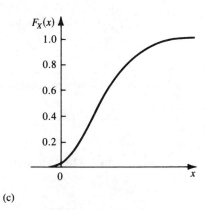

(c)

Figure 3.2   Comparing (a) the frequency and the cumulative frequency plots, (b) the relative frequency and the cumulative relative frequency plots, and (c) the probability density function (pdf) and the cumulative distribution function (cdf).

and we read the right side of (3.6b) as "the probability that the random variable X is less than or equal to x." If clarification of this abbreviated notation is needed, we will return to the more explicit (3.6a).[a]

Figure 3.3 presents examples of cdfs. The different shape of each cdf in the figure is chosen to emphasize that the shape of a cdf is determined by the statistical nature of its random variable. Each cdf in Figure 3.3 is a continuous function. This does not always have to be the case; we will soon see examples of cdfs with one or more discontinuities. However, when a cdf is continuous we say that the associated random variable is a **continuous random variable.** It is conventional in probability theory to use the uppercase F to designate a cdf. The different subscripts in Figure 3.3 show that the different cdfs relate to different random variables.

All cdfs are specified using (3.6b) and, as a result, they all have certain properties in common. For example, using (3.6b), we see that

$$F_X(\infty) = P(X \le \infty) = 1 \qquad (3.7)$$

which is a restatement of (3.2). Correspondingly,

$$F_X(-\infty) = P(X \le -\infty) = 0 \qquad (3.8)$$

since the event $(X \le -\infty)$ is the impossible event $\emptyset$, and $P(\emptyset) = 0$.

For the following development, we assume that a and b are two values on the real line, and that $a < b$. Then the two events $(X \le a)$ and $(a < X \le b)$ are disjoint, and

$$(X \le a) \cup (a < X \le b) = (X \le b)$$

Using the third axiom of probability,

$$P(a < X \le b) = P(X \le b) - P(X \le a)$$

From (3.6b),

$$P(a < X \le b) = F_x(b) - F_x(a) \qquad (3.9)$$

This is an important result because we will find many probabilities of the random variable X described over intervals on the x axis.

The second axiom of probability applied to (3.9) requires

$$F_X(b) - F_X(a) \ge 0 \qquad (3.10)$$

This means that a cdf must always be a nondecreasing function.

---

[a] With the notation in either (3.6a) or (3.6b), it is very important to keep in mind that the lowercase x is a specific number, presumedly a value under our control. The uppercase X, on the other hand, is a random variable, and stands for a range of observations (numbers).

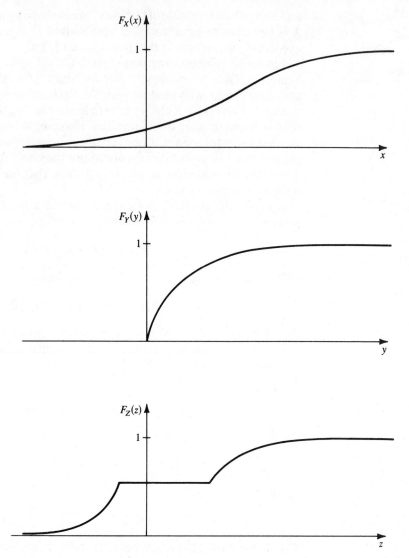

Figure 3.3   Examples of cdfs for the random variables X, Y, and Z.

◆ ◆

The density function in the integrand of (3.5) is called a **probability density function** (pdf). Using the fundamental theorem of the calculus:

$$f_X(x) = \frac{d}{dx} \int_{-\infty}^{x} f_X(\alpha)d\alpha$$

Therefore, the inverse relation to (3.5) is

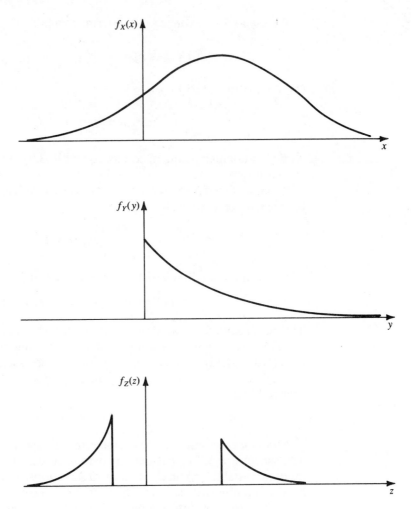

Figure 3.4   Examples of pdfs for the random variables X, Y, and Z.

◆ ◆

$$f_X(x) = \frac{d}{dx} F_X(x) \tag{3.11}$$

The derivative in (3.11) cannot be negative because the cdf must be nondecreasing, (3.10):

$$f_X(x) \geq 0 \tag{3.12}$$

The pdfs in Figure 3.4 are obtained from the cdfs in Figure 3.3 It is conventional to use the lowercase f to designate a pdf and, as with the cdf, a subscript relates the pdf to a specific random variable.

We use (3.5) to express (3.9) in terms of a pdf:

$$P(a < X \le b) = \int_{-\infty}^{b} f_X(x)dx - \int_{-\infty}^{a} f_X(x)dx$$

Combining these two integrals,

$$P(a < X \le b) = \int_{a}^{b} f_X(x)dx \tag{3.13}$$

As we commented before in connection with (3.9), this is an important result for our future work.

It follows that if $b \to \infty$ and $a \to -\infty$, and using (3.13), (3.7), (3.8), and (3.9), the area under a pdf is always unity:

$$\int_{-\infty}^{\infty} f_X(x)dx = 1 \tag{3.14}$$

Also, when the random variable is continuous, if $b \to a$, then using (3.9),

$$P(X=a) = F_X(a^+) - F_X(a) = 0 \tag{3.15}$$

This result says, for continuous random variables, that the probability of any specific observation is vanishingly small. Only intervals of observations, as indicated in (3.13), may have probabilities that are not zero. It also follows from (3.13) that if $a = x$ and $b = x + dx$, then $P(x < X \le x + dx)$ is a differential of probability dP, where

$$dP = f_X(x)dx \tag{3.16}$$

A random variable may be characterized by specifying either its pdf or cdf. The shape of a pdf or cdf may be helpful in describing the way in which a random variable produces random observations. For example, suppose we have a random variable in which observations occur **uniformly** in the interval $a < x < b$. By uniformly we mean that (3.16) becomes

$$dP = Adx$$

where $f_X(x) = A$ is a constant. The value of the constant A is $1/(b - a)$ because, from (3.14), the area under the pdf is unity; see Figure 3.5(a). It then follows from (3.5) that the cdf is as shown in Figure 3.5(b).

In summary, for a random variable uniformly distributed between a and b,

$$f_X(x) = \frac{1}{b - a}, \quad a < x < b \tag{3.17}$$

$$= 0, \qquad \text{otherwise}$$

$$F_X(x) = 1, \qquad b \le x < \infty \tag{3.18}$$

$$= \frac{x - a}{b - a}, \quad a \le x < b$$

$$= 0, \qquad -\infty < x < a$$

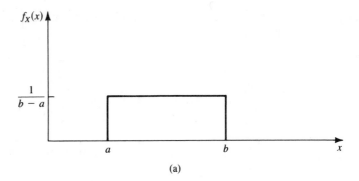

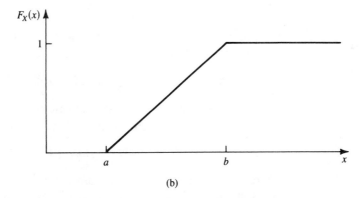

Figure 3.5   The (a) pdf and (b) cdf for the random variable X, which is uniformly distributed between a and b.

• •

$F_X(x)$ is a continuous function, hence X is a continuous random variable. Note how discontinuities in the derivative of the cdf in Figure 3.5(b) lead to discontinuities in the pdf in Figure 3.5(a). Discontinuities in the cdf, on the other hand, present no difficulties to us. They are integrable as required by (3.5).

Computer algorithms are available that simulate observations from a uniform random variable (see, for example URNG in Chapter 1 and Appendix A). Typically, these algorithms are normalized so $a = 0$ and $b = 1$. If X is a random variable that is uniform between zero and one, we can use the transformation

$$Y = (b - a)X + a \tag{3.19}$$

to produce the random variable Y, which is uniformly distributed[b] between a and b.

---

[b] We see this result intuitively. Functions of a single random variable are introduced later in this chapter, and this relation will be studied more carefully there.

Example 3.1   Consider the case of rounding a real number x at, say, the one-hundredths decimal place. This may be expressed as

$$y = [100x + 0.5]/100$$

where $[\cdot]$ is the operation of truncation, and where $[w + 0.5]$ rounds w to its nearest integer. For example, if $x = 1.762116 \ldots$, then its rounded value obtained from the expression above is $y = 1.76$.

Now we look at the reverse situation. Suppose we are given a value for y. What then can be said about x? A moment's reflection shows that

$$y - 0.005 \leq x < y + 0.005$$

If, for example, $y = 1.76$, then x could have any value in the range:

$$1.755 \leq x < 1.765$$

We can view this example from a probabilistic standpoint and say that X is a random variable with a range of observations

$$S_X = (1.755 \leq x < 1.765)$$

Without further information, all that can be said is that x can occur uniformly in S_X. What this means is, using (3.16),

$$dP = f_X(x)dx = A dx, \quad 1.755 \leq x < 1.765$$

where A is a constant. In other words, the pdf that applies in this example is uniform (constant) in the interval S_X. Then, in order for the area under the pdf to be unity, the constant value of the pdf must equal 100. The integral (3.5) of the pdf gives the cdf: $F_X(x) = 100(x - 1.755)$ for all x in S_X (see Figure 3.6).

◆ ◆ ◆ ◆ ◆

Example 3.2   The following pseudocode uses a URNG algorithm on a digital computer to simulate 10 independent observations of a normalized uniform random variable Z. Then, (3.19) is used to obtain 10 independent observations of the random variable X uniformly distributed between $a = 1.755$ and $b = 1.765$.

```
Set the SEED for the URNG
FOR I = 1 TO 10
    Z = URNG
    X = (1.765 − 1.755) * Z + 1.755
    PRINT I, Z, X
ENDFOR
```

Data obtained when the psuedocode was coded and run are shown in Table 3.1.

◆ ◆ ◆ ◆ ◆

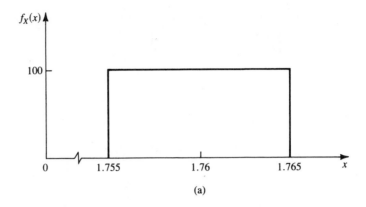

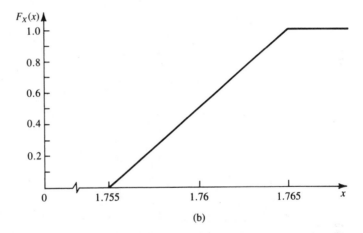

Figure 3.6   An example of (a) a pdf and (b) a cdf for the random variable X in Example 3.1.

● ●

Table 3.1   Data from the Pseudocode in Example 3.2

I	Z	X
1	0.589490	1.760895
2	0.557741	1.760577
3	0.948473	1.764485
4	0.986587	1.764866
5	0.561089	1.760611
6	0.224873	1.757249
7	0.447538	1.759475
8	0.769339	1.762693
9	0.284584	1.757846
10	0.003615	1.755036

The uniform random variable is but one illustration of a random variable specified by the pair of functions $f_X(x)$ and $F_X(x)$; we will encounter several others.

Section 3.2   EXPECTATION

◆   ◆   ◆   ◆   ◆

Inevitably, with any continuous random variable, observations in certain regions tend to occur more often than others. This relative frequency of occurrence leads us to define certain numbers, based on the geometric features of the pdf plot, to help us interpret how a random variable distributes its observations. We use the pdfs in Figure 3.7 to illustrate this.

A **mode** is a value of a continuous random variable at which its pdf is a maximum. A pdf may, in general, have more than one maximum; it may then be described as **multimodal.** Because the probability of occurrence of any specific value of a continuous random variable is zero (3.15), it follows that the probability a random variable exactly equals a mode is zero. We therefore do not say that the mode is a most likely value. Examples of modes are shown in Figure 3.7.

A **median** is a value of a continuous random variable that divides the area of a pdf in half:

$$P(X \le \text{median}) = P(X > \text{median}) = 1/2 \qquad \textbf{(3.20)}$$

The mode and the median are equal if the pdf has one mode and is symmetric about it, as is illustrated in Figure 3.7(a).

The **expectation** (or **expected value**) is a generalization of the idea behind a sample mean (1.1a), in which all the data in a sample are summed directly. If, however, the data are collected in a grouping of cells, as suggested in Figure 3.2(a), the sample mean may be approximated using the weighted sums (1.1a) and (1.22):

$$\bar{x} = \frac{1}{n} \sum_{k=1}^{k_M} n_k \tilde{x}_k \qquad \textbf{(3.21)}$$

where each of the n_k data in cell k is represented by $\tilde{x}_k$, and where the summation is over all cells. Using relative frequency (3.3), the sample mean in (3.21) is expressed as

$$\bar{x} = \sum_{k=1}^{k_M} \tilde{x}_k f_k \qquad \textbf{(3.22)}$$

We now assume $n \to \infty$, which means that our sample is enlarged to include all data in the same space S_X. In doing this we further assume the incremental width of each cell goes to zero, and the relative frequency become a pdf:

$$f_k \to f_X(x)dx$$

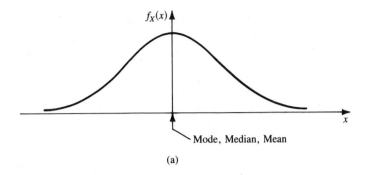

Mode, Median, Mean

(a)

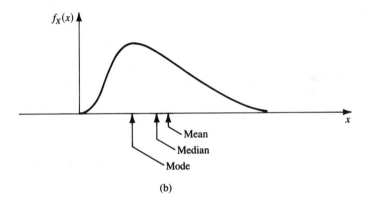

Mean
Median
Mode

(b)

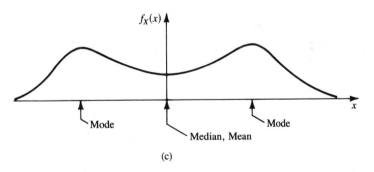

Mode   Mode
Median, Mean

(c)

Figure 3.7   Examples of various pdfs, illustrating the locations of modes, medians, and means.

• •

The sample mean (3.22) becomes the **sample space mean,** or more simply, the **mean:**

$$\bar{x} \rightarrow \mu_X, \quad \text{where } \mu_X = \int_{-\infty}^{\infty} x f_X(x) dx \qquad \textbf{(3.23)}$$

Symbols conventionally used for the mean are

$$\mu_X = \overline{X} = E[X] \tag{3.24}$$

Specifically, the last symbol in (3.24) is read as the **expectation** (or **expected value**) of X. The median and the expectation (mean) are equal if the pdf is symmetric as is illustrated in Figures 3.7(a) and 3.7(c).

While the concepts behind the mode and the median are important, they are relatively difficult to generalize. However, that is not true for expectation. We therefore focus considerable attention on the process of obtaining an expectation, and we consider expectation to be one of the most important features to emerge from our study of random variables.

Suppose that a random variable Y is related to a random variable X by a function:

$$Y = g(X) \tag{3.25}$$

Not only can we use (3.23) and (3.24) to write

$$E[X] = \int_{-\infty}^{\infty} x f_X(x) dx \tag{3.26}$$

but for the random variable Y we can write

$$E[Y] = \int_{-\infty}^{\infty} y f_Y(y) dy \tag{3.27}$$

where $f_X(x)$ and $f_Y(y)$ are, in general, two different pdfs. Using (3.25), we seek a method of writing $E[Y]$ in terms of $f_X(x)$, the pdf for X.

Figure 3.8 illustrates a portion of the plot of $y = g(x)$. Observations of Y occur between y and $y + dy$ with a probability

$$P(y < Y \leq y + dy) = P(x_1 < X \leq x_1 + dx_1) + P(x_2 - dx_2 < X \leq x_2)$$

All the differentials dy, dx_1, and dx_2 are positive. It then follows from (3.16) that

$$f_Y(y)dy = f_X(x_1)dx_1 + f_X(x_2)dx_2$$

Multiply both sides of this by y, and note that $y = g(x_1) = g(x_2)$,

$$y f_Y(y)dy = g(x_1)f_X(x_1)dx_1 + g(x_2)f_X(x_2)dx_2 \tag{3.28}$$

The relation (3.28) applies to Figure 3.8, and is presented as an illustration. If we generalize this illustration for an arbitrary (piecewise continuously increasing or decreasing) function $y = g(x)$, and if relations such as (3.28) are used such that each dx in the x axis is used only once, it then follows that

$$E[Y] = E[g(X)] = \int_{-\infty}^{\infty} g(x)f_X(x)dx \tag{3.29}$$

The expectation in (3.29) is fundamental to our study of probabilistic methods.

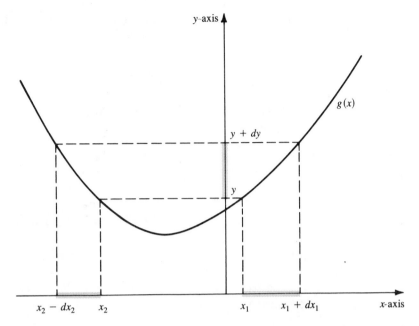

Figure 3.8   Illustration that the probability $f_Y(y)dy$ is equal to the sum of probabilities $f_X(x_1)dx_1$ and $f_X(x_2)dx_2$.

• •

The **expectation operator** is defined by the inegral in (3.29). As such, then, the expectation operator has certain useful features that can be written in operator notation, without explicitly writing an integral. For example, the expectation operator is linear:

$$E[g_1(X) + g_2(X)] = E[g_1(X)] + E[g_2(X)] \tag{3.30}$$

$$E[cg(X)] = cE[g(X)] \tag{3.31}$$

where g_1 and g_2 are different functions and c is a constant. Another simple but useful property, obtained from (3.29) and (3.14), is that the expected value of a constant c is the constant c:

$$E[c] = c \tag{3.32}$$

Moments about the origin are special cases of (3.29) in which

$$Y = X^n, n = 0, 1, 2, \ldots \tag{3.33}$$

When they exist, these moments are

$$E[X^n] = \int_{-\infty}^{\infty} x^n f_X(x)dx \tag{3.34}$$

When $n = 0$, we have (3.14) again. When $n = 1$, we have the mean (3.26). When $n = 2$, we have the mean square[c]:

$$E[X^2] = \int_{-\infty}^{\infty} x^2 f_X(x) dx \qquad (3.35)$$

Moments about the mean (or **central moments**), are another special case of (3.29) where

$$Y = (X - \mu_X)^n, \ n = 0, 1, 2 \ \ldots \qquad (3.36)$$

When central moments exist they are

$$E[(X - \mu_X)^n] = \int_{-\infty}^{\infty} (x - \mu_X)^n f_X(x) dx \qquad (3.37)$$

[It is possible that the integral in (3.37) does not converge. For example, see Exercise 14(b).]

The second central moment is called the **variance.** It is analogous to the sample variance introduced in Chapter 1:

$$\sigma_X^2 = \text{Var}[X] = E[(X - \mu_X)^2] = \int_{-\infty}^{\infty} (x - \mu_X)^2 f_X(x) dx \qquad (3.38)$$

The properties of the expectation operator may be used to find an equivalent expression for the variance. Starting with (3.38), and expanding the square:

$$\sigma_X^2 = E[X^2 - 2\mu_X X + \mu_X^2]$$

Using (3.30):

$$\sigma_X^2 = E[X^2] + E[-2\mu_X X] + E[\mu_X^2]$$

Then, with (3.31) and (3.32):

$$\sigma_X^2 = E[X^2] - 2\mu_X E[X] + \mu_X^2$$

And finally, using (3.24):

$$\sigma_X^2 = E[X^2] - \mu_X^2 \qquad (3.39)$$

Example 3.3   The pdf of a normalized uniform random variable X has a constant value of one for $0 < x < 1$, and is otherwise zero. Using (3.26), the mean of X is

$$\mu_X = \int_0^1 x \, dx = 1/2$$

---

[c] The **mean square** $E[X^2]$ must not be confused with the **square of the mean** μ_X^2.

Also, using (3.35), the mean square is

$$E[X^2] = \int_0^1 x^2 dx = 1/3$$

Then, using (3.39), the variance is

$$\sigma_X^2 = E[X^2] - \mu_X^2 = 1/12$$

In summary, the mean and variance of the normalized uniform random variable are

$$\mu_X = \tfrac{1}{2} \text{ and } \sigma_X^2 = \tfrac{1}{12}$$

◆ ◆ ◆ ◆ ◆

Example 3.4   The pdf of a **Rayleigh** random variable is

$$f_X(x) = \frac{x}{a^2} \exp\left(-\frac{x^2}{2a^2}\right), x \geq 0$$

$$f_X(x) = 0, \text{ otherwise}$$

Equation (3.23) is used to calculate the mean:

$$\mu_X = \frac{1}{a^2} \int_0^\infty x^2 \exp(-x^2/2a^2) dx$$

Using the *CRC Standard Mathematical Tables*[1] (No. 665),

$$\mu_X = a\sqrt{\pi/2}$$

The mean square (3.35) is

$$E[X^2] = \frac{1}{a^2} \int_0^\infty x^3 \exp(-x^2/2a^2) dx$$

Using the *CRC Standard Mathematical Tables*[1] (No. 667),

$$E[X^2] = 2a^2$$

Combining these results in (3.39) yields

$$\sigma_X^2 = \left(2 - \frac{\pi}{2}\right) a^2$$

◆ ◆ ◆ ◆ ◆

Suppose the random variables Y and X are related by

$$Y = \alpha X + \beta \qquad\qquad (3.40)$$

This occurs, for example, when we want to remove a constant value from a random variable, or when we want to scale its size. Using (3.30), (3.31), and (3.32),

$$\begin{aligned}
E[Y] &= E[\alpha X + \beta] \\
&= \alpha E[X] + \beta \\
&= \alpha \mu_X + \beta
\end{aligned}$$

(3.41)

Also, continuing with (3.38),

$$\begin{aligned}
\text{Var}[Y] &= E[(Y - \mu_Y)^2] \\
&= E[(\alpha X + \beta - \alpha \mu_X - \beta)^2] \\
&= \alpha^2 E[(X - \mu_X)^2] \\
&= \alpha^2 \text{Var}[X]
\end{aligned}$$

(3.42)

As a special case of (3.40), if $\alpha = 0$ then $Y = \beta$, and

$$\text{Var}[Y] = \text{Var}[\beta] = 0$$

(3.43)

This shows that the variance of a constant is zero.

Example 3.5   In (3.17) we described the pdf for an arbitrary uniform random variable, one that is uniformly distributed in the interval $a < X < b$. Transformation (3.19) shows how an arbitrary uniform random variable may be obtained from the normalized uniform random variable. Equation (3.40) may be used with this transformation to demonstrate that the mean of an arbitrary uniform random variable is, from (3.41),

$$\mu_Y = (b - a)/2 + a = \frac{b + a}{2}$$

and its variance is, from (3.42),

$$\sigma_Y^2 = \frac{(b - a)^2}{12}$$

◆ ◆ ◆ ◆ ◆

The asymmetry of a pdf is described by the third central moment:

$$\text{coefficient of skew} = E[(X - \mu_X)^3]/\sigma_X^3$$

(3.44)

If a pdf is symmetric about its mean, all of the odd central moments are zero. The third moment is the lowest order central moment sensitive to the presence of asymmetry, or skew.

Flatness of a pdf is described by the fourth central moment:

$$\text{coefficient of kurtosis} = E[(X - \mu_X)^4]/\sigma_X^4 \tag{3.45}$$

If a pdf is symmetric about its mean, and is very flat in the vicinity of its mean, the coefficient of kurtosis is relatively large.

Another parameter based on the moments, and which is sometimes used in comparing random variables, is the

$$\text{coefficient of variation} = \frac{\sigma_X}{\mu_X} \tag{3.46}$$

The **characteristic function** $\Phi_X(j\omega)$ is yet another special case of (3.29) where

$$Y = e^{j\omega X} \tag{3.47}$$

Thus,

$$\Phi_X(j\omega) = E[e^{j\omega X}] = \int_{-\infty}^{\infty} f_X(x)e^{j\omega x}dx \tag{3.48}$$

The characteristic function and the pdf are Fourier transform pairs:

$$f_X(x) = \frac{1}{2\pi} \int_{-\infty}^{\infty} \Phi_X(j\omega)e^{-j\omega x}d\omega \tag{3.49}$$

Note that the sign of each exponent in (3.48) and (3.49) is reversed from that which is used for the Fourier transform in most electrical engineering applications.

Moments about the origin may be obtained from a characteristic function. To see this, we note the following:

$$\frac{d^2}{d(j\omega)^2} \Phi_X(j\omega) = \int_{-\infty}^{\infty} x^n f_X(x)e^{j\omega x}dx$$

Then,

$$E[X^n] = \frac{d^n}{d(j\omega)^n} \Phi_X(j\omega) \Big|_{\omega=0} \tag{3.50}$$

If the shifting and scaling transformation (3.40) is used with characteristic functions,

$$\begin{aligned}
\Phi_Y(j\omega) &= E[e^{j\omega Y}] \\
&= E[e^{j\omega(\alpha X + \beta)}] \\
&= E[e^{j\omega\beta}e^{j\omega\alpha X}] \\
&= e^{j\omega\beta}E[e^{j(\alpha\omega)X}] \\
&= e^{j\omega\beta}\Phi_X(j\alpha\omega) \tag{3.51}
\end{aligned}$$

Example 3.6   The characteristic function for the normalized uniform random variable is, using (3.48),

$$\Phi_X(j\omega) = \int_0^1 e^{j\omega x}dx$$
$$= (e^{j\omega} - 1)/j\omega$$

An arbitrary uniform random variable may be obtained from the normalized version using the transformation (3.19). Combining this with (3.51) where $\alpha = b - a$ and $\beta = a$

$$\Phi_Y(j\omega) = e^{j\omega a}\Phi_X[j(b - a)\omega]$$

$$\Phi_Y(j\omega) = e^{j\omega a}\frac{e^{j(b-a)\omega} - 1}{j(b - a)\omega}$$

$$\Phi_Y(j\omega) = \frac{e^{j\omega b} - e^{j\omega a}}{j\omega(b - a)}$$

If the power series expansion is used for $\exp(j\omega)$, the characteristic function for the normalized random variable can be expressed as

$$\Phi_X(j\omega) = \sum_{n=1}^{\infty} \frac{(j\omega)^{n-1}}{n!}$$

It follows from (3.50) that

$$E[X] = \frac{d}{d(j\omega)}\Phi_X(j\omega)\bigg|_{\omega=0} = \frac{1}{2}$$

$$E[X^2] = \frac{d^2}{d(j\omega)^2}\Phi_X(j\omega)\bigg|_{\omega=0} = \frac{1}{3}$$

These results are the same as we found in Example 3.3.

◆ ◆ ◆ ◆ ◆

Moments calculated with a pdf, such as the mean and variance, are called **parameters**. Values obtained with sample data, such as the sample mean and the sample variance illustrated in Chapter 1, are called **statistics**. This distinction is conventional and useful.

Section 3.3   THE GAUSSIAN RANDOM VARIABLE

◆ ◆ ◆ ◆ ◆

Gaussian random variables frequently occur with observations that are made up from a sum of many independent perturbations. Noise is a good example: A noise voltage with Gaussian characteristics is generated by summing the voltages caused by random thermal agitation within the many separate atoms in a conductor. This phenomenon will be seen more clearly in Chapter 4. The reason the Gaussian random variable is so common attests to the many physical phenomena having additive independent random subphenomena.

We find it convenient to begin with a discussion of the **normalized** Gaussian random variable. After a study of the normalized form, a transformation is used to convert our results to a general description of the Gaussian random variable.

The pdf of the normalized Gaussian random variable Z is, for all z,

$$f_Z(z) = \frac{1}{\sqrt{2\pi}} \exp(-z^2/2) \tag{3.52}$$

The associated cdf is

$$F_Z(z) = \frac{1}{\sqrt{2\pi}} \int_{-\infty}^{z} \exp(-u^2/2)du \tag{3.53}$$

We note that when $z \to \infty$ the integral in (3.53) may be evaluated:

$$F_Z(\infty) = 1 \tag{3.54}$$

For example, see the *CRC Standard Mathematical Tables*[1] (No. 663).

Generally, (3.53) cannot be evaluated in closed form. We therefore provide in Appendix C an algorithm for calculating values of $F_Z(z)$. Tabulated values of $F_Z(z)$ for selected values of z between zero and four are also given there. We use the notation $\psi(z)$ in place of $F_Z(z)$ when we refer to the algorithm or the table in Appendix C:

$$\psi(z) = \frac{1}{\sqrt{2\pi}} \int_{-\infty}^{z} \exp(-u^2/2)du \tag{3.55}$$

Since the integrand in (3.55) is even, we may write the following, which equates areas on the left and the right of the pdf curve:

$$\frac{1}{\sqrt{2\pi}} \int_{-\infty}^{-z} \exp(-u^2/2)du = \frac{1}{\sqrt{2\pi}} \int_{+z}^{\infty} \exp(-u^2/2)du$$

Using (3.54), and using the fact that the area under the pdf curve is one, this integral relation may be written in terms of $\psi(z)$:

$$\psi(-z) = 1 - \psi(z) \tag{3.56}$$

Equation (3.56) provides us with a method for finding values of $\psi(z)$ when its argument is negative.

The characteristic function of the normalized Gaussian pdf in (3.52) is, from (3.48),

$$\Phi_Z(j\omega) = \frac{1}{\sqrt{2\pi}} \int_{-\infty}^{\infty} \exp(-z^2/2 + j\omega z)dz$$

To evaluate this integral, we use a technique that completes the square of the exponent in the integrand:

$$\Phi_Z(j\omega) = e^{-\omega^2/2} \frac{1}{\sqrt{2\pi}} \int_{-\infty}^{\infty} \exp[-(z-j\omega)^2/2]dz$$

If we use the complex change of variables $u = z - j\omega$ we obtain

$$\Phi_Z(j\omega) = e^{-\omega^2/2} \frac{1}{\sqrt{2\pi}} \int_{-\infty}^{\infty} \exp(-u^2/2)du$$

Equation (3.54) is then used to evaluate the integral and to obtain

$$\Phi_Z(j\omega) = \exp(-\omega^2/2) \tag{3.57}$$

The characteristic function for a Gaussian random variable X with arbitrary mean and variance can be obtained from (3.57). First, write (3.40) as

$$X = \sigma_X Z + \mu_X$$

where, in (3.40), $\alpha = \sigma_X$ and $\beta = \mu_X$. Then, using (3.51), we obtain the desired characteristic function,

$$\Phi_X(j\omega) = \exp\left(j\omega\mu_X - \frac{\omega^2\sigma_X^2}{2}\right) \tag{3.58}$$

We use (3.50) with (3.57) to obtain expected values of the normalized Gaussian random variable:

$$E[Z^n] = \frac{d^n}{d(j\omega)^n} \Phi_Z(j\omega)\Big|_{\omega=0}$$

The first four moments of Z are

$$\text{The mean, } E[Z] = \mu_Z = 0 \tag{3.59a}$$

$$\text{The variance, } E[Z^2] = \sigma_Z^2 = 1 \tag{3.59b}$$

$$\text{The coefficient of skew, } E[Z^3] = 0 \tag{3.59c}$$

$$\text{The coefficient of kurtosis, } E[Z^4] = 3 \tag{3.59d}$$

The Gaussian Random Variable with Arbitrary Mean and Variance

In general, the pdf for a Gaussian random variable X is, for all x,

$$f_X(x) = \frac{1}{\sqrt{2\pi\sigma_X^2}} \exp[-(x-\mu_X)^2/2\sigma_X^2] \tag{3.60}$$

The cdf associated with this is

$$F_X(x) = \frac{1}{\sqrt{2\pi\sigma_X^2}} \int_{-\infty}^{x} \exp[-(v - \mu_X)^2/2\sigma_X^2]dv$$

If we use the change of variable $u = (v - \mu_X)/\sigma_X$, then

$$F_X(x) = \frac{1}{\sqrt{2\pi}} \int_{-\infty}^{(x-\mu_X)/\sigma_X} \exp(-u^2/2)du$$

It then follows, using (3.55), that

$$F_X(x) = \psi\left(\frac{x - \mu_X}{\sigma_X}\right) \tag{3.61}$$

A general Gaussian random variable X is therefore related to the normalized Gaussian random variable with the transformation[d]:

$$Z = \frac{X - \mu_X}{\sigma_X} \tag{3.62a}$$

or

$$X = \sigma_X Z + \mu_X \tag{3.62b}$$

It follows directly from (3.62b) and (3.59a) that

$$E[X] = \sigma_X E[Z] + \mu_X = \mu_X \tag{3.63}$$

Also, it follows directly from (3.62a) that

$$E[(X - \mu_X)^n] = \sigma_X^n E[Z^n]$$

Then, using (3.59b),

$$\text{Var}[X] = \sigma_X^2 \tag{3.64}$$

It also follows from (3.44) and (3.45), along with (3.59c) and (3.59d), that the coefficients of skew and kurtosis are 0 and 3, respectively, for general Gaussian random variables.

Arbitrary Gaussian pdf and cdf curves are plotted in Figure 3.9. Note that the mean μ_X is a parameter that locates the mode of the pdf curve. The value of the pdf at its mean is, from (3.60),

$$f_X(\mu_X) = \frac{1}{\sqrt{2\pi\sigma_X^2}}$$

---

[d] The relations (3.62a) and (3.62b) are used frequently in applications of Gaussian random variables.

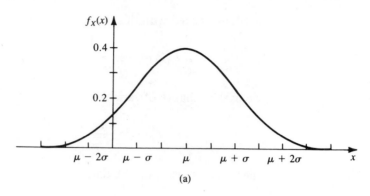

(a)

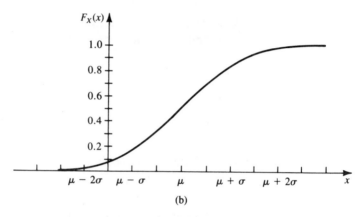

(b)

Figure 3.9   An example of (a) a pdf and (b) a cdf for a Gaussian random variable.

• •

When the standard deviation σ_X is relatively small, the pdf at the mean is relatively large, and vice versa. Recall that the area under the pdf must always be unity. Therefore, a small standard deviation gives a pdf curve that is peaked at its mean, and a large standard deviation gives a pdf curve that is flatter.

When dealing with errors modeled with a Gaussian random variable it is convenient to consider $1/\sigma_X$, the inverse of the standard deviation, as a **precision**; the system has greater precision if σ_X is small.

It should be clear that, as a model, the density function for a Gaussian random variable has weaknesses. For example, theoretically, the Gaussian pdf admits the possibility of values anywhere from $-\infty$ to $+\infty$. Parameter values that must be non-negative (e.g., resistance, capacitance, etc.) are allowed to have negative values somewhere under the Gaussian pdf if we look far enough to the left. What this means is that, when the Gaussian pdf is used to model a physical quantity, the regions under the curve that cannot be realized must be events of negligible probability. Gauss himself has discussed this subject, and it is interesting to read what he said.[2]:

> The function just found cannot, it is true, express rigorously the probabilities of the errors: for since the possible errors exceeding those limits ought always to be zero, while our formula always gives some value. However, this defect, which every analytical function must, from its nature, labor under, is of no importance in practice, because the value of our function decreases so rapidly, when $[(x - \mu_X)/\sqrt{2}\sigma_X]$ has acquired a considerable magnitude, that it can safely be considered as vanishing. Besides, the nature of the subject never admits of assigning with absolute rigor the limits of error.

Example 3.7 A calculation helps us to understand better what might, or might not, "safely be considered as vanishing." The probability that a Gaussian random variable is within $\pm 3\sigma_X$ of its mean is

$$
\begin{aligned}
P(\mu_X - 3\sigma_X < X \le \mu_X + 3\sigma_X) &= F(\mu_X + 3\sigma_X) - F(\mu_X - 3\sigma_X) \\
&= \psi(3) - \psi(-3) \\
&= \psi(3) - [1 - \psi(3)] \\
&= 2\psi(3) - 1 \\
&= 0.9973
\end{aligned}
$$

Thus, 99.73% of the time Gaussian observations will be within ± 3 standard deviations of the mean. However, as Gauss says, it is a matter of judgment, not "absolute rigor," whether the $\pm 3\sigma_X$ error limits are suitable for any application being studied.

Listed below are the probabilities of a Gaussian random variable being within $\pm \sigma_X$, $\pm 2\sigma_X$, or $\pm 3\sigma_X$ of its mean:

Region	Probability (%)
$\mu_X \pm \sigma_X$	68.3
$\mu_X \pm 2\sigma_X$	95.4
$\mu_X \pm 3\sigma_X$	99.7

Computations to verify two of these results are left to the reader.

◆ ◆ ◆ ◆ ◆

Example 3.8 A production drawing specifies a dimension on a certain device as 0.75 ± 0.002 M.

1. Assume that the process that manufactures the devices is such that the dimension is a Gaussian random variable Y, and that the man-

ufacturing process is accurate: $\mu_Y = 0.75$ M exactly. Assume that the precision of the manufacturing process is such that the standard deviation is $\sigma_Y = 0.0013$ M. We are interested in finding the percentage of devices having the dimension within the specified tolerance of 0.75 ± 0.002 M:

$$P(0.748 < Y \le 0.752) = F(0.752) - F(0.748)$$
$$= \psi\left(\frac{0.752 - 0.750}{0.0013}\right) - \psi\left(\frac{0.748 - 0.750}{0.0013}\right)$$
$$= \psi(1.5385) - \psi(-1.5385)$$
$$= 0.938 - 0.062 = 0.876$$

Thus, based on the given assumptions, we expect that 87.6% of the manufactured dimensions will be within the desired specifications.

2. We examine this Gaussian random variable example using the following assumptions: Let the precision be the same as before ($\sigma_Y = 0.0013$ M), and let the accuracy be slightly degraded ($\mu_Y = 0.7495$ M). The tolerance requirements remain unchanged:

$$P(0.748 < Y \le 0.752) = F(0.752) - F(0.748)$$
$$= \psi\left(\frac{0.752 - 0.7495}{0.0013}\right) - \psi\left(\frac{0.748 - 0.7495}{0.0013}\right)$$
$$= \psi(1.9231) - \psi(-1.1538)$$
$$= 0.973 - 0.124 = 0.849$$

These results are interesting because they illustrate the sensitivity of failure rates to manufacturing accuracy. Let the mean change from 0.7500 M to 0.7495 M. This is a change of 0.07%. Suppose that N devices are manufactured. The 0.07% change in the mean causes the number of failed devices to increase from $0.124N$ to $0.151N$, a 21.8% increase!

◆ ◆ ◆ ◆ ◆

When sample data are obtained from an experiment, it is straightforward to use the methods of Chapter 1 to calculate a sample mean and a sample variance (or sample standard deviation). Sometimes we are interested in whether or not the data approximate a Gaussian random variable. To answer this question we must, in effect, plot the frequency and/or the cumulative frequency data, and then see how well the data fit the theoretical curves for a Gaussian random variable. This task has been made easy for us because there is commercially available a special graph paper[3] on which cumulative relative frequency data (in percent) for a Gaussian random variable will plot as a straight line. We illustrate the use of this probability paper with an example.

Table 3.2   Frequency and Cumulative Frequency Data for Example 3.9. (The unit of x is diopter D)

Cell k	Boundaries x_1	Boundaries x_u	Frequency n_k	Cumulative Frequency N_k	Cumulative Relative Frequency $F_k(\%)$
1	−0.4	−0.2	2	2	0.9
2	−0.2	0.0	0	2	0.9
3	0.0	0.2	5	7	3.2
4	0.2	0.4	7	14	6.4
5	0.4	0.6	10	24	10.9
6	0.6	0.8	13	37	16.8
7	0.8	1.0	15	52	23.6
8	1.0	1.2	30	82	37.3
9	1.2	1.4	20	102	46.4
10	1.4	1.6	25	127	57.7
11	1.6	1.8	22	149	67.7
12	1.8	2.0	14	163	74.1
13	2.0	2.2	16	179	81.4
14	2.2	2.4	12	191	86.8
15	2.4	2.6	9	200	90.9
16	2.6	2.8	6	206	93.6
17	2.8	3.0	5	211	95.9
18	3.0	3.2	5	216	98.2
19	3.2	3.4	2	218	99.1
20	3.4	3.6	1	219	99.5
21	3.6	3.8	0	219	99.5
22	3.8	4.0	1	220	100.0

Source: Adapted,[4] and reprinted by permission of Kluwer Academic Publishers.

Example 3.9   Data from an experiment that measures the focal distance of the human eye in the dark for 220 subjects are shown in Table 3.2. The cumulative relative frequency data (in percent) from this table are plotted on the probability paper in Figure 3.10. A study of Figure 3.10 reveals the following:

1. A significant number of the data fall on an approximately straight line. The data that correspond to events at the extremes of the Gaussian density function deviate most markedly from the straight line. These events are of low probability and hence are of negligible significance.

2. The sample mean of the data $\bar{x}$ is estimated by finding the ordinate corresponding to the mean μ_X:

$$F(\mu_X) = \psi(0) = 0.5000 = 50\%$$

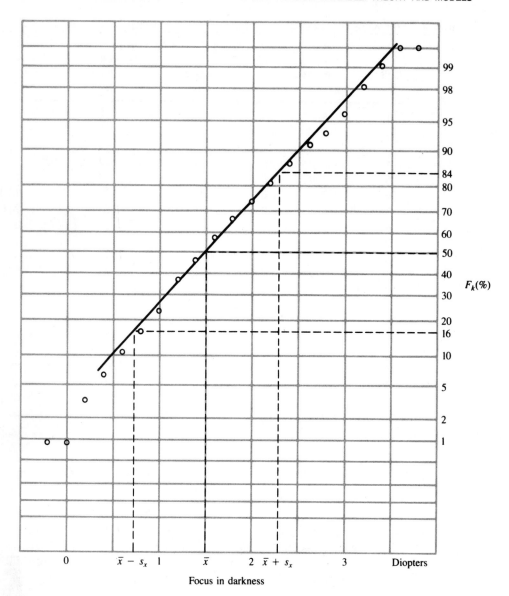

Figure 3.10   Cumulative frequency data from Table 3.2 plotted on probability paper.

Then reading to the abscissa using the straight line:

$$\bar{x} = 1.50 \ D \sim \mu_X$$

3. The sample standard deviation is estimated by finding the ordinate corresponding to $\mu_X - \sigma_X$:

$$F(\mu_X - \sigma_X) = \psi(-1) = 0.1587 \sim 16\%$$

Reading to the abscissa using the straight line: $x = 0.72\ D$. The sample standard deviation is then the difference between the abscissa value just found and the sample mean $\bar{x}$:

$$s_x = 1.50\ D - 0.72\ D = 0.78\ D \sim \sigma_x$$

Note that it is the values of x_u on Table 3.2 that are used to make the plot in Figure 3.10. This is necessary because the plot in Figure 3.10 is cumulative frequency, and each ordinate value includes the sum of all frequency data up to and including the abscissa value.

◆ ◆ ◆ ◆ ◆

Section 3.4   DISCRETE RANDOM VARIABLES

◆ ◆ ◆ ◆ ◆

To this point we have assumed observations obtained from a random experiment are a continuous set of numbers. Further, for a continuous random variable, the probability of observing any specific number is vanishingly small (3.15). There are, however, situations in which observations are discrete:

$$S_X = \{x_1, x_2, x_3, \ldots\}$$

Here the x_i are in a countable set (either finite or infinite) of numbers, and the random experiment is such that the probability of observing a specific $x_i \in S_X$ does not vanish:

$$P(X = x_i) = P(x_i) > 0, \quad i = 1, 2, 3, \ldots$$

When the range of observations S_X is discrete we say that X is a **discrete random variable**. A **mixed random variable** is also defined when a range of observations contains both continuous and discrete random variables.

The probability $P(x_i)$ associated with a discrete random variable is called a **probability mass function** (pmf). When all elementary discrete observations in a sample space are considered, their probabilities must sum to one:

$$\sum_i P(x_i) = 1 \qquad\qquad (3.65)$$

The definition of the cdf for the discrete random variable is the same as for the continuous random variable, (3.6b). The equality in this definition becomes important for discrete random variables. When $X = x_i$ the probability $P(x_i)$ is included in $P(X \leq x_i)$, and hence in $F_X(x_i)$. Refer to Figure 3.11, which illustrates a portion of a cdf for a discrete random variable. When x is slightly to the left of x_i, $x = x_i^-$, then

$$F_X(x_i^-) = F_X(x_{i-1})$$

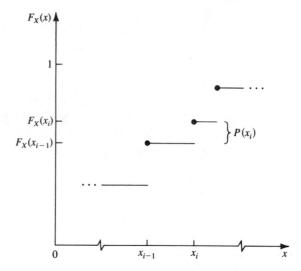

Figure 3.11   Illustrating the discontinuities occurring with the cdf of a discrete random variable; $F_X(x_i^+) = F_X(x_i)$ and $F_X(x_i^-) = F_X(x_{i-1})$.

• •

When x is slightly to the right of x_i, $x = x_i^+$, then the effect of the pmf at $x = x_i$ is included, and

$$F_X(x_i) = F_X(x_i^+) \tag{3.66}$$

Continuity is always from the right in a cdf. The discontinuity in the cdf at $x = x_i$ has a value determined by the pmf:

$$F_X(x_i^+) - F_X(x_i^-) = P(x_i)$$

The cdf can be described by a superposition of weighted step functions:

$$F_X(x) = \sum_i P(x_i)u(x - x_i) \tag{3.67}$$

where the step function is

$$u(x) = 1, \quad x \geq 0 \tag{3.68}$$
$$= 0, \quad x < 0$$

The Dirac-delta function $\delta(x)$, as it is commonly used in electrical engineering circuit theory,[e] is introduced:

_____

[e] The author believes that electrical engineering students will be familiar with the Dirac-delta function as introduced here. If that is not the case, the reader may prefer an alternative description that uses "a unit mass" concentrated at the point where the Dirac-delta function is located.

$$\delta(x) = = \frac{d}{dx} u(x) \tag{3.69}$$

Then, (3.11) represents the pdf of a discrete random variable:

$$f_X(x) = \sum_i P(x_i)\delta(x - x_i) \tag{3.70}$$

The effect of a Dirac-delta function is located only at the abscissa value where its argument is zero:

$$\int_a^b g(x)\delta(x - x_0)dx = g(x_0), \quad a < x_0 \le b \tag{3.71}$$
$$= 0, \quad \text{otherwise}$$

Using the Dirac-delta function, all results for pdfs for continuous random variables are extended to the case of discrete random variables.

Example 3.10   Suppose a discrete random variable is specified by the probability mass function in Table 3.3. Using (3.67) and these data, the cdf for this example random variable is

$$F_X(x) = \sum_{i=1}^4 P(x_i)u(x - x_i)$$
$$= 0.30u(x + 1.3) + 0.40u(x - 0.6) + 0.20u(x - 1.3) + 0.10u(x - 3.2)$$

Using (3.70), the pdf is

$$f_X(x) = \sum_{i=1}^4 P(x_i)\delta(x - x_i)$$
$$= 0.30\delta(x + 1.3) + 0.40\delta(x - 0.6) + 0.20\delta(x - 1.3) + 0.10\delta(x - 3.2)$$

Figures 3.12(a) and 3.12(b) show plots of the cdf and the pdf, respectively. The heavy vertical arrows in Figure 3.12(b) represent Dirac-delta functions.

Table 3.3   Data for a Random Variable in Examples 3.10 and 3.19

i	x_i	$P(x_i)$	$x_i P(x_i)$	$x_i^2 P(x_i)$
1	−1.3	0.30	−0.390	0.507
2	0.6	0.40	0.240	0.144
3	1.3	0.20	0.260	0.338
4	3.2	0.10	0.320	1.024
			0.430	2.013

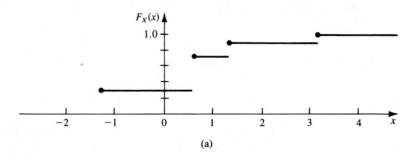

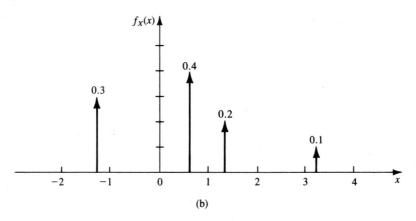

Figure 3.12   Plots of the (a) cdf and (b) pdf for the discrete random variable discussed in Example 3.10. Four Dirac-delta functions are shown in part (b). Each Dirac-delta function is of the form $P(x_i)\delta(x - x_i)$ where x_i specifies its location on the x axis and $P(x_i)$ is the pmf.

◆ ◆

As an example of a discontinuity in the cdf, refer to Figure 3.12(a) and note that

$$F_X(0.6^-) = 0.30$$

and

$$F_X(0.6) = F_X(0.6^+) = 0.70$$

◆ ◆ ◆ ◆ ◆

Expectation applied to discrete random variables follows directly from (3.29) and (3.70):

$$E[g(X)] = \int_{-\infty}^{\infty} g(x) \sum_i P(x_i)\delta(x - x_i)dx$$

Interchanging the integration and the sum:

$$E[g(X)] = \sum_i \int_{-\infty}^{\infty} g(x)\delta(x - x_i)dxP(x_i)$$

Then, using (3.71)

$$E[g(X)] = \sum_i g(x_i)P(x_i) \tag{3.72}$$

We use this result to show, for example, that the characteristic function (3.48) becomes, for a discrete random variable,

$$\Phi_X(j\omega) = \sum_i \exp(j\omega x_i)P(x_i) \tag{3.73}$$

Or moments about the origin (3.34) are

$$E[X^m] = \sum_i x_i^m P(x_i) \tag{3.74}$$

In particular, the mean of a discrete random variable is

$$\mu_X = E[X] = \sum_i x_i P(x_i) \tag{3.75}$$

The variance (3.38) of a discrete random variable is

$$\sigma_X^2 = \text{Var}[X] = \sum_i (x_i - \mu_X)^2 P(x_i) \tag{3.76}$$

Or, by using the mean square (3.35),

$$E[X^2] = \sum_i x_i^2 P(x_i) \tag{3.77}$$

the alternative expression for the variance (3.39) may be convenient.

Example 3.11   We continue the previous example to include the calculation of the discrete random variable's mean and variance. Table 3.3 includes values for $x_i P(x_i)$ and $x_i^2 P(x_i)$. Using these data,

$$\sum_{i=1}^{4} x_i P(x_i) = 0.430$$

$$\sum_{i=1}^{4} x_i^2 P(x_i) = 2.013$$

Then, using (3.75), (3.77), and (3.39), the mean and variance of the discrete random variable in this example are

$$\mu_X = 0.430 \quad \text{and} \quad \sigma_X^2 = 2.013 - (0.430)^2 = 1.828$$

◆ ◆ ◆ ◆ ◆

Section 3.5   FUNCTIONS OF A SINGLE RANDOM VARIABLE

◆ ◆ ◆ ◆ ◆

When we introduced expectation (3.29) we also introduced the idea of a function of a single random variable (3.25), i.e., $Y = g(X)$. Elaborating on this: Y must be a random variable because it is related to the random variable X through the function $g(\cdot)$. This assumes that Y has statistical consistency. That is, just as X has a pdf, a cdf, and a range of observations S_X, so also Y has a pdf, a cdf, and a range of observations S_Y. When we write $y = g(x)$ using the lowercase letters x and y we mean that x is an observation of X, and that the function $g(\cdot)$ provides the observation $y = g(x)$ of the random variable Y. Thus, the random variable $Y = g(X)$ is the totality of all observations

$$y = g(x) \in S_Y$$

In this section we assume that the random variable X is known. Then, given the function $g(\cdot)$, we seek a procedure to find the random variable Y.

Example 3.12   As an illustration of the procedure we use with functions of a single random variable, assume that (3.25) takes the form of the linear relation:

$$Y = \alpha X + \beta$$

Assume also that the slope α is positive so that a typical plot of $y = \alpha x + \beta$ appears as shown in Figure 3.13. From (3.6b),

$$F_Y(y) = P(Y \leq y)$$

Then, equating the probabilities of the regions illustrated in Figure 3.13, we have

$$P(Y \leq y) = P(X \leq x)$$

Using (3.6b) again,

$$P(X \leq x) = F_X(x)$$
$$= F_X\left(\frac{y - \beta}{\alpha}\right)$$

where the argument in the cdf for X is the inverse of $y = \alpha x + \beta$. We then have, by combining the statements above,

$$F_Y(y) = F_X\left(\frac{y - \beta}{\alpha}\right)$$

Using (3.11), the pdf for Y is obtained by differentiating $F_Y(y)$ with respect to y:

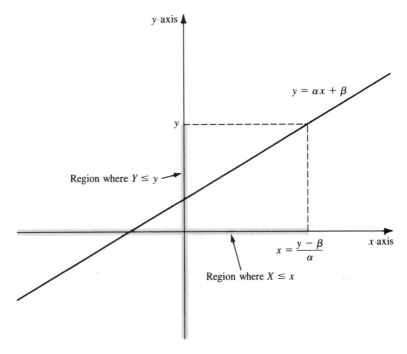

Figure 3.13   The plot of a function that is uniformly increasing. Observations occur in the region $(Y \le y)$ with the same probability as they occur in the region $(X \le x)$.

◆ ◆

$$f_Y(y) = f_X\left(\frac{y - \beta}{\alpha}\right)\frac{1}{\alpha}$$

If the range of observations S_X is the entire real line, then the range of observations S_Y is also the entire real line.

◆ ◆ ◆ ◆ ◆ ◆

In general terms, the procedure we used in Example 3.12 follows the five points below. This same general procedure[5] is repeated in several other examples.

1. Express the desired cdf for Y as a probability using (3.6b):

$$F_Y(y) = P(Y \le y)$$

2. Equate this probability of Y to a probability of X (or a combination of probabilities of X) using $Y = g(X)$.

3. Relate the cdf for X to the probability (or combination of probabilities) of X using (3.9).

4. Obtain the pdf $f_Y(y)$ from the cdf using (3.11) wherever the cdf is differentiable, or use the methods of discrete random variables if the cdf for Y has discontinuities.

5. Specify the range of observations S_Y from the given range of observations S_X.

Exercise 33 at the end of this chapter shows that results similar to those in Example 3.12 are obtained if the linear relation uses a negative α.

With a linear relation, the random variable Y is the same type as X. That is, if X is uniform then Y is also uniform; if X is Gaussian then Y is also Gaussian; etc. This observation is included in the next example.

Example 3.13   Suppose we want a random variable Y to have a range of observations

$$S_Y = \{900 \ \Omega < y < 1100 \ \Omega\}$$

We choose these values to model the variability that may occur when 1000 Ω resistors with a $\pm 10\%$ tolerance are selected randomly. Further, suppose we want to simulate observations of Y using URNG, which has a range of observations

$$S_X = \{0 < x < 1\}$$

We can do this with

$$Y = 200X + 900 \ \Omega$$

Using a result from Example 3.12:

$$f_Y(y) = f_X\left(\frac{y - \beta}{\alpha}\right)\frac{1}{\alpha}$$

With the values given in this example,

$$f_Y(y) = f_X\left(\frac{y - 900}{200}\right)\frac{1}{200}$$

Since $f_X(x) = 1$ for any argument $0 < x < 1$, it follows that

$$f_Y(y) = \frac{1}{200}, \quad y \in S_Y$$

Thus, the random variable Y is uniformly distributed between $1000 \pm 100 \ \Omega$.

♦ ♦ ♦ ♦ ♦

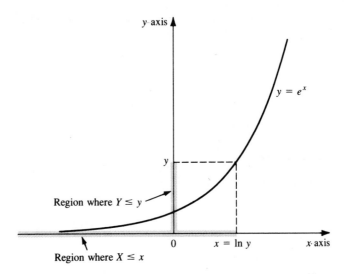

Figure 3.14   A plot of $y = e^x$. Observations occur in the region $(Y \leq y)$ with the same probability as they occur in the region $(X \leq x)$.

• •

Example 3.14   In this example, we use an exponential relation between the random variables X and Y, as shown in Figure 3.14:

$$Y = e^X$$

Proceeding with the five steps given above,

$$F_Y(y) = P(Y \leq y)$$

Since $y = e^X$ is a strictly monotone increasing function, we have

$$P(Y \leq y) = P(X \leq x) = P(X \leq \ln y)$$

where $\ln y$ is the inverse of e^x. Then, using (3.9), we have

$$P(X \leq \ln y) = F_X(\ln y)$$

Combining the above relations,

$$F_Y(y) = F_X(\ln y)$$

Then, using (3.11),

$$f_Y(y) = f_X(\ln y)\frac{1}{y}$$

If the range of observations S_X is the entire real line, then the range of observations S_Y is the positive half of the real line,

$$S_Y = \{0 < y < \infty\}$$

♦ ♦ ♦ ♦ ♦

Example 3.15   If the random variable X in Example 3.14 is Gaussian, then the random variable Y is the **lognormal** random variable. The expression for the pdf for Y, from Example 3.14, is

$$f_Y(y) = f_X(\ln y) \frac{1}{y}$$

Then, if $f_X(x)$ is an arbitrary Gaussian pdf (3.60), the pdf for Y is

$$f_Y(y) = \frac{1}{y\sigma_X\sqrt{2\pi}} \exp[-(\ln y - \mu_X)^2/2\sigma_X^2]$$

In working with the lognormal random variable, we use the change of variables

$$z = \frac{\ln y - \mu_X}{\sigma_X}$$

Since $X = \ln Y$ is Gaussian with a mean of μ_X, and a standad deviation of σ_X, it follows that Z is a normalized Gaussian random variable; its mean is zero and its standard deviation is one. With this change of variables, the lognormal cdf is

$$F_Y(y) = \psi[(\ln y - \mu_X)/\sigma_X]$$

The mean and the variance for the lognormal random variable are evaluated in Exercise 36 at the end of this chapter. However, practice generally favors describing the lognormal random variable Y with the parameters of the underlying Gaussian random variable. That is, we refer to a lognormal random variable Y using Gaussian parameters μ_X and σ_X.

♦ ♦ ♦ ♦ ♦

Example 3.16   Let (3.25) be $Y = X^2$. This example is interesting to us because the random variable Y is proportional to the **power** of the random variable X. The plot in Figure 3.15 assists in the analysis of this function of a single random variable. First,

$$F_Y(y) = P(Y \leq y)$$

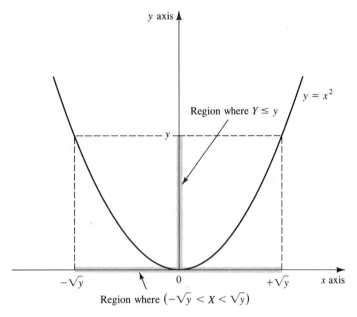

Figure 3.15   A plot of the function $y = x^2$. Observations occur in the region ($Y \leq y$) with the same probability as they occur in the region ($-\sqrt{y} < X < \sqrt{y}$).

• •

Then, equating probabilities of the regions illustrated in Figure 3.15,

$$P(Y \leq y) = P(-\sqrt{y} < X < \sqrt{y})$$

Using (3.9),

$$P(-\sqrt{y} < X < \sqrt{y}) = F_X(\sqrt{y}) - F_X(-\sqrt{y})$$

Combining these results, we have the cdf for Y:

$$F_Y(y) = F_X(\sqrt{y}) - F_X(-\sqrt{y})$$

Using (3.11), we obtain the pdf for Y:

$$f_Y(y) = [f_X(\sqrt{y}) + f_X(-\sqrt{y})]\frac{1}{2\sqrt{y}}$$

If the range of observations S_X is the entire real axis, then the range of observations for the random variable Y is

$$S_Y = \{0 < y < \infty\}$$

♦ ♦ ♦ ♦ ♦

Example 3.17   The pdf for the random variable Y given in Example 3.16 is

$$f_Y(y) = [f_X(\sqrt{y}) + f_X(-\sqrt{y})] \frac{1}{2\sqrt{y}}$$

Suppose that the random variable X used here is a Gaussian random variable (3.60) with a mean of zero and an arbitrary variance. Then,

$$f_Y(y) = \frac{1}{\sigma_X \sqrt{2\pi y}} \exp(-y/2\sigma_X^2)$$

This pdf is zero for all $y < 0$ because the range of observations for Y is $S_Y(y) = \{0 < y < \infty\}$. It is shown in Exercise 37 at the end of this chapter that the following moments can be calculated for the random variable Y:

$$E[Y] = E[X^2] = \sigma_X^2$$
$$E[Y^2] = E[X^4] = 3\sigma_X^4$$
$$\text{Var}[Y] = E[Y^2] - E[Y]^2 = 2\sigma_X^4$$

◆ ◆ ◆ ◆ ◆

Example 3.18   We illustrate a **simulation** of the power transformation $Y = X^2$ applied to a Gaussian random variable. Assume we have an algorithm that will simulate observations of a Gaussian random variable X with a mean of zero and a variance of one. (See Appendix A for such an algorithm.) The pdf for the random variable Y, obtained from Examle 3.17, is

$$f_Y(y) = \frac{1}{\sqrt{2\pi y}} \exp(-y/2)$$

We divide the abscissa between $y = 0$ and $y = 6$ into 24 cells, each with a width of 0.25. A twenty-fifth cell is added to collect all observations of Y that are greater than 6. We operate the algorithm $n = 1000$ times, and then construct a frequency plot showing how many times simulated observations occur in each cell. The following algorithm implements the desired simulation.

```
Dimension an array for integers — HISTOGRAM(25)
For I = 1 TO 1000 : We want n = 1000 observations
    X = Gaussian observation, μ_X = 0 and σ_X = 1
    Y = X² : Calculate the power of X
    K = [Y/0.25] + 1 : Calculate the cell number
    IF K > 25 THEN K = 25 : Collect in cell 25 the count of all
                            observations greater than 6
    HISTOGRAM(K) = HISTOGRAM(K) + 1 : Increment the
                            counter in the array for cell k
ENDFOR
```

Data from operating the algorithm are shown in Table 3.4.

Table 3.4   Frequency Data for the "Power" Random
Variable in Example 3.18 ($n = \Sigma\, n_k = 1000$)

Cell k	n_k	Cell k	n_k
1	390	14	9
2	128	15	4
3	106	16	9
4	62	17	6
5	44	18	5
6	50	19	4
7	36	20	1
8	25	21	1
9	24	22	3
10	35	23	0
11	24	24	1
12	10	25	11
13	12		

Figure 3.16 shows a plot of the theoretical pdf for this example. Also
shown in Figure 3.16 is a relative frequency plot, which is an estimate of the
theoretical pdf based on the data in Table 3.4. Here, for cells 2 through 24,
we used the approximation

$$f_Y(y_k)w \approx n_k/n$$

where y_k is the abscissa value at the center of cell k: $w = 0.25$ is the width of
each cell; n_k is the number of observations occurring in cell k; and $n = 1000$
is the total number of simulated observations.

An examination of cell 1 requires a different technique because the equation for the pdf is not defined at the origin; we equate corresponding probabilities of the X and Y random variables:

$$P(0 < Y < 0.25) = P(-\sqrt{0.25} < X < \sqrt{0.25})$$
$$= F_X(0.50) - F_X(-0.50)$$
$$= \psi(0.50) - \psi(-0.50) = 0.3829$$

This compares reasonably well with the relative frequency estimate of the
probability that Y is between 0 and 0.25. This is shown in cell 1 in Table
3.4: $390/1000 = 0.390$.

An examination of the data in cell 25 requires a technique similar to that
used for cell 1. Cell 25 includes observations from $y = 6$ to ∞. This includes
all observations of x from $-\infty$ to $-\sqrt{6}$, and from $\sqrt{6}$ to ∞. Therefore,

$$P(6 < Y < \infty) = 2P(\sqrt{6} < X < \infty)$$
$$= 2(F_X(\infty) - F_X(2.4495))$$
$$= 2(1 - \psi(2.4495)) = 0.0143$$

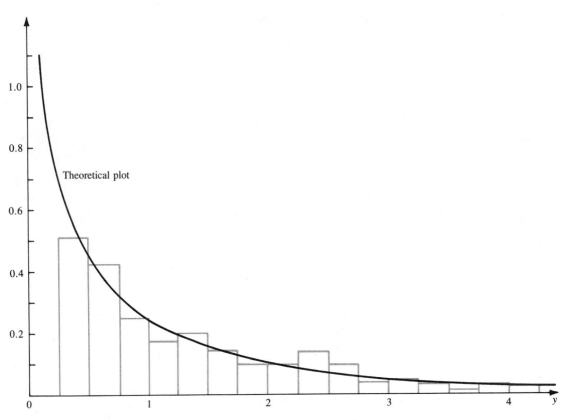

Figure 3.16   A plot of relative frequency data obtained using the algorithm for a power random variable in Example 3.18.

● ● ◆ ● ◆ ● ◆ ● ◆ ● ◆ ● ◆ ● ◆ ● ◆ ● ◆ ● ◆ ● ◆ ● ◆ ● ◆ ● ◆ ● ◆ ● ◆ ● ◆ ● ◆ ● ◆

This compares reasonably well with the simulated observations in cell 25 in Table 3.4 where we estimate $11/1000 = 0.0110$ for the same probability.

● ◆ ● ◆ ●

Assume that $Y = g(X)$ is used to transform one **discrete** random variable to another. The result is simply a different collection of probability mass functions. If the pmf for the random variable X is

$$P(x_i), \text{ all } i$$

and if the relation between observations of X and Y is $y = g(x)$, then the pmf for Y is

$$P(y_i), \text{ all } i$$

Example 3.19   Again, we use the data in Table 3.3 Let, for this example, $Y = X^2$. Then, the four terms in the pmf $P(x_i)$ are transformed into the pmf $P(y_i)$:

$$P(X = -1.3) = P(Y = 1.690) = 0.30$$

$$P(X = 0.6) = P(Y = 0.360) = 0.40$$

$$P(X = 1.3) = P(Y = 1.690) = 0.20$$

$$P(X = 3.2) = P(Y = 10.240) = 0.10$$

Notice in this example that the pmf for Y contains only three terms; $P(Y = 1.690) = 0.50$.

This probability mass function in this example may be incorporated into a cdf (3.67) and a pdf (3.70).

♦ ♦ ♦ ♦ ♦

The plot in Figure 3.17 gives us an interesting situation we have not yet discussed. Here, $y = g(x)$ is neither increasing nor decreasing when x is between a and b. For any x between a and b, the value of $y = g(x) = y_0$, a constant. When $y = y_0$, the random variable Y has the nature of a discrete random variable:

$$P(Y = y_0) = P(y_0) = P(a < X < b)$$

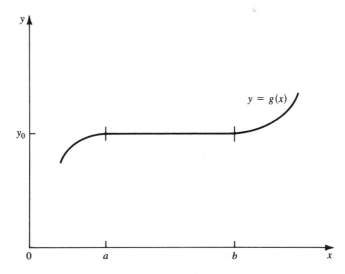

Figure 3.17   A plot of a function that is constant in the interval ($a < x < b$). The probability that $y = y_0$ is equal to the probability that x is in the interval ($a < x < b$).

♦ ♦

For all other observations of Y it is a continuous random variable. Therefore, Y is an example of a mixed random variable. This case is illustrated in the next example.

Example 3.20   Suppose we modify Example 3.16 as follows. Let $y = g(x)$ be the square-law rectifier function illustrated in Figure 3.18:

$$y = x^2, x \geq 0, \text{ and is zero otherwise}$$

When $y = 0$, it follows that

$$F_Y(0) = P(Y \leq 0)$$
$$= P(Y = 0)$$
$$= P(X \leq 0) = F_X(0)$$

Since the nature of the rectifying function requires that $F_Y(y) = 0$ for all $y < 0$, there is a discontinuity in the cdf for Y at $y = 0$.

When $y > 0$ it follows that

$$F_Y(y) = P(Y \leq y)$$
$$= F_X(0) + P(0 < X < \sqrt{y})$$
$$= F_X(0) + F_X(\sqrt{y}) - F_X(0)$$
$$= F_X(\sqrt{y})$$

• •

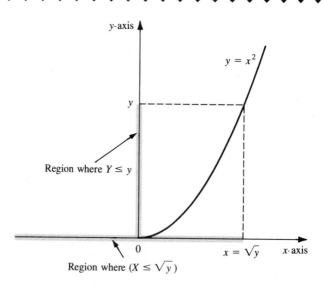

Figure 3.18   A rectifier function used in Example 3.20. Observations occur in the region $(Y \leq y)$ with the same probability as they occur in the region $(X \leq \sqrt{y})$.

The pdf for Y is obtained by differentiating $F_Y(y)$ with respect to y. The discontinuity of $F_Y(y)$ at $y = 0$ leads to probability mass value of $F_X(0)$. And, of course, the pdf for Y is zero for all $y < 0$. Therefore,

$$f_Y(y) = F_X(0)\delta(y) + f_X(\sqrt{y})\frac{1}{2\sqrt{y}}, \qquad y \geq 0$$

If the range of observations S_X is the entire real line, then the range of observations S_Y is the positive half line.

Exercise 48 contains an application of this example when X is a zero-mean Gaussian random variable.

◆   ◆   ◆   ◆   ◆

An algorithmic technique, useful for simulating observations of random variables, uses the uniform random number generator URNG. To see how this works, see Figure 3.19. The function $g(x)$ is increasing strictly monotone in the interval between zero and one on the x axis. Applying the five-step procedure for functions of a single random variable, we find

$$F_Y(y) = P(Y \leq y)$$

Then, equating the probabilities of the regions shown in Figure 3.19,

$$P(Y \leq y) = P(X \leq g^{-1}(y))$$

Relating the probability involving X to its pdf,

$$P[X \leq g^{-1}(y)] = F_X[g^{-1}(y)]$$

Because X is uniformly distributed between zero and one, its cdf has a constant slope of unity between $F_X(0) = 0$ and $F_X(1) = 1$.
Therefore,

$$F_X[g^{-1}(y)] = g^{-1}(y) = x$$

Combining the relations given above,

$$F_Y(y) = g^{-1}(y) = x \tag{3.78}$$

Then, solving this for y (if that is possible)

$$y = g(x) = F_Y^{-1}(x) \tag{3.79}$$

This relation describes how to obtain $g(x)$ knowing the cdf of the random variable we want to simulate. An example of its use follows.

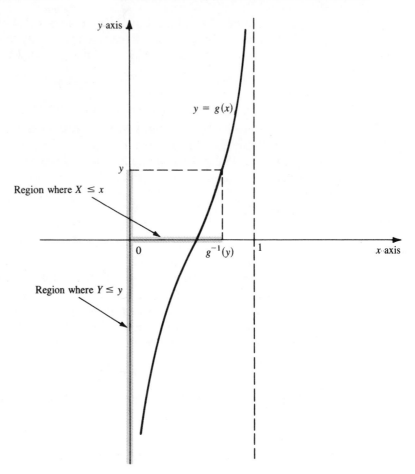

Figure 3.19   A graph of a typical function that increases strictly monotone when $0 < x < 1$.

• •

Example 3.21   Suppose we want an algorithm that can be used to simulate observations of an **exponential** random variable. The pdf for this random variable is

$$f_Y(y) = \lambda \exp(-\lambda y), \quad y \geq 0$$
$$= 0, \qquad\qquad y < 0$$

where λ is a constant. Using this pdf, we find the cdf (3.5)

$$F_Y(y) = 1 - \exp(-\lambda y), \quad y \geq 0$$
$$= 0, \qquad\qquad\quad y < 0$$

Starting with (3.78), and for $y \geq 0$,

$$1 - \exp(-\lambda y) = x$$

Then, solving for y as indicated by (3.79),

$$y = (-1/\lambda)\ln(1-x)$$

To illustrate the use of this algorithm, we (arbitrarily) let $\lambda = 2$, and use a computer to generate $n = 1000$ observations of y. We then estimate the pdf for Y using a relative frequency technique. The y axis between zero and three is divided into 24 cells, each with a width of 0.1250. We include a twenty-fifth cell to collect all simulated observations greater than three. Pseudocode for this algorithm is

```
Dimension an array for integers − HISTOGRAM(25)
FOR I = 1 TO 1000 : We want n = 1000 observations
    X = URNG
    Y = (−1/λ)ln(1−X): Calculate the exponential
                       random variable observation
    K = [Y/0.125] + 1 : Calculate the cell number
    IF K > 25 THEN K = 25 : Collect in cell 25 the count of all
                            observations greater than 3
    HISTOGRAM(K) = HISTOGRAM(K) + 1 : Increment the
                            counter in the array for cell K
ENDFOR
```

Data obtained from this algorithm are shown in Table 3.5. These data, summarized from $n = 1000$ simulated observations, are also plotted with $f_Y(y)$ in Figure 3.20. As in the previous example, we use the approximation

$$f_Y(y_k)w \approx n_k/n$$

Table 3.5   Frequency Data for the Exponential Random Variable in Example 3.21 $(n = \Sigma\, n_k = 1000)$

Cell k	n_k	Cell k	n_k
1	219	14	12
2	170	15	12
3	132	16	6
4	113	17	4
5	75	18	3
6	64	19	1
7	53	20	2
8	38	21	5
9	33	22	3
10	13	23	1
11	15	24	1
12	13	25	5
13	7		

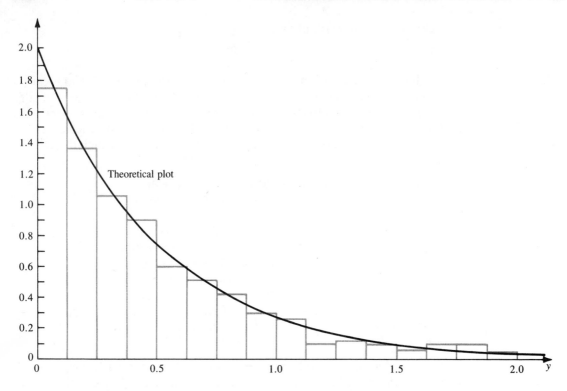

Figure 3.20   A plot of relative frequency data obtained using the algorithm for an exponential random variable in Example 3.21.

◆ ◆

where the cell width $w = 0.125$, and where y_k is the center of cell k. Examining Figure 3.20, the relative frequency approximation appears to work well, especially in those cells where there are more data.

◆ ◆ ◆ ◆ ◆

Section 3.6   CONDITIONED RANDOM VARIABLES

◆ ◆ ◆ ◆ ◆

Conditional probability is extended to include a **random variable conditioned by an event.** In this context, we combine the conditional probability (2.22) with the cdf (3.6b) to make the defining relation for $F_X(x|B)$, the **conditional cumulative distribution** function, or more succinctly, the **conditional cdf:**

$$F_X(x|B) = P(X \le x|B) = \frac{P(X \le x \cap B)}{P(B)} \qquad \textbf{(3.80)}$$

where $P(B) \neq 0$. The conditional cdf has all the properties and features any cdf has, but in addition, it includes the conditioning effect of some event B.

The **conditional probability density function**, or the **conditional pdf**, is related to a conditional cdf as follows:

$$f_X(x|B) = \frac{d}{dx} F_X(x|B) \tag{3.81}$$

$$F_X(x|B) = \int_{-\infty}^{x} f_X(\alpha|B)d\alpha \tag{3.82}$$

If we restrict B to a range of observations from the random variable X, then

$$B = \{a < X \leq b\} \tag{3.83}$$

The intersection in (3.80) may be written as

$$(X \leq x) \cap B = (X \leq x) \cap (a < X \leq b)$$

$$\begin{aligned}(X \leq x) \cap B &= \varnothing, & x \leq a \\ &= (a < X \leq x), & a < x \leq b \\ &= (a < X \leq b), & b < x\end{aligned}$$

Then, (3.80) becomes

$$\begin{aligned}F_x(x|B) &= 0, & x \leq a & \tag{3.84} \\ &= \frac{F_X(x) - F_X(a)}{P(B)}, & a < x \leq b \\ &= 1, & b < x\end{aligned}$$

and

$$f_X(x|B) = \frac{f_X(x)}{P(B)}, \quad a < x \leq b \tag{3.85}$$

and is zero otherwise. We illustrate the use of random variables conditioned by an event with two examples.

Example 3.22   Consider a production line designed to manufacture $8.2k\ \Omega$ resistors. Assume the line is adjusted so the resistors can be modeled as a Gaussian random variable with $\mu_X = 8200\ \Omega$ and $\sigma_X = 615\ \Omega$. Following manufacture, the resistors are tested, and all resistors having resistance values within $\pm 5\%$ of $8200\ \Omega$ ($8200 \pm 410\ \Omega$) are separated from the others in order to be marked and sold. We therefore define the conditioning event as

$$B = (7790\ \Omega < X \leq 8610\ \Omega)$$

and, we calculate the probability of B using the Gaussian cdf (3.60) with (3.9):

$$P(B) = F_X(8610) - F_X(7790)$$
$$= \psi(2/3) - \psi(-2/3) = 0.4950$$

Approximately half of the resistors produced by the production line fall within $\pm 5\%$ of the desired value of 8200 Ω. We are interested in finding the pdf of the random variable X on the condition of event B, that is, on the condition resistors with values outside of the $\pm 5\%$ range are deleted from consideration. To find this pdf we first use the conditional cdf (3.84):

If $x \le 7790$ then $(X \le x) \cap B = \emptyset$, and $P[(X \le x) \cap B] = 0$

If $7790 < x \le 8610$ then $(X \le x) \cap B = 7790 < X \le x$, and
$$P[(X \le x) \cap B] = F(x) - F(7790)$$

If $8610 < x$ then $(X \le x) \cap B = 7790 < X \le 8610$, and
$$P[X \le x) \cap B] = P(B)$$

Then,

$$\begin{aligned} F_X(x|B) &= 0, & x &\le 7790 \\ &= \frac{F_X(x) - F_X(7790)}{P(B)}, & 7790 &< x \le 8610 \\ &= 1, & 8610 &< x \end{aligned}$$

Finally, the desired conditional pdf (3.85) is

$$f_X(x|B) = \frac{f_X(x)}{P(B)}, \quad 7790 < x \le 8610$$

and is zero otherwise. Plots of $F_X(x|B)$ and $f_X(x|B)$ for this example are illustrated in Figure 3.21.

♦ ♦ ♦ ♦ ♦

The conditional pdf in (3.81) can be used to obtain expected values of a random variable conditioned by an event. For example, (3.29) can be used directly to write a conditional expectation:

$$E[g(X)|B] = \int_{-\infty}^{\infty} g(x) f_X(x|B) dx \qquad (3.86)$$

All features of expectation apply to the conditional expectation in (3.86).

Example 3.23   In Example 3.22 we found a conditional pdf

$$f_X(x|B) = \frac{f_X(x)}{0.4950}, \quad 7790 < x \le 8610$$

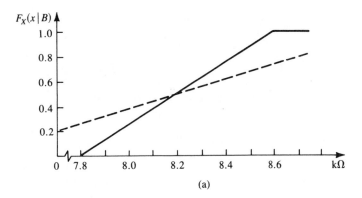

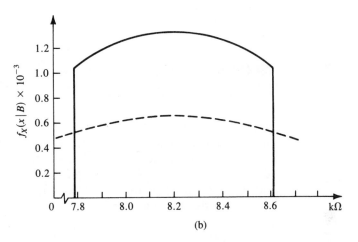

Figure 3.21   Plots of (a) a cdf conditioned by an event B, and (b) the corresponding conditional pdf. The dashed lines are, respectively, the cdf and the pdf of the resistance random variable in Example 3.22 prior to conditioning by B.

◆ ◆

and which is zero otherwise. $f_X(x)$ is Gaussian with a mean of 8200 Ω, and a standard deviation of 615 Ω. Because of symmetry, $E[X|B] = 8200$ Ω. However, its variance is

$$\text{Var}[X|B] = E[(X - \mu_X)^2|B]$$

$$= \int_{7790}^{8610} (x - \mu_X)^2 f_X(x|B)dx$$

$$= \frac{1}{0.4950\sqrt{2\pi}\sigma_X} \int_{7790}^{8610} (x - \mu_X)^2 \exp[-(x - \mu_X)^2/2\sigma_X^2]dx$$

Using the change of variable $z = (x - \mu_X)/\sigma_X$,

$$\text{Var}[X|B] = \frac{2\text{Var}[X]}{0.4950\sqrt{2\pi}} \int_0^{2/3} z^2 \exp(-z^2/2)dz$$

Then, integration by parts leads to

$$\text{Var}[X|B] = \frac{2\text{Var}[X]}{0.4950} [-0.2130 + \psi(2/3) - \psi(0)]$$

$$= 0.1394\text{Var}[X]$$

$$= .1394(615)^2 = 229.6$$

The standard deviation of the random variable X conditioned by event B is then 229.6 Ω.

◆ ◆ ◆ ◆ ◆

Section 3.7   INEQUALITIES

◆ ◆ ◆ ◆ ◆

Inequalities serve the important role of providing bounds on the size a probability can have. Sometimes, an inequality is used merely to obtain a number. At other times, an inequality is a theoretical tool used within a mathematical development. In this section we present the Markov inequality and several other inequalities that are derived from it.

Assume that the random variable Y is such that its observations are non-negative:

$$f_Y(y) = 0, \quad y < 0$$

The mean of Y is then

$$E[Y] = \int_0^\infty y f_Y(y)dy \leq \int_K^\infty y f_Y(y)dy$$

where K is some arbitrary positive number. In the integrand it is always true that $y \geq K$. Therefore,

$$E[Y] \geq K \int_K^\infty f_y(y)dy$$

The resultant integral is recognized as the probability that Y is greater than K. Therefore,

$$P(K < Y) \leq \frac{E[Y]}{K} \tag{3.87}$$

This is called the **Markov inequality.** Note that the inequality requires K to be greater than the mean if it is to convey any new information at all.

Let

$$Y = |X - c|^n$$

Y satisfies the constraint that $f_Y(y) = 0$, $y < 0$. Here, X is an arbitrary random variable, c is a constant, and n is an interger, $n = 1, 2, 3, \ldots$. Substitution of Y into (3.87) yields

$$P(K < |X - c|^n) \le E[|X - c|^n]/K$$

Substitute k^n for K. Then, since $k < |X - c|$ if $k^n < |X - c|^n$

$$P(k < |X - c|) \le E[|X - c|^n]/k^n \tag{3.88}$$

This result is called the **Bienaymé inequality.** The well-known inequality of **Chebyshev** is a special case of the Bienaymé inequality when $c = \mu_X$ and $n = 2$:

$$P(k < |X - \mu_X|) \le \sigma_X^2/k^2 \tag{3.89}$$

Another form of the Chebyshev inequality is obtained by letting $k = \epsilon \sigma_X$:

$$P(\epsilon \sigma_X < |X - \mu_X|) \le \frac{1}{\epsilon^2} \tag{3.90}$$

There is an alternative derivation for the Chebyshev inequality (3.89). It is based on the observation that, in the region **outside** of $x = \mu_X \pm k$,

$$(x - \mu_x)^2 \ge k^2$$

Then, using the integral expression for the variance (3.38), and using (3.13),

$$\sigma_X^2 \ge k^2[P(X < \mu_X - k) + P(\mu_x + k < X)]$$

Therefore,

$$\sigma_X^2 \ge k^2[P(|X - \mu_X| > k)]$$

and (3.89) follows directly.

Example 3.24   The random variable X is continuous, and has the mean μ_X and the variance σ_X^2. The pdf of X is not identified. Then, the probability that X deviates from its mean by more than three standard deviations is bounded as shown by (3.90):

$$P(3\sigma_X < |X - \mu_X|) \le 1/9 = 0.111$$

If the pdf is specified to be Gaussian, the results of Example 3.7 inform us that

$$P(3\sigma_X < |X - \mu_X|) = 0.003$$

As this example illustrates, the Chebyshev bound can be very conservative.

♦ ♦ ♦ ♦ ♦

Exercises

♦ ♦ ♦ ♦ ♦

1. The pdf for the random variable X is

$$f_X(x) = c(1 - x^2), \quad 0 < x < 1$$
$$= 0, \qquad \text{otherwise}$$

    a. Find the value of c.

    b. What is $F_X(0.5)$?

2. The pdf for the random variable Y is

$$f_Y(y) = \frac{c}{\sqrt{y}}, \quad 0 < y < 9$$
$$= 0, \quad \text{otherwise}$$

    a. Find the value of c.

    b. What is $F_Y(2)$?

3. The pdf for the random variable Z is

$$f_Z(z) = c\sqrt{z}, \quad 0 < z < 2$$
$$= 0, \quad \text{otherwise}$$

    a. Find the value of c.

    b. What is $F_Z(1.2)$?

4. The cdf for the random variable X is

$$F_X(x) = 1 - \exp(-x^2/4), \quad x \geq 0$$
$$= 0, \qquad \text{otherwise}$$

What is $P(1.1 < X < 2.1)$?

5. The cumulative distribution function for the random variable Y is

$$F_Y(y) = 1 - \exp(-0.4y^{0.5}), \quad y \geq 0$$
$$= 0, \qquad \text{otherwise}$$

What is $P(2.5 < Y < 6.2)$?

6. The cumulative distribution function for the random variable Z is

$$F_Z(z) = 1 - \exp(-2z^{3/2}), \quad z \geq 0$$
$$= 0, \qquad\qquad\qquad \text{otherwise}$$

What is $P(0.3 < Z < 0.7)$?

7. What are (a) the mean, (b) the mean square, and (c) the variance of the random variable X in Exercise 1?

8. What are (a) the mean, (b) the mean square, and (c) the variance of the random variable Y in Exercise 2?

9. What are (a) the mean, (b) the mean square, and (c) the variance of the random variable Z in Exercise 3?

10. The pdf for the **exponential** random variable is

$$f_X(x) = \lambda e^{-\lambda z}, \quad x \geq 0$$

and is zero otherwise, where λ is a **rate parameter** of the exponential random variable. Show that the mean and variance of X are $1/\lambda$ and $1/\lambda^2$, respectively.

11. The pdf of the **Laplace** random variable X is

$$f_X(x) = \frac{b}{2} \exp(-b|x|), \quad -\infty < x < \infty$$

where $b > 0$. Show that its mean and variance are

$$E[X] = 0, \quad \text{Var}[X] = 2/b^2$$

12. The **gamma function** is (using, for example, *CRC Standard Mathematical Tables*,[1] pp. 348–349):

$$\Gamma(n) = \int_0^\infty x^{n-1} e^{-x} dx, \quad n > 0$$
$$\Gamma(n + 1) = n\Gamma(n)$$
$$\Gamma(n + 1) = n! \text{ when } n \text{ is a positive integer}$$
$$\Gamma(1) = \Gamma(2) = 1$$
$$\Gamma(1/2) = \sqrt{\pi}$$

The **gamma** random variable is derived from these results; its pdf is

$$f_Y(y) = \frac{1}{b^a \Gamma(a)} y^{a-1} e^{-y/b}, \quad y > 0$$
$$= 0, \qquad\qquad\qquad\qquad \text{otherwise}$$

where $a,b > 0$. Show that the mean, the mean square, and the variance are

$$E[Y] = ab, \quad E[Y^2] = a(a + 1)b^2, \quad Var[Y] = ab^2$$

Also, show that the exponential random variable in Exercise 10 is a limiting case of the gamma random variable.

13. The **beta function** is (using, for example, *CRC Standard Mathematical Tables,*[1] p. 350):

$$B(m,n) = \int_0^1 z^{m-1}(1 - z)^{n-1} dz = \frac{\Gamma(m)\Gamma(n)}{\Gamma(m + n)}$$

where $m,n > 0$ and where $\Gamma(x)$ is a gamma function; its definition is given in Exercise 12. The **beta** random variable is derived from these results; its pdf is

$$f_Z(z) = \frac{\Gamma(a + b)}{\Gamma(a)\Gamma(b)} z^{a-1}(1 - z)^{b-1} \quad 0 < z < 1$$
$$= 0, \qquad\qquad\qquad\qquad \text{otherwise}$$

where $a,b > 0$. Show that the mean, the mean square, and the variance are

$$E[Z] = \frac{a}{a + b}, \quad E[Z^2] = \frac{a(a + 1)}{(a + b)(a + b + 1)}$$

$$Var[Z] = \frac{ab}{(a + b)^2(a + b + 1)}$$

Also, show that the uniform random variable is a limiting case of the beta random variable.

14. The **Cauchy** random variable has the pdf

$$f_X(x) = \frac{a}{\pi(x^2 + a^2)} \quad \text{for all } x$$

a. Find the median and the mode for the Cauchy random variable.

b. Verify that the mean and the variance do not exist for the Cauchy random variable.

c. Find the Cauchy cdf.

d. Use (3.49) to verify that $\Phi_X(j\omega) = \exp(-a|\omega|)$ is the Cauchy characteristic function.

15. The characteristic function of the random variable X is

$$\Phi_X(j\omega) = \frac{c^2}{(c + j\omega)^2}$$

Find the mean and variance of X.

16. The characteristic function of the random variable X is

$$\Phi_X(j\omega) = (0.25 + 0.75e^{j\omega})^{10}$$

Find the mean and variance of X.

17. The characteristic function of the random variable X is

$$\Phi_X(j\omega) = \exp(j10\omega - 2\omega^2)$$

Find the mean and variance of X.

18. A Gaussian random variable Y has the parameters $\mu_Y = 10$ and $\sigma_Y = 3$. Find (a) $P(7.0 < Y)$, (b) $P(Y \le 11.5)$, and (c) $P(7.0 < Y \le 11.5)$.

19. A Gaussian random variable Y has the parameters $\mu_Y = 20$ and $\sigma_Y = 5$. Find (a) $P(15.0 < Y)$, (b) $P(Y \le 24.5)$, and (c) $P(15.0 < Y \le 24.5)$.

20. Resistance values from a production line for resistors are Gaussian with a mean of 5100 Ω, and a standard deviation of 500 Ω. What is the probability of selecting a resistor from this line having a value within 5000 Ω $\pm 10\%$?

21. Use a Gaussian random number generator (GRNG—see Appendix A) to make $n = 1000$ numbers having a mean of 5100 and a standard deviation of 500. How many of these numbers occur within 5000 $\pm 10\%$? Compare this relative frequency answer with the theoretical answer in Exercise 20.

22. Inductance values of coils made on a production line are Gaussian with a mean of 1.2 mH and a standard deviation of 0.1 mH. What is the probability of selecting an inductor from this line having a value within 1.0 mH $\pm 10\%$?

23. Use a Gaussian random number generator (GRNG—see Appendix A) to make $n = 1000$ numbers having a mean of 0.0012 and a standard deviation of 0.0001. How many of these numbers occur within 0.001 $\pm 10\%$? Compare this relative frequency answer with the theoretical answer in Exercise 22.

24. Suppose a dimension and its tolerance are specified to be

$$y = 0.75 \pm 0.002 \text{ in.}$$

Y is a Gaussian random variable with the following parameters: the mean is 0.751 in. and the standard deviation is 0.0013 in. What percent of the observations of Y are within the specified tolerance?

25. Use a Gaussian random number generator (GRNG—see Appendix A) to make $n = 1000$ numbers having a mean of 0.751 and a standard deviation of 0.0013. How many of these values occur within 0.75 ± 0.002? Compare this relative frequency answer with the theoretical answer in Exercise 24.

26. Given the following frequency data:

Cell	Frequency	Cell	Frequency
1	0	11	10
2	0	12	14
3	0	13	6
4	2	14	10
5	2	15	1
6	6	16	0
7	8	17	2
8	12	18	2
9	11	19	0
10	13	20	1

The lower boundary of cell 1 is 0.01 μF, and each of the cells is 0.001 μF in width. For example, for cell 1, the lower boundary is $x = 0.010$ μF, and its upper boundary is $x = 0.011$ μF. Plot the data on $\times 90$ probability paper.[3] Determine $\bar{x}$ and s_x. Do the data appear to be Gaussian?

27. Given the following frequency data:

Cell	Frequency	Cell	Frequency
1	1	11	8
2	1	12	13
3	3	13	9
4	2	14	4
5	4	15	2
6	7	16	2
7	9	17	4
8	7	18	3
9	10	19	0
10	10	20	1

The lower boundary of cell 1 is 990 Ω, and the width of each cell is 10 Ω. For example, for cell 1, the lower boundary is $x = 990$ Ω, and its upper boundary is $x = 1000\ \Omega$. Plot the data on $\times 90$ probability paper.[3] Determine $\bar{x}$ and s_X. Do the data appear to be Gaussian?

28. Given the following frequency data:

Cell	Frequency	Cell	Frequency
1	0	11	11
2	0	12	10
3	0	13	6
4	0	14	11
5	5	15	8
6	7	16	5
7	4	17	1
8	9	18	0
9	8	19	1
10	14	20	0

The lower boundary of cell 1 is 0.008 H, and the width of each cell is 0.001 H. For example, for cell 1, the lower boundary is $x = 0.008$ H, and its upper boundary is $x = 0.009$ H. Plot the data on $\times 90$ probability paper.[3] Determine $\bar{x}$ and s_X. Do the data appear to be Gaussian?

29. A random variable Z has the discrete probabilities

$$P(Z = -3) = 0.10$$
$$P(Z = -1) = 0.13$$
$$P(Z = 0) = 0.43$$
$$P(Z = 2) = 0.20$$
$$P(Z = 4) = 0.14$$

a. Sketch the pdf and the cdf.

b. What is the value for $P(Z > 1.3)$?

c. What are the mean and the variance?

30. Given the following data:

j	Y_j	$P(Y_j)$
1	6.9	0.26
2	5.4	0.14
3	4.8	0.19
4	3.2	0.21
5	2.1	0.20

   a. Sketch the pdf and the cdf.

   b. What is the value for $P(Y > 4.0)$?

   c. What are the mean and the variance?

31. Given the following data:

i	X_i	$P(X_i)$
1	1.0	0.20
2	2.5	0.18
3	3.9	0.22
4	5.2	0.15
5	7.1	0.25

   a. Sketch the pdf and the cdf.

   b. What is the value for $P(X > 5.0)$?

   c. What are the mean and the variance?

32. The pdf for the random variable X is

$$f_X(x) = 0.20\delta(x - 1.0) + 0.25\delta(x - 3.0) + 0.15\delta(x - 3.5) \\ + 0.24\delta(x - 5.0) + 0.16\delta(x - 6.5)$$

   What are the mean and variance of X?

33. Repeat Example 3.12 where a function of a single random variable is the linear relation $y = \alpha x + \beta$, but, in this problem, let $\alpha < 0$. Show that

$$f_Y(y) = f_X\left(\frac{y - \beta}{\alpha}\right)\left(\frac{-1}{\alpha}\right)$$

34. The random variable X is uniformly distributed between zero and one. The random variable Y is

$$Y = -200X + 900$$

   Find the pdf for Y.

35. The random variable X is Gaussian with a mean of zero and a variance of one. The random variable Y is

$$Y = 200X + 900$$

   a. Find the pdf for Y.

b. If, in the given expression for Y, the $+200$ is changed to -200, what is the resultant pdf?

36. Use the technique of completing the square and (3.61), to show that moments about the origin for the lognormal random variable in Example 3.15 are

$$E[Y^n] = \exp(n\mu_X + n^2\sigma_X^2/2)$$

Then, using this, show that the mean and the variance of the lognormal random variable are

$$\mu_Y = \exp(\mu_X + \sigma_X^2/2)$$
$$\sigma_Y^2 = \exp(2\mu_X + \sigma_X^2)[\exp(\sigma_X^2) - 1]$$

37. In Example 3.17, the change of variable $Y = X^2$ is used when X is a Gaussian random variable with a mean of zero and a variance of σ_X^2. Use the expectation operator and (3.59) to show that the mean and variance of Y are

$$\mu_Y = \sigma_X^2 \quad \text{and} \quad \sigma_Y^2 = 2\sigma_X^4$$

38. The transformation $y = (x + 3)/3$ is applied to the random variable X, which is uniformly distributed between 0 and 1. Find the pdf for the random variable Y, and its mean and variance.

39. A Gaussian random variable X has a mean of 2 and a variance of 5. The random variable Y is obtained from $y = -2x + 3$. Find the mean of Y, its variance, and its pdf.

40. The transformation $y = x^2$ is applied to the random variable X, which has a Laplace pdf:

$$f_X(x) = \tfrac{1}{2} e^{-|x|}, \quad -\infty < x < \infty$$

Find the pdf for the random variable Y.

41. The transformation $y = V \sin(\omega x)$ is applied to the random variable X, which is uniformly distributed between $\pm(\pi/2\omega)$. Find the pdf for the random variable Y.

42. Simulate Exercise 41 on a computer using $n = 1000$ trials. Let $V = 1$ and $\omega = 1$. Use eight cells between $y = \pm 1$. Compare the simulated and the theoretical results.

43. The transformation $z = (1/4)|y|$ is applied to the random variable Y, which is Gaussian with a mean of zero and a variance of 3. Find the pdf for the random variable Z.

44. The transformation $y = c \tan(x)$ produces the Cauchy random variable when X is a random variable uniformly distributed between $\pm \pi/2$. Find the Cauchy pdf using this transformation.

45. Find the transformation (3.79) that will convert the random variable X uniformly distributed between 0 and 1 into the Laplace random variable Y with a pdf

$$f_Y(y) = (1/6)\exp(-|y|/3), \quad -\infty < y < \infty$$

46. Find the transformation (3.79) that will convert the random variable X uniformly distributed between 0 and 1 into the Cauchy random variable Y with a pdf

$$f_Y(y) = \frac{3}{\pi(y^2 + 9)}, \quad -\infty < y < \infty$$

47. A pdf for a mixed random variable X is

$$
\begin{aligned}
f_X(x) &= 0.3\delta(x) && \text{where } x = 0, \text{ and} \\
&= -a(x - 3)/3 && \text{where } 0 < x < 3, \text{ and} \\
&= 0, && \text{otherwise}
\end{aligned}
$$

Find (a) the value of the constant a and (b) $F_X(x)$.

48. Y is a zero-mean Gaussian random variable with a variance of 3. If Y is transformed by

$$
\begin{aligned}
z &= 2y^2, && y \geq 0 \\
&= 0, && \text{otherwise}
\end{aligned}
$$

What is the pdf for the random variable Z?

49. The random variable X is uniformly distributed between -2 and $+5$. The random variable Y is obtained from X by

$$
\begin{aligned}
y &= x/6, && y \geq 0 \\
&= 0, && \text{otherwise}
\end{aligned}
$$

Find the pdf and the cdf for the random variable Y.

50. The random variable X is Gaussian with a mean of zero and a variance of 4. The random variable Y is obtained using the transformation

$$
\begin{aligned}
y &= 100x, && x \geq 0 \\
&= 0, && \text{otherwise}
\end{aligned}
$$

Find the pdf and the cdf for the random variable Y.

51. The random variable Z in Exercise 29 is transformed by

$$x = 0.5z^2 + 1$$

Find the mean and variance of X.

52. The random variable Y in Exercise 30 is transformed by

$$z = 2y + 7$$

Find the mean and variance of Z.

53. The random variable X in Exercise 31 is transformed by

$$y = 3x + 5$$

Find the mean and variance of Y.

54. The pdf for a mixed random variable is a constant c between $x = \pm 10$, and is zero otherwise, except for $0.3\delta(x - 10)$. Find (a) the value of c, (b) the mean, and (c) the variance of the random variable.

55. X is a Gaussian random variable with a mean of 300 and a standard deviation of 50. Two events are defined as follows:

$$A = (200 < X \le 325), \quad B = (280 < X \le 400)$$

Use this information to calculate $P(A|B)$, and compare that with $P(A)$.

56. Event A is binary: $P(A) = 0.65$. When A occurs, a random variable X is Gaussian with a mean of 10 and a variance of 25. When $\overline{A}$ occurs, the random variable X is still Gaussian, but its mean is 0 and its variance is 64. A detection level of $x = 5$ has been set:

> If $X \ge 5$ then A is said to occur.
>
> If $X < 5$ then $\overline{A}$ is said to occur.

a. Find the probability of making an error, and saying that A occurs when $\overline{A}$ has occurred.

b. Find the probability of making an error, and saying that $\overline{A}$ occurs when A has occurred.

c. What is the probability of making an error?

57. A system may be either in state A or B. They are mutually exclusive states. If in state A, its output is a Gaussian random variable with a mean of 500 and a standard deviation of 50. However, in state B, the output is still Gaussian, but the mean is 250 and the standard deviation is 125.

A decision level of $d = 425$ has been determined: If the output is greater than, or equal to, 425, then we say that the system is in state A, otherwise, state B.

a. What is the probability of making the mistake of saying the system in state B when it is actually in A?

b. What is the probability of making the mistake of saying the system is in state A when it is actually in B?

c. If A and B are equally likely, what is the probability of making an error?

58. The lifetime of a system expressed in months is a Rayleigh random variable X:

$$f_X(x) = (x/200)\exp(-x^2/400), \quad x > 0$$
$$= 0, \qquad\qquad\qquad\qquad \text{otherwise}$$

Find the pdf that applies for the lifetime of the system if it is given that the system has survived for 15 months.

59. The random variable Y is exponential:

$$F_Y(y) = 1 - e^{-y/4}, \quad y > 0$$
$$= 0, \qquad\qquad \text{otherwise}$$

All outcomes corresponding to the event $\{Y > \mu_Y\}$ are excluded. What is the pdf for Y conditioned by this exclusion?

60. A random variable X has an unknown density function, but its mean and variance are known to be 3 and 1/5, respectively. Find an upper bound on the probability that X deviates by more than 2 from its mean.

61. A random variable Z is known to have a mean of 2.1 and a variance of 2.25. Calculate an upper bound on the following probability:

$$P[(Z < \mu_z - 4) \cup (\mu_z + 4 < Z)]$$

References

♦   ♦   ♦   ♦   ♦

1. Beyer, William H. ed. *CRC Standard Mathematical Tables.* 28th ed. Boca Raton, Florida: CRC Press, Inc., 1987.

2. Gauss, Karl F. *Theoria Motus* (Motion of the Heavenly Bodies moving about the Sun in Conic Sections, an English translation by C. H. Davis) Boston: Little, Brown and Company, 1857, p. 259.

3. Probability graph paper "×90 DIVISIONS" is available, for example, from the Dietzgen Corporation (No. 340-PS), and Keuffel & Esser Company (#46-8003).

4. Leibowitz, H. W. and D. A. Owens, "New Evidence for the Intermediate Position of the Relaxed Accomodation," *Documenta Ophthalmologica,* 46, 1:133–147, 1978.

5. The author is grateful to Alan C. Bovik, Stark Centennial Endowed Associate Professor, ECE Department, University of Texas, Austin, for the suggestion of, and discussion on, this method.

Additional Readings

◆　◆　◆　◆　◆

The five numbered references in Chapter 2 also serve as additional reading for this chapter.

4 Multiple Random Variables: Theory and Models

. . . .

But to us, probability is the very guide of life.

Bishop Joseph Butler, 1692–1752

Introduction When we want to describe a random experiment involving n random variables, we begin with an n'th-order joint probability,

$$P(A) = P(A_1 \cap A_2 \cap \cdots \cap A_n) \tag{4.1}$$

where $A_i = (X_i \leq x_i)$, $i = 1, 2, \ldots, n$.

The first step in learning how to work with (4.1) is to learn the case for the **bivariate random variables:**

$$P(A) = P(A_1 \cap A_2) \tag{4.2}$$

A theory for bivariate random variables, such as X_1 and X_2, must do at least two things:

1. It must be a logical and direct extension of the theory for a single random variable as presented in Chapter 3.

2. It must be directly capable of expansion to the case of $n > 2$ random variables in (4.1).

What we desire is that all the conceptual foundations for relating one random variable to another be done when only two are involved. Then, extensions to three, four, or more random variables will introduce, perhaps, more labor, but no new concepts.

Section 4.1   BIVARIATE RANDOM VARIABLES

♦ ♦ ♦ ♦ ♦

When two random variables are considered at once we say that they are bivariate random variables. Bivariate random variables occur when, for example, the input to a system at some instant of time is a random variable X, and the output from the system, at the same instant of time, is a random variable Y. Also, the common situation of working simultaneously with a signal random variable X and a noise random variable Y is an example of bivariate random variables.

We define the **joint cumulative distribution function** (joint cdf) of the bivariate random variables X and Y as

$$F_{XY}(x,y) = P[(X \le x) \cap (Y \le y)] \tag{4.3}$$

This definition is a direct extension of the cdf for a single random variable (3.6b).

Correlations between bivariate random variables are important to us; therefore we do not consider X and Y separately, but as a pair (X,Y). Also, we visualize observations of X and Y as points on an x,y plane. Then, as is illustrated in Figure 4.1, the joint cdf (4.3) is the probability of a bivariate observation occurring in the quarter-plane to the left of, and below, the point (x,y).

Consider a joint cdf evaluated once at (x,y) and once again at $(x + dx, y + dy)$ as shown in Figure 4.2; we assume both dx and dy are positive. The difference between these two joint cdfs is a probability dP, which must be non-negative because it represents the probability of observations occurring in the shaded area of Figure 4.2. Using a two-dimensional Taylor's expansion,

$$dP = F_{XY}(x+dx, y+dy) - F_{XY}(x,y)$$
$$\approx \frac{\partial}{\partial x} F_{XY}(x,y)dx + \frac{\partial}{\partial y} F_{XY}(x,y)dy$$

The joint cdf is non-negative because it is a probability. The differentials dx and dy are positive by assumption. Therefore, the joint cdf must increase monotonically in both the x and y directions.

Certain special cases for the joint cdf are examined: The event $(X \le -\infty)$ is the impossible event $\varnothing$. When this happens (4.3) simplifies as:

$$F_{XY}(-\infty, y) = P[\varnothing \cap (Y \le y)] = P(\varnothing)$$

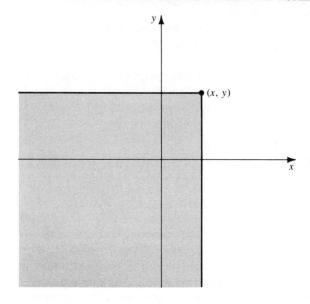

Figure 4.1   The shaded region is the region covered by $(X \le x) \cap (Y \le y)$. The probability of bivariate observations (x,y) occurring in this region is, by definition, the joint cdf $F_{XY}(x,y)$.

◆ ◆

Therefore, (2.16) shows us that

$$F_{XY}(-\infty,y) = 0 \tag{4.4}$$

Similarly, it follows that

$$F_{XY}(x,-\infty) = 0 \tag{4.5}$$

$$F_{XY}(-\infty,-\infty) = 0 \tag{4.6}$$

In another special case, the event $(X \le +\infty)$ is the certain event S_X. It then follows from (4.3) that

$$F_{XY}(\infty,y) = P[S_X \cap (Y \le y)] = P(Y \le y)$$

Therefore, using (3.6b),

$$F_{XY}(\infty,y) = F_Y(y) \tag{4.7}$$

This is the cdf for the single random variable Y. Similarly,

$$F_{XY}(x,\infty) = F_X(x) \tag{4.8}$$

which is the cdf for the single random variable X. These cdf relations are called **marginal cumulative distribution functions.** If both x and y are arbitrarily large,

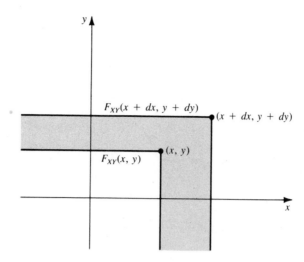

Figure 4.2   Illustrating that $F_{XY}(x,y)$ must be nondecreasing in the x and the y directions; dx and dy are positive. The shaded area indicates an increase in area in which observations of the bivariate random variables X and Y can occur. The probability of this happening is $dP \geq 0$.

• •

$$F_{XY}(\infty,\infty) = 1 \tag{4.9}$$

The results in (4.4) through (4.9) are indicated in Figure 4.3 and are, of course, consistent with the requirement that $F_{XY}(x,y)$ be nondecreasing in both the x and the y directions.

The **joint probability density function** (joint pdf) is defined as the following derivative of the joint cdf:

$$f_{XY}(x,y) = \frac{\partial^2}{\partial x \partial y} F_{XY}(x,y) \tag{4.10}$$

It follows from (4.10), and from the fact that the joint cdf increases monotonically in both the x and y directions, that a joint pdf is always non-negative. We assume the differentiability of the joint cdf, or we admit the use of Dirac-delta functions as we did for discrete and mixed single random variables.

The inverse relation of (4.10) is

$$F_{XY}(x,y) = \int_{-\infty}^{y} \int_{-\infty}^{x} f_{XY}(\alpha,\beta)d\alpha d\beta \tag{4.11}$$

The volume under the surface of the joint pdf is unity, as can be seen by combining (4.9) and (4.11):

$$F_{XY}(\infty,\infty) = \int_{-\infty}^{\infty} \int_{-\infty}^{\infty} f_{XY}(x,y)dxdy = 1 \tag{4.12}$$

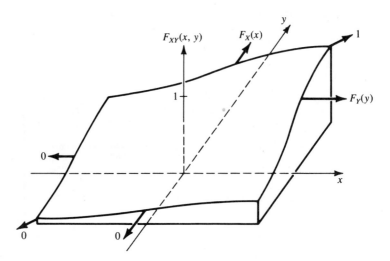

Figure 4.3   Illustration of a joint cumulative distribution function. Note the marginal cumulative distribution functions $F_X(x)$ and $F_Y(y)$.

• •

A differential area $dA = dxdy$ is shown in Figure 4.4. We determine the probability of an observation occurring in this area as follows. First, we find the probability of a bivariate observation occurring in a strip, shown in Figure 4.4, of width dx, and extending from $-\infty$ to $y+dy$. That probability is, using the integral relation (4.11),

$$F_{XY}(x+dx,y+dy) - F_{XY}(x,y+dy) = \int_x^{x+dx} \int_{-\infty}^{y+dy} f_{XY}(\alpha,\beta)d\alpha d\beta$$

Second, we perform a similar calculation for a strip of the same width dx, but extending from $-\infty$ to only y. The probability of an observation occurring in this strip is

$$F_{XY}(x+dx,y) - F_{XY}(x,y) = \int_x^{x+dx} \int_{-\infty}^{y} f_{XY}(\alpha,\beta)d\alpha d\beta$$

The probability of a bivariate occurrence in the differential area $dA = dxdy$ is the difference between these two results,

$$P[(x,y) \in dA] = \int_x^{x+dx} \int_{y}^{y+dy} f_{XY}(\alpha,\beta)d\alpha d\beta$$
$$\approx f_{XY}(x,y)dxdy$$

Therefore, volumes under a joint pdf are probabilities. Specifically, let $P[(x,y) \in R]$ be the probability that data (in x,y pairs) are contained in a re-

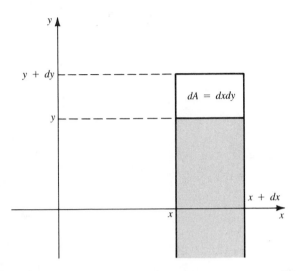

Figure 4.4 Illustrating how the differential area $dA = dxdy$ is constructed from the difference between two semi-infinite strips of width dx. The first strip extends from $-\infty$ to $y+dy$, and the second, which is shaded, extends from $-\infty$ to y.

• •

gion R:

$$P[(x,y) \in R] = \int_R f_{XY}(x,y)dxdy \qquad (4.13)$$

Now, we return our attention to the joint pdf. Combining (3.11) with (4.8) we have

$$f_X(x) = \frac{d}{dx} F_{XY}(x,\infty)$$

Then, using (4.11),

$$f_X(x) = \frac{d}{dx} \int_{-\infty}^{x} \int_{-\infty}^{\infty} f_{XY}(\alpha,y)dyd\alpha$$

$$= \int_{-\infty}^{\infty} f_{XY}(x,y)dy \qquad (4.14)$$

Similarly, it follows that

$$f_Y(y) = \int_{-\infty}^{\infty} f_{XY}(x,y)dx \qquad (4.15)$$

The pdfs in (4.14) and (4.15) are referred to as **marginal probability density functions.** Figures 4.5(a) and 4.5(b) are examples of joint pdfs for the bivariate random variables X and Y.

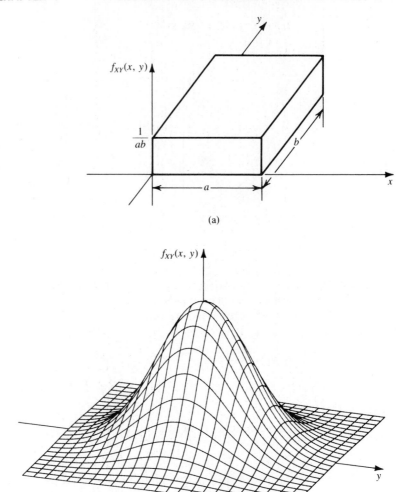

(a)

(b)

Figure 4.5   Illustration of two joint pdfs.

If the random variables X and Y are independent, then (2.34) applies, and the joint cdf (4.3) separates:

$$F_{XY}(x,y) = P(X \leq x)P(Y \leq y)$$

$$F_{XY}(x,y) = F_X(x)F_Y(y) \tag{4.16}$$

Using (4.10), the joint pdf also separates:

$$f_{XY}(x,y) = \frac{d}{dx} F_X(x) \frac{d}{dy} F_Y(y)$$

$$f_{XY}(x,y) = f_X(x)f_Y(y) \tag{4.17}$$

Example 4.1   Refer to Figure 4.5(a), which shows a joint pdf that is rectangular in shape. For simplicity, let $a = b = 1$, so that the joint pdf has the constant value of one within the unit square of the x,y plane, and is zero otherwise. The purpose of this example is to illustrate how a joint cdf may be calculated from its joint pdf using the integral relation in (4.11).

Figure 4.6 shows a top view of the joint pdf. Also shown in this figure is a point (x,y) within the unit square occupied by the joint pdf. Extending downward and to the left of (x,y) are shaded lines indicating the region covered by the range of integration of the integral (4.11). This is, of course, the same region illustrated in Figure 4.1.

Therefore, to evaluate the joint cdf for any (x,y) inside the unit square,

$$F_{XY}(x,y) = \int_0^x d\alpha \int_0^y d\beta = xy$$

This same technique that we just used with (x,y) located in the unit square can be used again within the semi-infinite strip above the unit square: $0 < x < 1$ and $1 < y < \infty$. If we do, the result is

$$F_{XY}(x,y) = \int_0^x d\alpha \int_0^1 dy = x$$

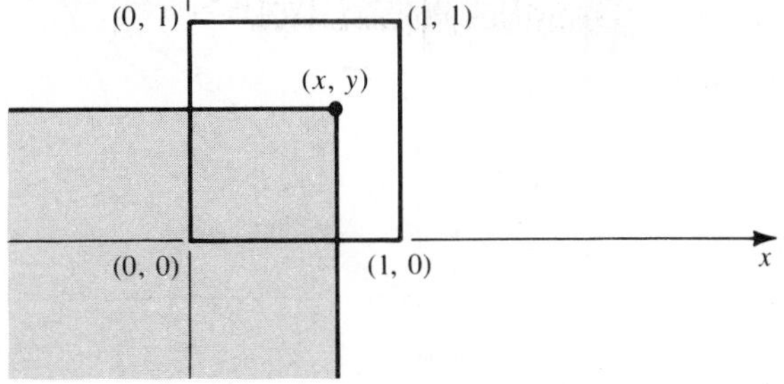

Figure 4.6   A top view of the joint pdf of Example 4.1.

Similarly, for the semi-infinite strip to the right of the unit square: $0 < y < 1$ and $1 < x < \infty$,

$$F_{XY}(x,y) = \int_0^1 dx \int_0^y dy = y$$

These results for the joint cdf are summarized in Figure 4.7(a). To complete this picture we note that if (x,y) is below the x axis or to the left of the y axis then $F_{XY}(x,y) = 0$ because the joint pdf is outside the ranges of integration

◆ ◆

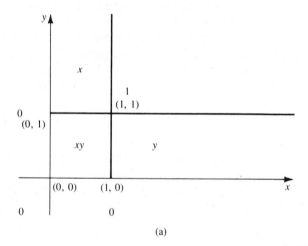

(a)

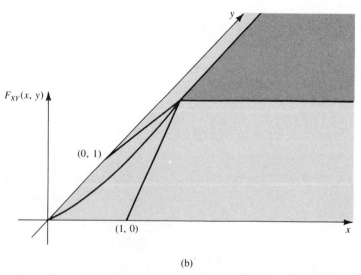

(b)

Figure 4.7   Showing a top view (a) and an oblique view (b) of the joint cdf in Example 4.1.

in (4.11). Finally, if (x,y) is anywhere above $y = 1$ *and* to the right of $x = 1$ then $F_{XY}(x,y) = 1$ because the entire joint pdf will always be within the ranges of integration. A sketch of how this joint cdf appears is shown in Figure 4.7(b).

◆ ◆ ◆ ◆ ◆

Example 4.2   Assume that the joint pdf $F_{XY}(x,y)$ is discrete, and that it has the value of 0.25 at each of the four points $(-1,-1)$, $(-1,1)$, $(1,-1)$, and $(1,1)$. What are (a) $F_{XY}(0,0)$ and (b) $F_{XY}(0.5,10)$?

To answer (a), we note that the point $(-1,-1)$ is the only point of the given four points that is located to the left and below $(0,0)$. Therefore, the value of the joint cdf at $(0,0)$ is 0.25. The reader should note that $F_{XY}(x,y) = 0.25$ for the same reason for every point (x,y) **within** the square defined by the four points given above.

By similar reasoning, $F_{XY}(0.5,10) = 0.50$ because two points, $(-1,-1)$ and $(-1,1)$, are located to the left and below the point $(0.5,10)$ and because each of these two points occurs with a probability of 0.25.

◆ ◆ ◆ ◆ ◆

In Appendix D there is a derivation of the Gaussian and Rayleigh probability density functions for an important class of applications. It is appropriate to refer the reader to Appendix D at this stage because the derivation requires an understanding of a joint pdf. While this derivation is not necessary for the reader to continue in this book, it is important to recognize that there are physical origins for these two powerful pdfs.

Section 4.2   EXPECTATION

◆ ◆ ◆ ◆ ◆

The expectation operator, introduced with a single random variable in (3.29), is applied to bivariate random variables with

$$E[g(X,Y)] = \int_{-\infty}^{\infty} \int_{-\infty}^{\infty} g(x,y) f_{XY}(x,y) dx dy \qquad (4.18)$$

where $g(x,y)$ is an arbitrary function of two variables.

If the function $g(x,y)$ happens to depend on only one of the variables, say x, then (4.18) reverts to the case of the single random variable X:

$$E[g(X)] = \int_{-\infty}^{\infty} g(x) \int_{-\infty}^{\infty} f_{XY}(x,y) dy dx$$

Then, using (4.14) to obtain the marginal pdf $f_X(x)$,

$$E[g(X)] = \int_{-\infty}^{\infty} g(x) f_X(x) dx$$

This means that all expectations introduced with a single random variable, such as μ_X, μ_Y, σ_x^2, and σ_Y^2, are included within the bivariate case.

A bivariate expectation of extreme importance to us is the **correlation,** denoted R_{XY}; it is the expected value of the product of X and Y:

$$R_{XY} = E[XY] = \int_{-\infty}^{\infty} \int_{-\infty}^{\infty} xy f_{XY}(x,y) dx dy \qquad \textbf{(4.19)}$$

Correlation, including its extension to correlation functions (in Chapter 8), provides the single most important tool we have for engineering signal processing and detection systems. Correlation is, of course, related to the sample correlation coefficient discussed in Chapter 1.

Suppose that the random variables X and Y have means of zero. We say there is a positive correlation between the random variables X and Y when their observations tend to have the same sign,

$$R_{XY} = E[XY] > 0$$

However, if observations of the bivariate random variables have a tendency to have opposite signs, the resultant correlation will be negative:

$$R_{XY} = E[XY] < 0$$

If the random variables X and Y do not have means of zero then, in effect, we remove the respective means from the bivariate random variables and interpret the results as before. Correlation with the means removed is defined as the **covariance:**

$$\text{Cov}[XY] = E[(X - \mu_x)(Y - \mu_Y)] \qquad \textbf{(4.20)}$$

If the expectation in (4.20) is expanded, the covariance becomes

$$\text{Cov}[XY] = R_{XY} - \mu_X \mu_Y \qquad \textbf{(4.21)}$$

Note that both (4.20) and (4.21) become the familiar expressions for variance if the random variables X and Y are the same.

If the bivariate random variables are independent, then using (4.17), the correlation (4.19) becomes

$$R_{XY} = \int_{-\infty}^{\infty} x f_X(x) dx \int_{-\infty}^{\infty} y f_Y(y) dy$$

$$R_{XY} = E[XY] = E[X]E[Y] = \mu_X \mu_Y \qquad \textbf{(4.22)}$$

By definition, the random variables X and Y are **uncorrelated** if (4.22) applies. That is, if $R_{XY} = \mu_X \mu_Y$. We see from (4.22) that whenever X and Y are independent they are also uncorrelated. However, the reverse is not true in general; it may not be said that whenever X and Y are uncorrelated that they are also independent. This restriction may better be appreciated if we note that when X and Y are independent then

$$E[X^n Y^m] = E[X^n]E[Y^m]$$

The case of uncorrelated random variables refers only to the case of $n = m = 1$.

By definition, if $R_{XY} = 0$ then the random variables X and Y are said to be **orthogonal.** One relatively common situation in which orthogonality occurs is where X and Y are independent and one or the other has a mean of zero. Then, (4.22) shows that X and Y are orthogonal. An example of this is the correlation of a signal X with a zero-mean noise Y.

The covariance (4.20) may be normalized with respect to the standard deviations of the random variables X and Y. The normalized covariance is called the **correlation coefficient** and is denoted by ρ. It is a figure of merit that describes the correlation between the random variables X and Y, but which is independent of the relative magnitudes of X and Y, as well as their means:

$$\rho = \frac{\text{Cov}[XY]}{\sigma_X \sigma_Y} \tag{4.23}$$

Whenever the random variables X and Y are uncorrelated the covariance, and therefore the correlation coefficient, vanishes. If, on the other hand, X and Y are related by the linear relation (3.40), then $Y = \alpha X + \beta$,

$$\mu_Y = E[Y] = \alpha \mu_X + \beta$$

and

$$\sigma_Y^2 = E[(Y - \mu_X)^2] = \alpha^2 \sigma_X^2$$

Further, the covariance becomes

$$\text{Cov}[XY] = E[(X - \mu_X)(Y - \mu_Y)]$$
$$= \alpha \sigma_X^2$$

Substituting these results into (4.23) yields

$$\rho = \frac{\alpha}{\sqrt{\alpha^2}} = \pm 1$$

Therefore, if X and Y are linearly related, the correlation coefficient will always have a magnitude of one, and its sign will be the sign of the coefficient α.

The magnitude of the correlation coefficient is bounded by one in all circumstances. We demonstrate this by starting with the following inequality, the left side of which cannot be negative:

$$E\left[\left(\frac{X-\mu_X}{\sigma_X} \pm \frac{Y-\mu_Y}{\sigma_Y}\right)^2\right] \geq 0$$

This inequality remains after the square is expanded:

$$E\left[\left(\frac{X-\mu_X}{\sigma_X}\right)^2 \pm 2\frac{(X-\mu_X)(Y-\mu_Y)}{\sigma_X\sigma_Y} + \left(\frac{Y-\mu_Y}{\sigma_Y}\right)^2\right] \geq 0$$

Then, performing the expectation operations,

$$1 \pm 2\rho + 1 \geq 0$$

And this reduces to

$$|\rho| \leq 1 \tag{4.24}$$

The correlation coefficient therefore is a convenient figure of merit because both its sign and magnitude can be interpreted independently of the means and variances of the bivariate random variables.

Example 4.3   We continue Example 4.1, which is based on the joint pdf in Figure 4.5(a), where $a = b = 1$. The reader may easily verify, using (4.18), that the expectations for the random variable X are

$$E[X] = 1/2 \quad \text{and} \quad \text{Var}[X] = 1/12$$

Similarly, for the random variable Y,

$$E[Y] = 1/2 \quad \text{and} \quad \text{Var}[Y] = 1/12$$

Our interest here is mainly with the correlation; using (4.19),

$$R_{XY} = \int_0^1 x\,dx \int_0^1 y\,dy = \frac{1}{4}$$

Thus, we see in this example that the bivariate random variables X and Y are uncorrelated because $R_{XY} = \mu_X\mu_Y$. Therefore, $\text{Cov}[XY] = \rho = 0$.

◆ ◆ ◆ ◆ ◆

Example 4.4   We are given that the bivariate random variables X and Y have the following parameters:

$$\mu_X = 1 \quad \text{and} \quad \sigma_X^2 = 2$$
$$\mu_Y = 3 \quad \text{and} \quad \sigma_Y^2 = 4$$
$$\rho = 0.5$$

What is the correlation R_{XY}? Using (4.21), we have an expression for the correlation:

$$R_{XY} = \text{Cov}[XY] + \mu_X \mu_Y$$

Then, using (4.23),

$$R_{XY} = \rho \sigma_X \sigma_Y + \mu_X \mu_Y$$

Finally, using the given data,

$$R_{XY} = (0.5)(\sqrt{2})(2) + (1)(3) = 4.414$$

♦ ♦ ♦ ♦ ♦

Example 4.5   In this example we are given that the variances of the bivariate random variables X and Y are 7.05 and 5.36, respectively. We are also given that the correlation coefficient for X and Y is $\rho_{XY} = -0.48$. Then, given the linear transformation,

$$U = 2X + Y$$
$$V = X + 2Y$$

we are asked to find the covariance for U and V, $\text{Cov}[UV]$. To solve this problem, we start with the definition of the covariance (4.20),

$$\text{Cov}[UV] = E[(U - \mu_U)(V - \mu_V)]$$

Using the relations given for U and V, we can write the following expressions for the means of U and V:

$$\mu_U = 2\mu_X + \mu_Y$$
$$\mu_V = \mu_X + 2\mu_Y$$

Then, the covariance becomes

$$\text{Cov}[UV] = E[(2X + Y - 2\mu_X - \mu_Y)(X + 2Y - \mu_X - 2\mu_Y)]$$

Rearranging this, we find

$$\text{Cov}[UV] = E[[2(X - \mu_X) + (Y - \mu_Y)][(X - \mu_X) + 2(Y - \mu_Y)]]$$

If the multiplication is carried out we obtain

$$\text{Cov}[UV] = 2E[(X - \mu_X)^2] + 5E[(X - \mu_X)(Y - \mu_Y)] + 2E[(Y - \mu_Y)^2]$$

This is recognized as

$$\text{Cov}[UV] = 2\sigma_X^2 + 5\text{Cov}[XY] + 2\sigma_Y^2$$

Finally, using (4.23) and the values given in this example, we have

$$\text{Cov}[UV] = 2(7.05) - (5)(0.48)\sqrt{(7.05)(5.36)} + 2(5.36) = 10.07$$

Note that it was not necessary to know the values of μ_X and μ_Y to calculate the required covariance.

Using similar methods, the variances $\text{Var}[U]$ and $\text{Var}[V]$ may also be calculated. The resultant values are

$$\text{Var}[U] = 21.76 \quad \text{and} \quad \text{Var}[V] = 16.69$$

(The calculations used to reach these variances are left to the reader.) It then follows that the correlation coefficient (4.23) for the bivariate random variables U and V is

$$\rho_{UV} = \frac{10.07}{\sqrt{(21.76)(16.69)}} = 0.53$$

◆ ◆ ◆ ◆ ◆

Section 4.3   BIVARIATE GAUSSIAN RANDOM VARIABLES

◆ ◆ ◆ ◆ ◆

Applications frequently require the use of Gaussian bivariate random variables; they are extensions of the single Gaussian random variables in Chapter 3. However, the possibility of two Gaussian random variables being correlated is new and provides the focus for this section.

Let X_1 and X_2 be bivariate random variables, and let the correlation coefficient between X_1 and X_2 be ρ_X. We define the joint pdf of the **normalized Gaussian bivariate random variables** as

$$f_X(x_1, x_2) = \frac{1}{2\pi\sqrt{1 - \rho_X^2}} \exp\left[-(x_1^2 - 2\rho_X x_1 x_2 + x_2^2)\frac{1}{2(1 - \rho_X^2)}\right] \quad \textbf{(4.25)}$$

It is not enough merely to define (4.25) as a joint pdf. We must justify this definition by verifying that it meets all the requirements of a joint pdf. Inspection shows that the bivariate function in (4.25) cannot be negative for any point (x_1, x_2). We now verify that the volume under the joint pdf is unity, (4.12): The quadratic relation

$$Q(x_1, x_2) = x_1^2 - 2\rho_X x_1 x_2 + x_2^2$$

in the exponent of (4.25) can, by completing the square, be written as

$$Q(x_1, x_2) = (x_1 - \rho_X x_2)^2 + (1 - \rho_X^2)x_2^2 \quad \textbf{(4.26)}$$

Then,

$$\int_{-\infty}^{\infty}\int_{-\infty}^{\infty} f_X(x_1,x_2)dx_1dx_2$$

$$= \frac{1}{\sqrt{2\pi}}\int_{-\infty}^{\infty}\exp(-x_2^2/2)\frac{1}{\sqrt{2\pi(1-\rho_X^2)}}\int_{-\infty}^{\infty}\exp\left[-\frac{(x_1-\rho_X x_2)^2}{2(1-\rho_X^2)}\right]dx_1dx_2$$

We recognize that the right-hand part of the integrand is in the standard form of a Gaussian pdf (3.60). Its mean and variance are, respectively, $\rho_X X_2$ and $(1-\rho_X^2)$. The variable x_2 is held constant while integration with respect to x_1 is performed. Then, using (3.14), the right-hand integral, including the constant in front of it, equals one. Therefore,

$$\int_{-\infty}^{\infty}\int_{-\infty}^{\infty} f_X(x_1,x_2)dx_1dx_2 = \frac{1}{\sqrt{2\pi}}\int_{-\infty}^{\infty}\exp(-x_2^2/2)dx_2$$

Finally, the integrand on the right is recognized as the normalized Gaussian pdf, and using (3.54),

$$\int_{-\infty}^{\infty}\int_{-\infty}^{\infty} f_X(x_1,x_2)dx_1dx_2 = 1$$

The technique of completing the square in the quadratic form (4.26) can be used with pdf (4.25) to verify by integration that

$$E[X_1] = 0 = E[X_2] \tag{4.27}$$

and

$$\text{Var}[X_1] = 1 = \text{Var}[X_2] \tag{4.28}$$

We use these results with (4.23) to write

$$\text{Cov}[X_1 X_2] = \rho_X \tag{4.29}$$

Therefore, using the definition in (4.25), normalized Gaussian bivariate random variables have (1) means of zero, (2) variances of one, and (3) a covariance (which in this normalized case is also a correlation coefficient) that is arbitrary within its allowed range of $|\rho_X| \leq 1$.

It is possible to use normalized Gaussian bivariate random variables that are uncorrelated to construct Gaussian bivariate random variables with arbitrary variances, and with an arbitrary correlation coefficient. We will only illustrate this situation with an example, and then refer interested readers to Peebles' text[1] for further details.

Example 4.6   Let X and Y be uncorrelated normalized Gaussian random variables ($\rho_{XY} = 0$). We use the following transformation to obtain the bivariate random variables U and V:

$$U = 5X \cos \phi - 2Y \sin \phi$$

$$V = 5X \sin \phi + 2Y \cos \phi$$

where we let $\phi = -10$ degrees. Since X and Y have means of zero, U and V also have means of zero. And, since X and Y have variances of one, it follows directly that

$$\text{Var}[U] = E[U^2] = 25 \cos^2\phi + 4 \sin^2\phi$$

$$\text{Var}[V] = E[V^2] = 25 \sin^2\phi + 4 \cos^2\phi$$

$$\text{Cov}[UV] = E[UV^2] = (25 - 4) \sin \phi \cos \phi$$

Using the given data, we find

$$\sigma_U^2 = 24.37, \quad \sigma_V^2 = 4.63, \quad \text{Cov}[UV] = -3.59$$

The correlation coefficient (4.23) for U and V is $\rho_{UV} = -0.34$.

♦ ♦ ♦ ♦ ♦

If the Gaussian random variables X_1 and X_2 are uncorrelated, then $\rho_X = 0$, and (4.25) becomes simply the product of two normalized Gaussian random variables:

$$f_X(x_1, x_2) = \frac{1}{\sqrt{2\pi}} \exp\left(\frac{-x_1^2}{2}\right) \frac{1}{\sqrt{2\pi}} \exp\left(\frac{-x_2^2}{2}\right)$$

or,

$$f_X(x_1, x_2) = f_{X_1}(x_1) f_{X_2}(x_2)$$

In words, if bivariate Gaussian random variables are uncorrelated, they are also independent. This remarkable result is an exception to the general case described in Section 4.2.

Section 4.4   SUMS OF TWO INDEPENDENT RANDOM VARIABLES

♦ ♦ ♦ ♦ ♦

A general class of problems in probability theory occurs when two independent random variables are added to produce a third:

$$Z = X + Y \tag{4.30}$$

where

$$f_{XY}(x,y) = f_X(x)f_Y(y)$$

It also follows from the assumed independence that X and Y are uncorrelated.

Applications of (4.30) occur, for example, when a noise random variable V is added to a signal random variable S:

$$Z = S + V, \quad E[SV] = \mu_S \mu_V$$

As another example, when different observations of the same random variable X are summed, then

$$Z = X_1 + X_2, \quad E[X_1 X_2] = \mu_X^2$$

If the means and variances of both X and Y are known, then the mean and the variance of Z are readily obtained using the properties of the expectation operator (3.30) through (3.32):

$$E[Z] = E[X + Y]$$
$$\mu_Z = \mu_X + \mu_Y \tag{4.31}$$

$$\begin{aligned}
\mathrm{Var}[(Z] &= E[Z - \mu_Z)^2] \\
&= E[(X + Y - \mu_X - \mu_Y)^2] \\
&= E[(X - \mu_X)^2 + 2(X - \mu_X)(Y - \mu_Y) + (Y - \mu_Y)^2] \\
&= \mathrm{Var}[X] + \mathrm{Var}[Y]
\end{aligned} \tag{4.32}$$

The covariance in (4.32) vanishes because X and Y are, by assumption, independent.

We now seek to find the pdf for the random variable Z assuming that the pdfs for X and Y are known. The cdf function (3.6b) for the random variable Z is, using (4.30),

$$F_Z(z) = P(X + Y \le z)$$

This involves the bivariate random variables X and Y; the region R in (4.13) is illustrated in Figure 4.8:

$$P(X + Y \le z) = P(x,y \in R)$$

$$P(X + Y \le z) = \int_R f_{XY}(x,y)dxdy$$

$$P(X + Y \le z) = \int_{-\infty}^{\infty} \left[\int_{-\infty}^{z-x} f_{XY}(x,y)dy \right] dx$$

Then, using (3.11),

$$f_Z(z) = \int_{-\infty}^{\infty} f_{XY}(x,z-x)dx$$

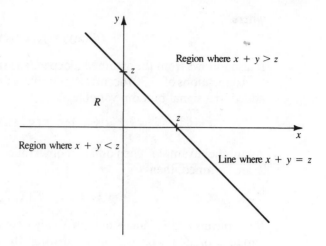

Figure 4.8   A view of the x,y plane showing the region R where $x + y \leq z$. Or, stated another way, showing the region R where observations (x,y) occur satisfying the relation $X + Y \leq z$.

• •

And, because of the assumed independence of X and Y,

$$f_Z(z) = \int_{-\infty}^{\infty} f_X(x) f_Y(z-x) dx \qquad \textbf{(4.33a)}$$

This is a convolution integral; it does not matter which factor in the integrand is given the "shifting and rotation." We therefore denote the convolution by

$$f_Z(z) = f_X(x) * f_Y(y) \qquad \textbf{(4.33b)}$$

The reader should verify that an equivalent expression for the pdf for Z is

$$f_Z(z) = \int_{-\infty}^{\infty} f_Y(y) f_X(z-y) dy \qquad \textbf{(4.33c)}$$

Since the pdf for the random variable Z is a convolution, a convenient relation for the characteristic function for Z is obtained in terms of the characteristic functions for X and Y. Using (3.48) and (4.33a),

$$\Phi_Z(j\omega) = \int_{-\infty}^{\infty} \int_{-\infty}^{\infty} f_X(x) f_Y(z-x) dx\, e^{j\omega z} dz$$

Changing the order of integration,

$$\Phi_Z(j\omega) = \int_{-\infty}^{\infty} f_X(x) \int_{-\infty}^{\infty} f_Y(z-x) e^{j\omega z} dz\, dx$$

Then, using the change of variables $u = z - x$,

$$\Phi_Z(j\omega) = \int_{-\infty}^{\infty} f_X(x)e^{j\omega x}dx \int_{-\infty}^{\infty} f_Y(u)e^{j\omega u}du$$

$$\Phi_Z(j\omega) = \Phi_X(j\omega)\Phi_Y(j\omega) \tag{4.34}$$

Example 4.7   Let the random variable X be exponential:

$$f_X(x) = \lambda e^{-\lambda x}, \quad x \geq 0$$
$$= 0, \qquad x < 0$$
$$\mu_X = 1/\lambda, \quad \sigma_X^2 = 1/\lambda^2$$
$$\Phi_X(j\omega) = \lambda(\lambda - j\omega)^{-1}$$

Let the random variable Y be the sum of two independent observations of X,

$$Y = X_1 + X_2$$

Then, we use the convolution integral (4.33a), and we let Y have only non-negative observations. The two factors in the integrand of the convolution integral are plotted in Figure 4.9. Aided by these plots, we write

$$f_Y(y) = \int_0^y \lambda e^{-\lambda x}\lambda e^{-\lambda(y-x)}dx, \quad y \geq 0$$
$$= \lambda^2 y e^{-\lambda y}, \qquad\qquad y \geq 0$$

This is a pdf for an **Erlang** random variable of order two. Using (4.31) and (4.32),

• •

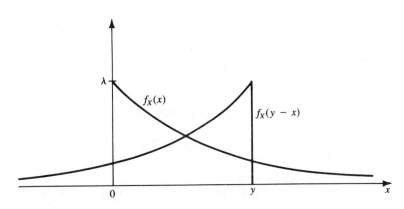

Figure 4.9   A plot of the two factors in the integrand of the convolution integral in Example 4.7.

$$\mu_Y = \frac{2}{\lambda} \quad \text{and} \quad \sigma_Y^2 = \frac{2}{\lambda^2}$$

And, using (4.34), the characteristic function of the Erlang random variable of order two is

$$\Phi_Y(j\omega) = \lambda^2(\lambda - j\omega)^{-2}$$

◆ ◆ ◆ ◆ ◆

Example 4.8 Let the random variable X be Gaussian with a mean of zero and a variance of σ_X^2. It was shown in Example 3.17 that if the Gaussian random variable X is squared, the following pdf is obtained:

$$f_Y(y) = \frac{1}{\sigma_x\sqrt{2\pi y}} \exp(-y/2\sigma_X^2), \quad y \geq 0$$

Related to this pdf are the expectations

$$\mu_Y = \sigma_X^2 \quad \text{and} \quad \sigma_Y^2 = 2\sigma_X^4$$

$$\Phi_Y(j\omega) = (1 - j2\sigma_X^2\omega)^{-1/2}$$

Let the random variable Z be the sum of two independent observations of Y,

$$Z = Y_1 + Y_2$$

$$Z = X_1^2 + X_2^2$$

Then, using a convolution integral (4.33), and recognizing that observations of Z must be positive, the pdf for Z is

$$f_Z(z) = \int_{-\infty}^{\infty} f_Y(y)f_Y(z-y)dy$$

$$= \int_{-\infty}^{\infty} \frac{1}{\sigma_x\sqrt{2\pi y}} \exp(-y/2\sigma_X^2) \frac{1}{\sigma_x\sqrt{2\pi(z-y)}} \exp[-(z-y)/2\sigma_X^2]dy$$

$$= \frac{\exp(-z/\sigma_X^2)}{2\pi\sigma_x^2} \int_0^z y^{-1/2}(z-y)^{-1/2}dy, \quad z > 0$$

Using the change of variables $y = zu$,

$$f_Z(z) = \frac{\exp(-z/\sigma_X^2)}{2\pi\sigma_x^2} \int_0^1 \frac{du}{\sqrt{u(1-u)}}, \quad z > 0$$

This integral can be found in tables of definite integrals (see Exercise 3.13):

$$f_Z(z) = \frac{\Gamma^2(1/2)}{2\pi\sigma_x^2} \exp(-z/2\sigma_X^2), \quad z > 0$$

where $\Gamma(x)$ is the gamma function. Since $\Gamma(1/2) = \sqrt{\pi}$,

$$f_Z(z) = \frac{1}{2\sigma_X^2} \exp(-z/2\sigma_X^2), \quad z > 0$$

The random variable Z is exponential; see Example 4.7 where

$$\lambda = \frac{1}{2\sigma_X^2}$$

It follows from (4.31), (4.32), and (4.34) that the random variable Z has the expectations

$$\mu_Z = 2\sigma_X^2 \quad \text{and} \quad \sigma_Z^2 = 4\sigma_X^4$$
$$\Phi_Z(j\omega) = (1 - j2\sigma_X^2\omega)^{-1}$$

If $\sigma_X = 1$, the pdf and its expectations are those of the chi-square random variable of order two.

◆ ◆ ◆ ◆ ◆

Example 4.9 Consider the random variable

$$W = \sqrt{X_1^2 + X_2^2}$$

This random variable is of interest in applications where we find root-mean-square (rms) values from independent observations of zero-mean Gaussian random variables. To find the pdf of the random variable W, we begin with the method of functions of a single random variable as discussed in Chapter 3:

$$F_W(w) = P(W \le w), \quad \text{where } F_W(w) = 0 \text{ when } w < 0$$

Then, using $w = +\sqrt{z}$,

$$P(W \le w) = P(0 < Z < w^2)$$

Introducing the cdf for Z, we have

$$P(0 < Z < w^2) = F_Z(w^2)$$

Combining the above results,

$$F_W(w) = F_Z(w^2)$$

Differentiating to obtain the desired pdf,

$$f_W(w) = 2wf_Z(w^2)$$

Observations of w must be non-negative. Then, using the pdf for Z obtained in Example 4.8,

$$f_W(w) = \frac{w}{\sigma_X^2} \exp(-w^2/2\sigma_X^2), \quad w \geq 0$$

$$= 0, \qquad\qquad\qquad w < 0$$

Thus, w is a Rayleigh random variable. Its mean and variance are obtained using results in Example 3.4:

$$\mu_W = \sigma_X \sqrt{\frac{\pi}{2}} \quad \text{and} \quad \sigma_W^2 = \left(2 - \frac{\pi}{2}\right) \sigma_X^2$$

Frequently, the constant σ_X^2 in the Rayleigh pdf is replaced by an arbitrary parameter, say a^2. However, using the variance underscores a possible origin for a Rayleigh random variable: a "square root of the sum of the squares" combination of two independent Gaussian random variables with means of zero, and variances of σ_X^2.

♦ ♦ ♦ ♦ ♦

Suppose X and Y are independent but otherwise arbitrary Gaussian random variables. Their characteristic functions (3.58) are

$$\Phi_X(j\omega) = \exp(j\omega\mu_X - \omega^2\sigma_X^2/2)$$

$$\Phi_Y(j\omega) = \exp(j\omega\mu_Y - \omega^2\sigma_Y^2/2)$$

Then, using (4.34), the characteristic function of Z is

$$\Phi_Z(j\omega) = \exp[j\omega(\mu_X + \mu_Y) - \omega^2(\sigma_X^2 + s_Y^2)/2] \qquad\qquad \textbf{(4.35)}$$

This result establishes that **the sum of two independent Gaussian random variables is Gaussian.** This is another very important result making bivariate Gaussian random variables extremely useful in practice.

Section 4.5   SUMS OF INDEPENDENT IDENTICALLY DISTRIBUTED RANDOM VARIABLES

♦ ♦ ♦ ♦ ♦

In the last section we derived expressions for the mean, variance, pdf, and characteristic function for the sum of two independent random variables. These expressions provide us with a method to analyze the sum of an arbitrary number of random variables. Specifically, we apply this method in the case when each random variable in the sum is related to the same pdf. This case is denoted as **independent and identically distributed** (IID) random variables.

Let

$$Y = \sum_{i=1}^{n} X_i \qquad (4.36)$$

where

$$E[X_i] = E[X] = \mu_X$$
$$\text{Var}[X_i] = \text{Var}[X] = \sigma_X^2$$

and where

$$E[X_i X_j] = E[X^2], \quad i = j$$
$$\qquad\quad = \mu_X^2, \qquad i \neq j \qquad (4.37)$$

and where the pdf associated with each X_i is $f_X(x)$. We begin with the case when $n = 2$:

$$Y_2 = X_1 + X_2 \qquad (4.38)$$

Using (4.31) and (4.32),

$$E[Y_2] = 2\mu_X \quad \text{and} \quad \text{Var}[Y_2] = 2\sigma_X^2$$

When $n = 3$,

$$Y_3 = X_1 + X_2 + X_3$$

and, using (4.38),

$$Y_3 = Y_2 + X_3 \qquad (4.39)$$

Application again of (4.31) and (4.32) yields

$$E[Y_3] = 3\mu_X \quad \text{and} \quad \text{Var}[Y_3] = 3\sigma_X^2$$

We can continue this way, using pairs of random variables, until (4.36) becomes

$$Y = Y_{n-1} + X_n \qquad (4.40)$$

Then it follows that

$$\mu_Y = E[Y] = n\mu_X \qquad (4.41)$$
$$\sigma_Y^2 = \text{Var}[Y] = n\sigma_X^2 \qquad (4.42)$$

As we can see in (4.33), the pdf for Y_2 in (4.38) is the convolution of $f_X(x)$ with itself. Continuing, the pdf for Y_3 in (4.39) is the result of two convolutions. Finally, the pdf for Y in (4.40) is the result of $n - 1$ convolutions involving $f_X(x)$; typically this is a formidable task. It may be less formidable, mathematically, to use the characteristic function $\Phi_X(j\omega)$; (4.34) leads directly to

$$\Phi_Y(j\omega) = \Phi_X^n(j\omega) \tag{4.43}$$

for a sum of n IID random variables.

Example 4.10　　In Example 4.7 we used the exponential random variable:

$$f_X(x) = \lambda e^{-\lambda x}, \quad x \geq 0$$
$$= 0, \qquad x < 0$$
$$\mu_X = 1/\lambda \quad \text{and} \quad \sigma_X^2 = 1/\lambda^2$$
$$\Phi_X(j\omega) = \lambda(\lambda - j\omega)^{-1}$$

We showed that, for the sum of two independent random variables,

$$f_{Y_2}(y) = \lambda^2 y e^{-\lambda y}, \quad y \geq 0$$
$$= 0, \qquad y < 0$$

This corresponds to (4.38). The pdf for Y_3 in (4.39) is

$$f_{Y_3}(y) = f_{Y_2}(y) * f_X(x)$$

$$f_{Y_3}(y) = \int_{-\infty}^{\infty} f_{Y_2}(z) f_X(y-z)dz$$

where z is a convenient dummy variable of integration. Then,

$$f_{Y_3}(y) = \int_0^y \lambda^2 z e^{-\lambda z} \lambda e^{-\lambda(y-z)} dz$$

$$f_{Y_3}(y) = \lambda^3 e^{-\lambda y} \int_0^y z\, dz$$

$$f_{Y_3}(y) = \frac{\lambda^3 y^2}{2} e^{-\lambda y}, \quad y \geq 0$$
$$= 0, \qquad y < 0$$

Continuing this convolution process, you may verify that the general pdf for the sum of n IID exponential random variables is

$$f_Y(y) = \frac{\lambda^n y^{n-1}}{(n-1)!} e^{-\lambda y}, \quad y \geq 0$$
$$= 0, \qquad y < 0$$

The random variable Y is named the **Erlang** random variable of order n, where $n = 1, 2, \ldots$. Equations (4.41) and (4.42) show that the mean and variance of the Erlang random variable are

$$\lambda_Y = \frac{n}{\lambda} \quad \text{and} \quad \sigma_Y^2 = \frac{n}{\lambda^2}$$

Using (4.43), the characteristic function for the Erlang random variable is

$$\Phi_Y(j\omega) = \lambda^n(\lambda - j\omega)^{-n}$$

Erlang random variables find applications in some reliability studies.

◆ ◆ ◆ ◆ ◆

Example 4.11   We begin this example by summarizing some of the results in Example 4.8; for our purposes, the parameter σ_X in that example is set equal to one:

$$f_Y(y) = \frac{1}{\sqrt{2\pi y}}\, e^{-y/2}, \quad y > 0$$

$$= 0, \qquad\qquad y < 0$$

$$\mu_Y = 1 \quad \text{and} \quad \sigma_Y^2 = 2$$

$$\Phi_Y(j\omega) = (1 - j2\omega)^{-1/2}$$

In Example 4.8 we showed that

$$Z_2 = Y_1 + Y_2$$

leads to the following pdf for Z:

$$f_{Z_2}(z) = \frac{1}{2}\, e^{-z/2}, \quad z \geq 0$$

$$= 0, \qquad\quad z < 0$$

We now continue by extending the results in Example 4.8:

$$Z_3 = Y_1 + Y_2 + Y_3$$

$$Z_3 = Z_2 + Y_3$$

Then, according to (4.33), the pdf for Z_3 is obtained by convolving the probability density functions for Z_2 and Y_3:

$$f_{Z_3}(z) = f_{Z_2}(z)*f_Y(y)$$

$$f_{Z_3}(z) = \int_0^z \frac{1}{\sqrt{2\pi x}}\, \exp(-x/2)\, \frac{1}{2}\, \exp[-(z-x)/2]\,dx$$

where x is a convenient dummy of integration. Then,

$$f_{Z_3}(z) = \frac{e^{-z/2}}{2\sqrt{2\pi}} \int_0^z x^{-1/2}dx$$

$$f_{Z_3}(z) = \frac{z^{1/2}e^{-z/2}}{\sqrt{2\pi}}, \quad z \geq 0$$

$$= 0, \qquad\qquad z < 0$$

The reader may demonstrate that, for arbitrary $n = 1, 2, \cdots,$

$$Z = \sum_{i=1}^{n} Y_i$$

$$f_Z(z) = \frac{1}{\Gamma(n/2)2^{n/2}} z^{(n/2)-1} e^{-z/2}, \quad z > 0$$

$$= 0, \qquad\qquad\qquad z < 0$$

where $\Gamma(x)$ is the gamma function. Using (4.41) through (4.43),

$$\mu_Z = n \quad \text{and} \quad \sigma_Z^2 = 2n$$

$$\Phi_Z(j\omega) = (1 - 2j\omega)^{-n/2}$$

Z is the chi-square random variable of order n, $n = 1, 2, \ldots$. It finds application in the statistical analysis of sample variances. Figure 4.10 illustrates some typical chi-square probability density functions.

♦ ♦ ♦ ♦ ♦

The sum in (4.36) has a very interesting feature if n is allowed to increase to arbitrarily large values. But before we let $n \to \infty$ we normalize Y, we define

$$W = \frac{Y - \mu_Y}{\sigma_Y} \qquad\qquad \textbf{(4.44)}$$

Then the mean and variance of W are

$$\mu_W = 0 \quad \text{and} \quad \sigma_W^2 = 1$$

Using (4.36), (4.41), and (4.42),

$$W = \frac{1}{\sqrt{n}\sigma_X} \left(\sum_{i=1}^{n} X_i - n\mu_X \right)$$

$$W = \frac{1}{\sqrt{n}} \sum_{i=1}^{n} \left(\frac{X_i - \mu_X}{\sigma_X} \right)$$

$$W = \frac{1}{\sqrt{n}} \sum_{i=1}^{n} Z_i \qquad\qquad \textbf{(4.45)}$$

where Z is another normalized IID random variable:

$$\mu_Z = 0 \quad \text{and} \quad \sigma_Z^2 = 1$$

By definition (3.48), the characteristic function for W is

$$\Phi_W(j\omega) = E[e^{j\omega W}]$$

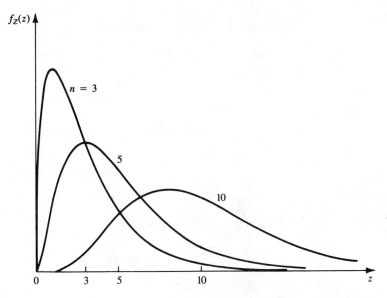

Figure 4.10   Illustration of typical plots of the chi-square pdf. The parameter used is n in $f_Z(z)$ discussed in Example 4.11.

• •

Using (4.45),

$$\Phi_W(j\omega) = E\left[\exp\left(\frac{j\omega}{\sqrt{n}}\sum_{i=1}^{n} Z_i\right)\right]$$

Assuming that each of the Z_i is independent of the other, we have

$$\Phi_W(j\omega) = \Pi_{i=1}^{n}\, E\left[\exp\left(\frac{j\omega}{\sqrt{n}}\, Z_i\right)\right]$$

By assuming that the Z_i are identically distributed,

$$\Phi_W(j\omega) = \left\{E\left[\exp\left(\frac{j\omega}{\sqrt{n}}\, Z\right)\right]\right\}^n$$

$$\Phi_W(j\omega) = \left[\Phi_Z\left(\frac{j\omega}{\sqrt{n}}\right)\right]^n$$

This last statement again uses (3.48), the definition of the characteristic function.

If there is a power series for $\Phi_Z(j\omega)$, it is

$$\Phi_Z(h) \approx \Phi_Z(0) + h\Phi_Z'(0) + \frac{h^2}{2!}\,\Phi_Z''(0) + R_3$$

where $h = \dfrac{j\omega}{\sqrt{n}}$. The remainder term is $R_3 = Kh^3$ where K is some constant.

From (3.50), the n'th derivative of the characteristic function is related to the n'th moment about the origin:

$$\Phi_Z^{(n)}(0) = E[Z^n]$$

It is always true that $\Phi_Z(0) = 1$. And, since the random variable Z is normalized,

$$\Phi_Z'(0) = \mu_Z = 0$$

$$\Phi_Z''(0) = E[Z^2] = \sigma_Z^2 = 1$$

Combining these results leads to

$$\Phi_Z\left(\frac{j\omega}{\sqrt{n}}\right) \approx 1 - \frac{\omega^2}{2n} + R_3$$

The characteristic equation for W is then

$$\Phi_W(j\omega) \approx \left(1 - \frac{\omega^2}{2n} + R_3\right)^n$$

Rewriting:

$$\Phi_W(j\omega) \approx \left(1 + \frac{-\omega^2/2 + nR_3}{n}\right)^n$$

In the limit as $n \to \infty$, the effect of the remainder vanishes:

$$\lim_{n \to \infty} nR_3 = \lim_{n \to \infty} n\left(\frac{j\omega}{\sqrt{n}}\right)^3 K = 0$$

Then, using a familiar result from the calculus,

$$\lim_{n \to \infty} \Phi_W(j\omega) = \lim_{n \to \infty} \left(1 + \frac{-\omega^2/2}{n}\right)^n$$

$$\Phi_W(j\omega) = \exp(-\omega^2/2)$$

Compare this result with (3.57) and see that it is the characteristic function for the normalized Gaussian random variable. We now recall (4.44):

$$Y = \sigma_Y W + \mu_Y$$

As a result of this linear relation, Y is Gaussian with mean μ_Y and variance σ_Y^2.

This development may be summarized in a theorem, one of several forms of the **central limit theorem**. Briefly, the theorem says that if the random variables

X_i are IID, and if

$$Y = \sum_{i=1}^{n} X_i$$

and if the moments of X about the origin are finite, then, as n becomes large, Y approaches a Gaussian random variable with the following mean and variance:

$$\mu_Y = n\mu_X \quad \text{and} \quad \sigma_Y^2 = n\sigma_X^2$$

Example 4.12   According to the central limit theorem just developed, an Erlang pdf of some higher order ought to begin looking like a Gaussian pdf. We investigate this heuristically; let $n = 25$ and $\lambda = 1$ in the Erlang pdf given in Example 4.10:

$$f_Y(y) = \frac{y^{24}}{24!} e^{-y}, \quad y \geq 0$$
$$= 0, \qquad y < 0$$

The mean and variance are

$$\mu_Y = 25 \quad \text{and} \quad \sigma_Y^2 = 25$$

Figure 4.11 shows a plot of this Erlang pdf for values of y in the interval $\mu_Y \pm 2\sigma_Y$. For comparison, this figure also shows the Gaussian pdf having the same mean and variance. While the Gaussian and Erlang pdfs approxi-

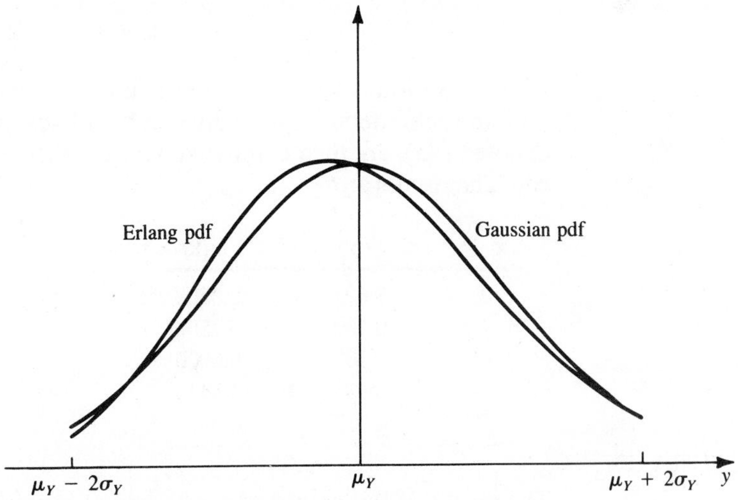

• •

Figure 4.11   Comparing the pdfs for an Erlang random variable ($n = 25$, $\lambda = 1$, $\mu_Y = 25$, and $\sigma_Y^2 = 25$) and a Gaussian random variable having the same mean and variance.

mate each other, differences between the two are noticeable, but the effect of the central limit theorem is demonstrated.

◆ ◆ ◆ ◆ ◆

Example 4.13   We illustrate the central limit theorem another way. Here we let the random variable X be the normalized uniform random variable, URNG,

$$\mu_X = 1/2 \quad \text{and} \quad \sigma_X^2 = 1/12$$

If we let a new random variable Y be

$$Y = \sum_{i=1}^{12} X_i - 6$$

then, by (4.41) and (4.42), Y is normalized:

$$\mu_Y = 0 \quad \text{and} \quad \sigma_Y^2 = 1$$

Using a relative frequency technique and the URNG algorithm from Appendix A, we calculate $n = 1000$ observations of Y. Each observation is examined to see if it is

$$X \leq -2$$
$$X \leq -1$$
$$X \leq 0$$
$$X \leq 1$$
$$X \leq 2$$

An observation is couned each time it occurs in each of these intervals. The total in each interval is then divided by n to estimate $\psi(x)$. These estimates, denoted $\hat{\psi}(x)$, are then compared with the theoretical normalized Gaussian cdf. The results are:

x	$\hat{\psi}(x)$	$\psi(x)$
-2	0.024	0.0228
-1	0.150	0.1587
0	0.506	0.5000
1	0.835	0.8413
2	0.972	0.9772

The results of this empirical study, and of others, suggest that this technique, based on the central limit theorem, is quite reasonable for us to use as an algorithm for generating observations simulating the normalized Gaussian random variable. This is the reason behind the Gaussian random number generator (GRNG) in Appendix A.

♦ ♦ ♦ ♦ ♦

A very important sum of IID random variables occurs with the equation used in averaging:

$$Y = \frac{1}{n} \sum_{i=1}^{n} X_i \tag{4.46}$$

We can study this using the results obtained from (4.36). First, write (4.46) as

$$Y = \sum_{i=1}^{n} \left(\frac{X_i}{n} \right)$$

Then, since $E[X/n] = \mu_X/n$ and $\text{Var}[X/n] = \sigma_X^2/n^2$, we can use (4.41) and (4.42) to write

$$\mu_Y = \mu_X \quad \text{and} \quad \sigma_Y^2 = \frac{\sigma_X^2}{n} \tag{4.47}$$

We also know from the central limit theorem that the random variable Y in (4.46) tends to become Gaussian with large n.

Example 4.14   The random variable x has the parameters of $E[X] = 4/7$ and $\text{Var}[X] = 1.7$. The random variable Y is obtained using

$$Y = \frac{1}{47} \sum_{i=1}^{47} X_i$$

Here, the X_i are IID. It then follows from (4.47) that

$$E[Y] = 4/7 = 0.571$$

$$\text{Var}[Y] = 1.7/47 = 0.0362$$

♦ ♦ ♦ ♦ ♦

Section 4.6   CONDITIONAL JOINT PROBABILITIES

♦ ♦ ♦ ♦ ♦

In this section we introduce conditional joint probabilities, and then use the resultant theory to derive the Cauchy pdf (Example 4.15) and the pdf for the t distribution (Example 4.16). If desired, this section may be omitted upon the first reading of this textbook.

Bivariate random variables may be conditioned in the same manner as the single random variables we discussed in Chapter 3. We define the joint cdf conditioned by an event B using

$$F_{XY}(x,y|B) = \frac{P[(X \le x) \cap (Y \le y) \cap B]}{P(B)} \tag{4.48}$$

All the properties of a conditional joint cdf follow from this definition. In particular, the joint pdf conditioned by an event B is

$$f_{XY}(x,y|B) = \frac{\partial^2}{\partial x \partial y} F_{XY}(x,y|B) \tag{4.49}$$

The event B is a set of bivariate observations (x,y) in the x,y plane as suggested in Figure 4.12. The probability of event B is

$$P(B) = \int\int_B f_{XY}(x,y)dxdy$$

The event B takes on the role of a sample space for the conditioned random variables, and we therefore express (4.49) as

$$f_{XY}(x,y|B) = \frac{f_{XY}(x,y)}{P(B)}, \quad (x,y) \in B$$
$$= 0, \qquad \text{otherwise} \tag{4.50}$$

Similar to what we did in (4.15), this conditional joint pdf may be integrated to obtain a conditional marginal pdf:

$$f_Y(y|B) = \int_{-\infty}^{\infty} f_{XY}(x,y|B)dx \tag{4.51}$$

Suppose we are given a specific value of the random variable X; say, $X = x$. Based on this condition, what can we say about the pdf for Y? To answer this question we start with (4.51):

$$f_Y(y|B) = \int_x^{x+dx} f_{XY}(u,y|B)du$$

where $B = (x < X \le x+dx)$. Using (4.50),

$$f_Y(y|B) = \int_x^{x+dx} \frac{f_{XY}(u,y)}{P(B)} du \approx \frac{f_{XY}(x,y)dx}{P(B)}$$

where $x \in B$. Now, from (3.16), $P(B)$ itself may be expressed as

$$P(B) = P(x < X \le x+dx)$$
$$= \int_x^{x+dx} f_X(x)dx \approx f_X(x)dx$$

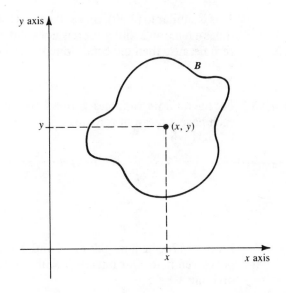

Figure 4.12   Illustration of an event B in the x,y plane, which is used to condition random variables X and Y.

◆ ◆

Therefore,

$$f_Y(y|B) = \frac{f_{XY}(x,y)dx}{f_X(x)dx}$$

and as $dx \to 0$, $B \to (X = x)$, and

$$f_Y(y|X=x) = \frac{f_{XY}(x,y)}{f_X(x)}$$

This is usually denoted as

$$f_{Y|X}(y|x) = \frac{f_{XY}(x,y)}{f_X(x)} \tag{4.52}$$

The symmetrical relation is

$$f_{X|Y}(x|y) = \frac{f_{XY}(x,y)}{f_Y(y)} \tag{4.53}$$

These last two equations may be combined to form another case of Bayes' theorem:

$$f_{X|Y}(x|y)f_Y(y) = f_{Y|X}(y|x)f_X(x) \tag{4.54}$$

This is similar to (2.30), Bayes' theorem for total probabilities. However, (4.54) states a relation about pdfs; it is not valid where either the pdf for X or Y equals zero because then the conditioned pdf in either (4.52) or (4.53) is undefined.

Example 4.15 Let the random variables X and Y be independent and Gaussian, and let each have a mean of zero and a variance of σ^2. Therefore,

$$f_X(x) = \frac{1}{\sigma\sqrt{2\pi}} \exp(-x^2/2\sigma^2)$$

$$f_Y(y) = \frac{1}{\sigma\sqrt{2\pi}} \exp(-y^2/2\sigma^2)$$

From (4.17), the joint pdf for X and Y is the product of the two marginal pdfs given here. Our interest is with the single random variable obtained by dividing X by Y:

$$Z = a\frac{X}{Y}$$

where a is a positive constant. If we had a joint pdf for the random variable Z and, say, Y, then using (4.14) we could obtain the pdf for Z:

$$f_Z(z) = \int_{-\infty}^{\infty} f_{ZY}(z,y)dy$$

Then using (4.53),

$$f_Z(z) = \int_{-\infty}^{\infty} f_{Z|Y}(z|y)f_Y(y)dy$$

The conditional pdf $f_{Z|Y}(z|y)$ assumes that y is fixed at some value. Using this for guidance, we make Z a function of the single random variable X:

$$Z = \frac{a}{y}X$$

According to Section 3.5 on functions of a single random variable,

$$F_{Z|Y}(z|y) = P(Z \le z|y) \text{ when } z = \left(\frac{a}{y}\right)x$$

Then,

$$P(Z \le z|y) = P\left(X \le \frac{yz}{a}\right) = F_X\left(\frac{yz}{a}\right)$$

Combining these relations,

$$F_{Z|Y}(z|y) = F_X\left(\frac{yz}{a}\right)$$

Differentiating to obtain the pdf and noting that the sign of y can be either positive or negative,

$$f_{Z|Y}(z|y) = f_X\left(\frac{yz}{a}\right)\left|\frac{y}{a}\right|$$

Then, substituting into this the expression for $f_X(x)$ given at the beginning of this example,

$$f_{Z|Y}(z|y) = \frac{|y|}{a\sigma\sqrt{2\pi}}\exp\left(-\frac{y^2z^2}{2a^2\sigma^2}\right)$$

Combining all of these results into the integral,

$$f_Z(z) = \frac{1}{2\pi a\sigma^2}\int_{-\infty}^{\infty}|y|\exp[-(y^2 + y^2z^2/a^2)/2\sigma^2]dy$$

The integrand is even; therefore,

$$f_Z(z) = \frac{1}{\pi a\sigma^2}\int_{0}^{\infty}\exp[-(y^2 + y^2z^2/a^2)/2\sigma^2]ydy$$

Then, using the change of variables,

$$u = y^2(1 + z^2/a^2)/2\sigma^2$$
$$du = ydy(1 + z^2/a^2)/\sigma^2$$

it follows that

$$f_Z(z) = \frac{1}{\pi a\sigma^2}\frac{\sigma^2}{1 + z^2/a^2}\int_{0}^{\infty}e^{-u}du$$

The definite integral evaluates to be one, and we obtain

$$f_Z(z) = \frac{a}{\pi(z^2 + a^2)}, \quad -\infty < z < \infty$$

This pdf is called Cauchy; the Cauchy random variable was discussed in Exercise 14 at the end of Chapter 3 where you were asked to show that the characteristic function of the Cauchy random variable is

$$\Phi_Z(j\omega) = \exp(-a|\omega|)$$

Derivatives of this characteristic function with respect to $j\omega$ do not exist when $\omega = 0$. When this observation is combined with (3.50), we then say

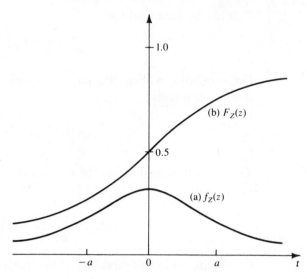

Figure 4.13   Illustration of typical plots for (a) the pdf and (b) the cdf for a Cauchy random variable discussed in Example 4.15.

• •

that the mean and variance of the Cauchy random variable do not exist. This is another viewpoint showing that we can have a valid pdf for which moments do not exist.

This example suggests an algorithm for simulating the Cauchy random variable on a computer: Choose the desired parameter a, and divide observations from two IID Gaussian random variables.

Some typical plots of the Cauchy pdf and cdf are shown in Figure 4.13.

• • • • •

Example 4.16   The **t distribution** (or, Student's t distribution) finds application in statistical estimation theory and is obtained from the relation

$$T = \frac{U}{\sqrt{V/r}}$$

where U is a Gaussian random variable with a mean of zero and variance of unity.

$$f_U(u) = \frac{1}{\sqrt{2\pi}} \exp(-u^2/2). \quad -\infty < u < \infty$$

and V is a chi-square random variable of order r, where r is an integer;

$r = 1, 2, 3, \ldots$:

$$f_V(v) = \frac{1}{\Gamma(r/2)2^{r/2}} v^{(r-2)/2} \exp(-v/2), \quad 0 < v < \infty$$

and $\Gamma(x)$ is the gamma function. The parameter r in the defining relation for T is the same r that is in the pdf for the chi-square random variable V. Assume that U and V are independent. We are interested in finding the pdf $f_T(t)$. From (4.14),

$$f_T(t) = \int_{-\infty}^{\infty} f_{TV}(t,v)dv$$

Using (4.53),

$$f_T(t) = \int_{-\infty}^{\infty} f_{T|V}(t|v)f_V(v)dv$$

We let the random variable V be fixed: $V = v$, and

$$T = \frac{U}{\sqrt{v/r}}$$

Again, according to Section 3.5 on functions of a single random variable,

$$F_{T|V}(t|v) = P(T \le t|v)$$

Then,

$$P(T \le t|v) = P(U \le t\sqrt{v/r}) = F_U(t\sqrt{v/r})$$

Combining the relations above,

$$F_{T|V}(t|v) = F_U(t\sqrt{v/r})$$

Then, differentiating with respect to t,

$$f_{T|V}(t|v) = f_U(t\sqrt{v/r})\sqrt{v/r}$$

Using the pdf given in this example for the random variable U,

$$f_{T|V}(t|v) = \frac{1}{\sqrt{2\pi}}\sqrt{v/r}\exp(-vt^2/2r)$$

Combining this with the integral given above,

$$f_T(t) = \int_0^{\infty} \frac{1}{\sqrt{2\pi r}} v^{1/2} \exp(-vt^2/2r) \frac{1}{\Gamma(r/2)2^{r/2}} v^{(r-2)/2} \exp(-v/2)dv$$

In simplifying this, we use the change of variables

$$w = (v/2)(1 + t^2/r)$$

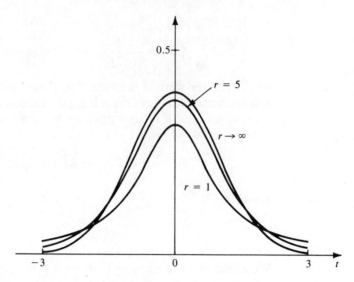

Figure 4.14   Illustrating typical plots of the t distribution pdf discussed in Example 4.16.

• •

and we use the integral relation for the gamma function:

$$\Gamma(a) = \int_0^\infty x^{a-1}\, e^{-x}\, dx, \quad a > 0$$

It then follows that the pdf for the t distribution is

$$f_T(t) = \frac{\Gamma[(r+1)/2]}{\sqrt{\pi r}\ \Gamma(r/2)(1 + t^2/r)^{(r+1)/2}}$$

where $-\infty < t < \infty$, and $r = 1, 2, 3, \ldots$.

The pdf for the t distribution is shown in Figure 4.14 for several values of the parameter r; $F_T(t)$ is symmetric about $t = 0$, and

$$E[T] = 0, \quad \mathrm{Var}[T] = \frac{r}{r-2}, \quad r > 2$$

• • • • •

Exercises

• • • • •

1. The joint pdf for the random variables X and Y is

$$\begin{aligned}
f_{XY}(x,y) &= C(1 + xy), \quad 0 < x < 1, \quad 0 < y < 2 \\
&= 0, \qquad\qquad\quad \text{otherwise}
\end{aligned}$$

a. Find the value of C.

b. Are X and Y independent?

c. Find the joint cdf $F_{XY}(x,y)$.

d. What is $P[(X < 1) \cap Y < 1)]$?

2. The random variable X is uniformly distributed between ± 1, and the random variable Y is uniformly distributed between ± 2. X and Y are independent.

a. Find $f_{XY}(x,y)$.

b. Find $F_{XY}(x,y)$.

c. Find the value for $F_{XY}(0,1)$.

3. A joint pdf is

$$f_{XY}(x,y) = \frac{1}{3}\delta(x)\delta(y-1) + \frac{1}{3}\delta(x-1)\delta(y) + \frac{1}{3}\delta(x-1)\delta(y-1)$$

Or, in other words, the bivariate random variables X and Y have probability mass densities of $1/3$ at the points $(0,1)$, $(1,0)$, and $(1,1)$.

a. Are X and Y independent?

b. Find the value of $F_{XY}(0.5, 1.5)$.

4. The mean and variance of random variable X are -2 and 3; the mean and variance of Y are 3 and 5. The correlation coefficient $\rho = 0.7$. What are

a. the covariance $\text{Cov}[XY]$?

b. the correlation $E[XY]$?

5. The mean and variance of random variable X are -2 and 3; the mean and variance of Y are 3 and 5. The covariance $\text{Cov}[XY] = -0.8$. What are

a. the correlation coefficient ρ?

b. the correlation $E[XY]$?

6. The mean and variance of random variable X are -2 and 3; the mean and variance of Y are 3 and 5. The correlation $E[XY] = -8.7$. What are

a. the covariance $\text{Cov}[XY]$?

b. the correlation coefficient ρ?

7. The mean and variance of random variable X are -2 and 3; the mean and variance of Y are 3 and 5. X and Y are orthogonal. Given

$$W = 7X + 2Y - 5$$

    a. What is the correlation $E[WX]$?

    b. What is the correlation $E[WY]$?

8. X and Y are random variables: $\mu_X = 3$, $\text{Var}[X] = 49$, $\mu_Y = 5$, $\text{Var}[Y] = 144$, and $\rho = 0.6$. The random variables U and V are obtained using

$$U = X + CY, \quad V = X - CY$$

What values can the C have if U and V are uncorrelated?

9. A joint pdf is

$$f_{XY}(x,y) = \frac{1}{3}\delta(x)\delta(y-1) + \frac{1}{3}\delta(x-1)\delta(y) + \frac{1}{3}\delta(x-1)\delta(y-1)$$

Find $E[X]$, $E[Y]$, and $E[XY]$.

10. The bivariate random variables X_1 and X_2 have means of zero and variances $\text{Var}[X_1] = 10$ and $\text{Var}[X_2] = 15$. The correlation coefficient is $\rho_X = 0.7$. X_1 and X_2 are transformed using

$$Y_1 = X_1 + X_2$$
$$Y_2 = X_1 - 2X_2$$

Find $\text{Var}[Y_1]$, $\text{Var}[Y_2]$, and $\text{Cov}[Y_1 Y_2]$.

11. The zero-mean bivariate random variables X_1 and X_2 have the following variances: $\text{Var}[X_1] = 2$ and $\text{Var}[X_2] = 4$. Their correlation coefficient is 0.8. Random variables Y_1 and Y_2 are obtained from

$$Y_1 = 3X_1 + 4X_2$$
$$Y_2 = -X_1 + 2X_2$$

Find $\text{Var}[Y_1]$, $\text{Var}[Y_2]$, and $\text{Cov}[Y_1 Y_2]$.

12. Use the technique of completing the square, illustrated in (4.26), to demonstrate that a marginal pdf, say, $f_{X_1}(x_1)$, obtained from the Gaussian joint pdf (4.25) is Gaussian.

13. Make $n = 1000$ uncorrelated pairs of zero-mean Gaussian random variables U_1 and U_2 using GRNG (Appendix A) or an equivalent algorithm. Use $\text{Var}[U_1] = 26.13$ and $\text{Var}[U_2] = 2.87$. Then, use the transformation

$$Y_1 = U_1\cos\theta - U_2\sin\theta$$
$$Y_2 = U_1\sin\theta + U_2\cos\theta$$

where $\theta = -12.74$ deg. Finally, estimate values for Var[Y_1], Var[Y_2], and ρ_Y using the $n = 1000$ pairs of data.

14. Make $n = 1000$ uncorrelated pairs of zero-mean Gaussian random variables U_1 and U_2 using GRNG (Appendix A) or an equivalent algorithm. Use Var[U_1] = 4.655 and Var[U_2] = 22.345. Then, use the transformation

$$Y_1 = U_1\cos\theta - U_2\sin\theta$$
$$Y_2 = U_1\sin\theta + U_2\cos\theta$$

where $\theta = -21.355$ deg. Finally, estimate values for Var[Y_1], Var[Y_2], and Cov[$Y_1 Y_2$] using the $n = 1000$ pairs of data.

15. Make $n = 1000$ uncorrelated pairs of zero-mean Gaussian random variables U_1 and U_2 using GRNG (Appendix A) or an equivalent algorithm. Use Var[U_1] = 0.897 and Var[U_2] = 7.104. Then, use the transformation

$$Y_1 = U_1\cos\theta - U_2\sin\theta$$
$$Y_2 = U_1\sin\theta + U_2\cos\theta$$

where $\theta = 7.41$ deg. Finally, estimate values for Var[Y_1], Var[Y_2], and ρ_Y using the $n = 1000$ pairs of data.

16. The random variable X is uniformly distributed between ± 3.

   a. Find the pdf for $W = X_1 + X_2$, where X_1 and X_2 are independent.

   b. What are the mean and variance of W?

17. The random variable X is uniformly distributed between zero and one, and the random variable Y is uniformly distributed between zero and four. X and Y are independent. Let

$$Z = X + Y$$

   a. Find the pdf for Z.

   b. What are the mean and variance of Z?

18. Let the random variable U be uniformly distributed between ± 5. Also, let the pdf for the random variable V be

$$f_V(v) = 3e^{-3v}u(v)$$

U and V are independent and $W = U + V$.

   a. What is the pdf for W?

   b. What are the mean and variance of W?

19. It is given that $f_X(x)$ is uniformly distributed between ± 3. Also,

$$f_Y(y) = 7e^{-7y}u(y)$$

where $W = X + Y$; X and Y are independent. Find the pdf for W.

20. Probability density functions for the two independent random variables X and Y are

$$f_X(x) = ae^{-ax}\, u(x)$$
$$f_y(y) = (a^3/2)y^2e^{-ay}\, u(y)$$

where $a = 3$. If $Z = X + Y$, what is $f_Z(z)$?

21. A discrete random variable Y has the pdf

$$f_Y(y) = 0.3\delta(y+1) + 0.7\delta(y-2)$$

Let $W = Y_1 + Y_2$, where the Y are independent. What is the pdf for W?

22. The pdf of the discrete random variable X is

$$f_X(x) = 0.6\delta(x-2) + 0.4\delta(x-1)$$

We have $Z = X_1 + X_2$, where the two observations of X are independent. What is the pdf $f_Z(z)$?

23. Consider the case where two independent random variables are subtracted:

$$Z = X - Y$$

Find a general (integral) expression of the pdf for Z by first writing

$$Z = X + W, \quad W = -Y$$

Then use the function of a single random variable (in Chapter 3) to find the pdf for W.

24. Let X and Y be independent Cauchy random variables:

$$f_X(x) = \frac{a/\pi}{x^2 + a^2}, \quad f_Y(y) = \frac{b/\pi}{y^2 + b^2}$$

If $Z = X + Y$, show that Z is also a Cauchy random variable. (*Hint:* Use characteristic functions.)

25. The pdfs for the uncorrelated random variables X, Y, and Z are not known. However, it is known that

$$\mu_X = 9, \quad \mu_Y = 6, \quad \mu_Z = 10$$

and

$$\sigma_X^2 = 4, \quad \sigma_Y^2 = 1, \quad \sigma_Z^2 = 6$$

If $W = X + Y - Z$, find μ_W and σ_W.

26. The mean and the variance of the random variable X are 3.74 and 1.46, respectively. Let

$$Y = n^{-1/2} \sum_{k=1}^{n} (X_k - 3.74)$$

The X_k are IID. Find $E[Y]$ and $\text{Var}[Y]$.

27. The random variable U has a mean of 1/3 and a variance of 1.5.

    a. Find μ_Y and σ_Y^2 if

    $$Y = \frac{1}{53} \sum_{i=1}^{53} U_i, \text{ where the } U_i \text{ are IID}$$

    b. Find μ_Y and σ_Y^2 if

    $$Y = \sum_{i=1}^{53} U_i, \text{ where the } U_i \text{ are IID}$$

28. The random variables $X_i = 5 + V_i$ where V_i are IID Gaussian random variables with a mean of zero and a variance of 30. The random variable Y is

    $$Y = \frac{1}{n} \sum_{i=1}^{n} X_i, \quad n = 70$$

    What are μ_Y and σ_Y^2?

29. Given the sum

    $$Y = \frac{1}{n} \sum_{k=1}^{n} X_k, \quad \text{the } X_k \text{ are IID}$$

    where $E[X] = 1$ and $E[X^2] = 4$. What is the minimum integer n if the following is true:

    $$\text{Var}[Y] < 0.05\sigma_X^2$$

30. Suppose we average n independent observations of Y, a Gaussian random variable with a mean of zero and a variance of 7.3. How large should n be if the standard deviation of the average is not to exceed 0.1?

31. The random variables X_i are IID, each with a mean of 1200 and a variance of 2500. We average n observations of X using

$$Y = \frac{1}{n} \sum_{i=1}^{n} X_i$$

Use the central limit theorem to find the minimum value of n for the following to be true:

$$P(Y > 1205) < 10\%$$

32. A random variable X has an exponential pdf:

$$f_X(x) = \frac{1}{6} \exp(-x/6)u(x)$$

The random variable Y is the sum of 20 independent observations of X. Use the central limit theorem to estimate the probability that $Y > 100$.

33. Simulate Exercise 32 using $n = 1000$ trials on a computer. Count the number of times realizations of the exponential random variable Y occurs in the range $Y > 100$. Then, use the relative frequency technique to estimate the probability $P(Y > 100)$. Compare this ratio with the theoretical result.

34. A random variable X has a mean of 0.5 and a variance of 1.0. The random variable Y is obtained by summing $n = 20$ independent realizations of X. Use the central limit theorem to estimate the probability that the random variable Y is in the interval between $-\infty$ and 9.

35. To simulate Exercise 34 on a computer, we can proceed as follows: Suppose Z is a random variable uniformly distributed between zero and one, as with URNG. Then, using

$$X = 3.464Z - 1.232$$

X is a random variable with a mean of 0.5 and a variance of 1. It may therefore be used to simulate X in Exercise 34. Then, according to that problem,

$$Y = \sum_{i=1}^{20} X_i$$

Observations of Y are calculated for $n = 1000$ trials. Count the number of times an observation of Y is less than 9, and use the relative frequency technique to estimate the probability $P(Y < 9)$. Compare this result with the theoretical value.

36. The random variable X is Rayleigh, and has the pdf

$$f_X(x) = (2x/7) \exp(-x^2/7) \, u(x)$$

If 20 independent observations of X are summed, estimate (using the central limit theorem) the probability of the sum being between 40 and 50.

37. Simulate Exercise 36 using $n = 1000$ trials on a computer. If Z is a random variable uniformly distributed between zero and one, as with URNG, then

$$X = [-7\ln(1 - Z)]^{1/2}$$

will simulate the random variable X in Exercise 36. Then, according to that problem,

$$Y = \sum_{i=1}^{20} X_i$$

Observations of Y are calculated for $n = 1000$ trials. Count the number of times an observation of Y is greater than 40 and less than 50. Use the relative frequency technique to estimate the probability $P(40 < Y < 50)$. Compare this result with the theoretical value.

38. Repeat Example 4.13 using URNG and your seed.

References

• • • • •

1. Peebles, Peyton Z., Jr. *Probability, Random Variables, and Random Signal Principles.* 2d ed. New York: McGraw-Hill Book Company, 1987.

Additional References

• • • • •

Cooper, George R., and Clare D. McGillem. *Probabilistic Methods of Signal and System Analysis.* 2d ed. New York: Holt, Rinehart and Winston, 1986.

Helstrom, Carl W. *Probability and Stochastic Processes for Engineers.* New York: Macmillan Publishing Company, 1984.

Larson, Harold J., and Bruno O. Shubert. *Probabilistic Models in Engineering Sciences, Volume I: Random Variables and Stochastic Processes.* New York: John Wiley and Sons, 1979.

Leon-Garcia, Alberto. *Probability and Random Processes for Electrical Engineering.* Reading, Mass.: Addison-Wesley Publishing Company, 1989.

Shanmugan, K. Sam, and Arthur M. Breipohl. *Random Signals— Detection, Estimation and Data Analysis.* New York: John Wiley and Sons, 1988.

5 Counting Processes

• •

$$I\ like\ to\ count:\ 1,\ 2,\ 3,\ \ldots,\ (n-1)! = \Gamma(n) = \int_0^\infty x^{n-1}e^{-x}dx$$

The Count[a]

Introduction   Counting is a form of measuring and is one of the basic human experiences common to us all. In many of these counting experiences we deal with events that occur randomly. Examples are legion: scores in games, numbers of children in a family, votes in an election, etc. In our technical world too, simple counting of random events is ubiquitous: How many units out of a thousand manufactured cannot pass a final production test? How many electrons per second will drift across a potential barrier in a semiconductor? How many computer tasks are in a queue waiting for execution?

Counting random events suggests a counting random variable:

$$X = 0, 1, 2, 3, \ldots, n, \ldots$$

---

[a] With permission of the *Children's Television Workshop*, One Lincoln Plaza, New York, NY 10023.

And because a counting random variable is discrete, we look for probability mass functions to model counting phenomena. As a foundation for this chapter, we introduce three probabilistic models of counting:

1. The **binomial** model, which comes directly from the repeated independent trials we studied in Chapter 2.

2. The **hypergeometric** model, which is important in sampling. It differs from the binomial model in that successive trials are not independent.

3. The **Poisson** model, which is similar to the binomial in that events are independent. However, it is different from the binomial and hypergeometric models in that the upper limit of the counting random variable can, in theory at least, be arbitrarily large; $n \to \infty$.

Under some conditions the mathematical expressions contained in our models of counting present computational difficulties. These difficulties may be alleviated with some approximations, called "continuity correction techniques," which are also discussed in this chapter. Queues, and p charts from statistical process control, are presented at the end of this chapter and illustrate some useful engineering applications of counting processes.

You may find it helpful to scan Appendix B which presents a review of the notation and also some properties and results of a mathematical description of counting.

Section 5.1   THE BINOMIAL COUNTING PROCESS

• • • • •

A Bernoulli random experiment, as introduced in Chapter 2, produces two mutually exclusive events, A and $\overline{A}$. The probabilities of these events are denoted

$$P(A) = p, \quad P(\overline{A}) = q, \quad \text{where } p + q = 1$$

We introduce a **counting random variable** X by assigning the integers one and zero as follows:

$$X(A) = 1 \quad \text{and} \quad X(\overline{A}) = 0$$

Now, consider n independent trials with outcomes in $\{A, \overline{A}\}$. Then the counting function

$$Y = \sum_{i=1}^{n} X_i \tag{5.1}$$

will add a value of one to Y each time the event A occurs; an event $\bar{A}$ contributes zero to the sum in Y. In this way we count the outcomes of A in a sequence of n Bernoulli trials. Note that Y may have any integer value between zero and n. The zero occurs when each X in the sum is zero, and the n occurs when each X in the sum is 1.

The probability mass function (pmf) introduced with X is

$$P(X=1) = p, \quad P(X=0) = q$$

Using these, the pdf and cdf for the discrete random variable X are

$$f_X(x) = q\delta(x) + p\delta(x-1)$$
$$F_X(x) = qu(x) + pu(x-1)$$

The pdf may be used to calculate the mean and the variance for the Bernoulli random variable:

$$\mu_X = p \quad \text{and} \quad \sigma_X^2 = pq \tag{5.2}$$

If a sequence of n Bernoulli experiments is performed, and if the experiments are independent, then (4.41) and (4.42) show that the mean and the variance for Y are

$$\mu_Y = np \quad \text{and} \quad \sigma_Y^2 = npq \tag{5.3}$$

Further, the binomial terms in (2.47) form the pmf for the random variable Y:

$$P_n(k) = \binom{n}{k} p^k q^{n-k}, \quad 0 \le k \le n$$

Y is therefore named a **binomial random variable,** and the pdf and cdf for Y are, respectively,

$$f_Y(y) = \sum_{k=0}^{n} P_n(k)\delta(y-k) \tag{5.4}$$

$$F_Y(y) = \sum_{k=0}^{n} P_n(k)u(y-k) \tag{5.5}$$

Example 5.1   In Example 2.15 we considered the case of a computer pod with 10 terminals on which people independently signed on to three different computers (A, B, and C) via a network. We say that the event A occurs when an individual connects to computer A, and that $\bar{A}$ occurs when an individual connects to either computer B or C. In that example we stipulated that

$$P(A) = p = 0.25 \quad \text{and} \quad P(\bar{A}) = q = 0.75$$

At any particular time we can look into the pod and count the number of individuals connected to computer A. The smallest possible number is zero;

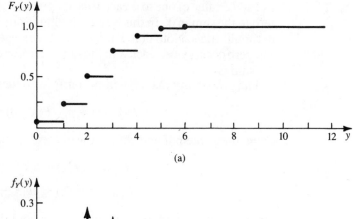

Figure 5.1   The (a) cdf and (b) the pdf (probability mass function) for a binomial counting process with parameters $n = 10$ and $p = 0.25$.

• •

the largest is 10. Table 2.3 lists the pmf for all 11 cases. Using (5.4), we plot the pdf for this example in Figure 5.1(b). This pdf for the discrete random variable Y can, of course, be used to find probabilities of interest to us. For example, if we want to know the probability that more than one but no more than four people in this pod are using computer A, we write

$$P(1 < Y \le 4) = \int_{1+}^{4} f_Y(y)dy$$

$$= \sum_{k=2}^{4} P_n(k) = 0.6779$$

We plot the cdf for this binomial random variable in Figure 5.1(a). We can also use (5.3) to calculate the average number of people in the pod who will be using computer A:

$$\mu_Y = np = 2.50$$

The variance of this is $\sigma_Y^2 = npq = 1.875$.

• • • • • •

In developing the theory for the binomial random variable, we stipulated that there were to be exactly n Bernoulli trials. A variation on this counting process happens when we place no limit on the number of Bernoulli trials; we count them as far as necessary to find the m'th occurrence of A. For example, if we are interested in the third occurrence of A, and if we are given the following sequence of Bernoulli trials,

$$\overline{A}, \overline{A}, A, \overline{A}, A, A, \ldots$$

we count six trials before the third occurrence of the event A. Perhaps in the next sequence we would count five, or seven, or more trials before the third occurrence of A. This counting process is called the **Pascal** counting process. Another name for it is the **negative binomial** counting process.

The pmf for the Pascal random variable is derived as follows. For the m'th occurrence of A on the k'th Bernoulli trial both of the following conditions must occur:

1. A occurs on the k'th trial.

2. Exactly $m - 1$ realizations of A occur in the preceding $k - 1$ trials.

We assume independence for all k Bernoulli trials. Therefore:

1. The probability of A on the k'th trial is p.

2. The probability of $m - 1$ occurrences of A in $k - 1$ trials is:

$$\binom{k-1}{m-1} p^{m-1} q^{k-1-(m-1)}$$

The desired pmf for the Pascal random variable is therefore

$$P(k,m) = p \binom{k-1}{m-1} p^{m-1} q^{k-m}$$

$$= \binom{k-1}{m-1} p^m q^{k-m} \tag{5.6}$$

If the Pascal random variable is denoted by Z, then

$$P(k,m) = P(Z=k), \quad k = m, m+1, m+2, \ldots$$

The Pascal pdf and cdf are

$$f_Z(z) = \sum_{k=m}^{\infty} P(k,m)\delta(z - k) \tag{5.7}$$

$$F_Z(z) = \sum_{k=m}^{\infty} P(k,m)u(z - k) \tag{5.8}$$

The mean and the variance for the Pascal random variable are[1]:

$$\mu_Z = \frac{m}{p} \quad \text{and} \quad \sigma_Z^2 = \frac{mq}{p^2} \tag{5.9}$$

A special case of the Pascal random variable occurs when $m = 1$. Here we ask for the number of trials it takes for the first occurrence of A to appear. This special case is called the **geometric random variable**, and the pmf (5.6) simplifies to

$$P(k,1) = pq^{k-1} \tag{5.10}$$

where k can be any integer greater than zero.

Example 5.2   Consider a four-bit binary word: If any bit in the word is inadvertently reversed, perhaps because of noise, the word contains an error. Let the probability of this error be $q = 10^{-4}$, and let the four bits be independent. Then, using a binomial random variable, the probability of at least one error in the four bits of the word is one minus the probability of no error:

$$P(\text{error} \geq 1) = 1 - P_4(4)$$
$$= 1 - \binom{4}{4} p^4 q^0$$
$$= 1 - (1 - 10^{-4})^4 \approx 4q, \quad q \ll 1$$
$$= 0.000400$$

We continue this example by introducing the idea of an error detecting code: Before a four-bit word is transmitted, a fifth bit, called a **parity bit**, is added, making a five-bit word. Whether the parity bit is a one or a zero depends on the original four-bit word. To explain how this is done, we assume an **even parity error detecting code**, which is described as follows.

1. If the number of ones in the four-bit word is even, then the parity bit is set to zero.

2. If the number of ones in the four-bit code is odd, then the parity bit is set to one.

In either case, the five-bit word always has an even number of ones in it before it is transmsitted. (An **odd parity error detecting code** could also be defined.)

When a four-bit word and its parity bit are received, an odd number of errors occurring in the five bits is detected, and the erroneous word is rejected. The system then asks that the original word be transmitted again. However, if zero, two, or four errors occur, the four-bit word is accepted as accurate. The probability of two and four errors occurring in five bits is

$$P(\text{exactly two errors}) = P(\text{exactly three correct})$$

$$= \binom{5}{3} p^3 q^2$$

$$= 9.997 \times 10^{-8}$$

$$P(\text{exactly four errors}) = P(\text{exactly one correct})$$

$$= \binom{5}{1} pq^4$$

$$= 5 \times 10^{-16}$$

Combining these results for the parity bit technique, the probability of making a mistake and accepting a word containing errors is approximately 10^{-7}. This is a significant improvement over the case in which no parity bit is used. Using the theory for the geometric random variable, we let $p = 10^{-7}$. Then (5.9) tells us that this kind of error will occur on the average every $1/p = 10$ million words. Notice that the standard deviation is also approximately 10^7 words.

♦ ♦ ♦ ♦ ♦

Section 5.2   THE HYPERGEOMETRIC COUNTING PROCESS

♦ ♦ ♦ ♦ ♦

This section deals with counting items in a **sample**. We assume the sample has n items, and that they are drawn from a larger collection of N items called the **population**:

$$0 \leq n \leq N$$

when we sample an item we remove it from the population; we may not sample it again. This is referred to as **sampling without replacement**. Because we sample without replacement, the probabilities of selecting the various items from the population change as the sampling proceeds. In other words, the sampling trials are not independent.

The hypergeometric counting process applies when, for example, 10 microchips are randomly selected for testing from a box of 50 microchips that are nominally identical.

Samples are drawn from the population randomly. This means we use the assumption of equally likely events: We will draw any single item from the population as equally likely as any other item. In practical situations we must do everything reasonable to ensure that the sampling is random.

We assume that the population contains two identifiable disjoint groups: One group, called R items, has a size of r, and the other group, called B items has a size of b:

$$r + b = N$$

Usually, it is the proportion of these groups within the population that we want to discover by using the sampling process. The number of R items found in a sample is designated by the integer k:

1. The smallest value k can have is zero if none of the R items happens to appear in the sample.

2. The greatest value k can have is either n (if all the samples happen to be R items) or r (if the sample happens to draw all the R items).

Therefore, the bounds on the integer k are

$$0 \le k \le \min(n,r)$$

Denote the counting random variable by X. Then $P(X=k)$ is the pmf for X and we calculate it as follows.

1. We find the number of all possible samples of size n that can be drawn from the population N; this is the combination $\binom{N}{n}$.

2. We find the number of ways into which the R items can be combined into groups of size k in the sample; this is the combination $\binom{r}{k}$. For each of these ways, we can combine the remainder of the sample (which can only have B items) in $\binom{b}{n-k}$ ways.

Then,

$$\binom{r}{k}\binom{b}{n-k}$$

is the total number of ways we can draw a sample with exactly k of the R items. Finally, the pmf is

$$P(X=k) = \frac{\binom{r}{k}\binom{b}{n-k}}{\binom{N}{n}} \tag{5.11}$$

where $k = 0, 1, 2, \ldots, \min(n,r)$. X is called the **hypergeometric** random variable.

The Vandermonde convolution relation:

$$\sum_{k=0}^{\min(n,r)} P(X=x) = 1$$

assures us that the union of all the disjoint hypergeometric events is the certain event. It then follows that the pdf and cdf for the hypergeometric random variable are

$$f_X(x) = \sum_{k=0}^{\min(n,r)} P(X=k)\delta(x-k) \tag{5.12}$$

$$F_X(x) = \sum_{k=0}^{\min(n,r)} P(X=k)u(x-k) \tag{5.13}$$

We state without proof the following features of the hypergeometric random variable. Its mean and variance are[1]:

$$\mu_X = n\frac{r}{N} \quad \text{and} \quad \sigma_X^2 = n\frac{r}{N}\left(1 - \frac{r}{N}\right)\frac{N-n}{N-1} \tag{5.14}$$

Example 5.3   Assume we have a population of $N = 30$ items, which are partitioned into $r = 10$ R items and $b = 20$ B items. A sample of size $n = 5$ is taken from the population. We calculate the first value for the pmf using (5.11):

$$P(X=0) = \frac{\binom{10}{0}\binom{20}{5}}{\binom{30}{5}} = 0.109$$

Continuing in his way with (5.11),

$$P(X=1) = 0.340$$
$$P(X=2) = 0.360$$
$$P(X=3) = 0.160$$
$$P(X=4) = 0.029$$
$$P(X=5) = 0.002$$

Note that the sum of all terms in the pmf is one, as required by the Vandermonde convolution relation for any pmf. Using (5.14), the mean and variance are

$$\mu_X = 1.67 \quad \text{and} \quad \sigma_X^2 = 0.958$$

We illustrate the pdf and cdf for this example of the hypergeometric random variable in Figure 5.2.

◆ ◆ ◆ ◆ ◆

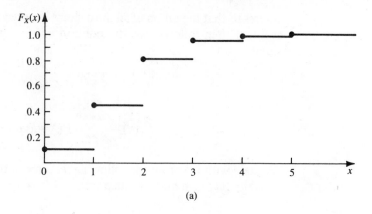

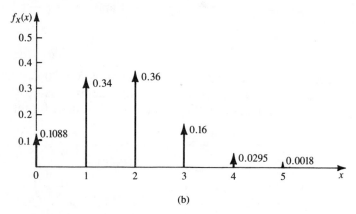

Figure 5.2 The (a) cdf and (b) the pdf (probability mass function) for the hypergeometric random variable in Example 5.3.

◆ ◆

The hypergeometric pmf becomes the same as the pmf for the binomial random variable as N becomes arbitrarily large. We anticipate this result by defining

$$p = \frac{r}{N} \quad \text{and} \quad q = \frac{b}{N} \tag{5.15}$$

where p and q are defined, of course, such that $p + q = 1$. First, we write the pmf in (5.11) in terms of the elemental factorials:

$$P(X=k) = \frac{r!b!n!(N-n)!}{k!(r-k)!(n-k)!(b-n+k)!N!} \tag{5.16a}$$

Then we group the factorial terms in (5.16a) as follows:

$$P(X=k) = \frac{n!}{k!(n-k)!} \cdot \frac{(N-n)!}{N!} \cdot \frac{r!}{(r-k)!} \cdot \frac{b!}{(b-n+k)!} \quad (5.16b)$$

We use the first group of factorials directly as a combination:

1.
$$\frac{n!}{k!(n-k)!} = \binom{n}{k}$$

We investigate the next three groups in (5.16b) as N becomes large:

2.
$$\frac{(N-n)!}{N!} = \frac{(N-n)!}{N(N-1) \ldots (N-n+1)(N-n)!}$$

$$= \frac{1}{N(N-1) \ldots (N-n+1)}$$

And, as $N \to \infty$, it follows that

$$\frac{(M-n)!}{N!} \approx \frac{1}{N^n}$$

3.
$$\frac{r!}{(r-k)!} = \frac{r(r-1) \ldots (r-k+1)(r-k)!}{(r-k)!}$$

$$= r(r-1) \ldots (r-k+1)$$

Using (5.15), we write this as

$$\frac{r!}{(r-k)!} = N^k p \left(p - \frac{1}{N}\right) \ldots \left(p - \frac{k}{N} + \frac{1}{N}\right)$$

Then, as $N \to \infty$, we have

$$\frac{r!}{(r-k)!} \approx N^k p^k$$

4.
$$\frac{b!}{(b-n+k)!} = \frac{b(b-1) \ldots [b-(n-k)+1][b-(n-k)]!}{[b-(n-k)]!}$$

$$= b(b-1) \ldots [b-(n-k)+1]$$

Using (5.15), this becomes

$$\frac{b!}{(b-n+k)!} = N^{n-k} q \left(q - \frac{1}{N}\right) \ldots \left(q - \frac{n-k}{N} + \frac{1}{N}\right)$$

And, as $N \to \infty$, this becomes

$$\frac{b!}{(b-n+k)!} \approx N^{n-k} q^{n-k}$$

Combining these four groups, as in (5.16b), we have

$$P(X=k) \approx \binom{n}{k} \cdot \frac{1}{N^n} \cdot N^k p^k \cdot N^{n-k} q^{n-k}$$

Finally, as $N \to \infty$,

$$P(X=k) \approx \binom{n}{k} p^k q^{n-k} \tag{5.17}$$

This approximate result for the hypergeometric random variable is the same as the pmf $P_n(k)$ for the binomial random variable. What this says is that if a population is large enough with respect to sample size, the sample selections all have (approximately) equal probability; therefore, selections become independent. Then, the hypergeometric random variable becomes (asymptotically) the same as the binomial random variable. Because of the independence, which comes along with the binomial random variable, it also says that the binomial random variable can be referred to as **sampling with replacement.**

Section 5.3   THE POISSON COUNTING PROCESS

◆ ◆ ◆ ◆ ◆

Suppose we examine discrete random events and the times they occur. For example, radioactive decay occurs randomly. Telephone calls coming into a communications trunk arrive randomly. A noise voltage exceeds a threshold randomly. These examples are among many having this in common: The events being discussed are discrete, the time between events is random, and a random number of events can occur in a finite interval of time.

Let t represent a positive interval of time, and let the random variable X be the number of events occurring in that interval:

$$X = k, \quad k = 0, 1, 2, \ldots$$

Clearly, the smallest number of events possible in an interval is zero. At the other extreme, however, we cannot determine the maximum number of events in a finite interval. For any k we can always think of the possibility of having one more event. As an example, if radioactive decay produces 10 events per minute on the average, we cannot exclude the possibility of having 11 (or 111!) events per minute. One of the features distinguishing this process from the binomial and hypergeometric processes is that we cannot specify *a priori* any finite upper bound on k.

We define a probability mass function $P(k,t)$ to be the probability that there are exactly k events in a time interval t:

$$P(k,t) = P(k \text{ events in time interval } t)$$

Then we assume the following.

1. *Independent increments:* Occurrences in any interval are independent of occurrences in any other disjoint interval.

2. *Bernoulli trials:* When an interval is arbitrarily small, such as $\Delta t \rightarrow$
   0, we assume that at most one event can occur in the interval. The
   probability of that happening is $p = \lambda \Delta t$. The parameter λ is positive and, as we shall see later, is physically interpreted as an average
   rate of occurrence for the process being studied. The probability of
   not having an event occur in Δt is $q = 1 - \lambda \Delta t$. As required by a
   Bernoulli event, $p + q = 1$.

Suppose we start by assuming the special case when *no* events occur in
interval t. The probability of this happening is $P(0,t)$. Also, the probability of no
events between time-zero and $t + \Delta t$ is $P(0,t+\Delta t)$. Now,

$$P(0,t+\Delta t) = P\{[\text{no events in } (0,t)] \cap [\text{no events in } (t,t+\Delta t)]\}$$

Because of the assumption of independent increments, this becomes

$$P(0,t+\Delta t) = P[\text{no events in } (0,t)]P[\text{no events in } (t,t+\Delta t)]$$

Then, using the notation we have established,

$$P(0,t+\Delta t) = P(0,t)q = P(0,t)(1 - \lambda \Delta t)$$

Rewriting,

$$\frac{P(0,t+\Delta t) - P(0,t)}{\Delta t} = -\lambda P(0,t)$$

Letting $\Delta t \rightarrow 0$ and, if a limit exists, we have the differential equation

$$\frac{d}{dt} P(0,t) = -\lambda P(0,t), \quad t \geq 0$$

The probability of having any event in an interval of zero length is zero.
Therefore, the probability of having zero events in an interval of zero length is
one. This gives us the initial condition for the differential equation:

$$P(0,0) = 1$$

Its solution is

$$P(0,t) = e^{-\lambda t}, \quad t \geq 0 \tag{5.18}$$

Now suppose that we have exactly k events in the interval between zero and
$t + \Delta t$ and k has integer values greater than 0. These k events can happen in one
of two mutually exclusive ways. Either

1. we have k events within 0 to t, and no event in the interval from t to $t + \Delta t$, or

2. we have $k - 1$ events between 0 and t, and exactly one event in the interval from t to $t + \Delta t$.

Using this we write

$$P(k,t+\Delta t) = P(k,t)q + P(k-1,t)p$$

Using our notation for Bernoulli trials,

$$P(k,t+\Delta t) = P(k,t)(1 - \lambda\Delta t) + P(k-1,t)\lambda\Delta t$$

Rearranging,

$$\frac{P(k,t+\Delta t) - P(k,t)}{\Delta t} = -\lambda P(k,t) + \lambda P(k-1,t)$$

Again, letting $\Delta t \to 0$, and assuming the derivative exists,

$$\frac{d}{dt}P(k,t) + \lambda P(k,t) = \lambda P(k-1,t)$$

The initial condition is $P(k,0) = 0$ because the probability of having k events in an interval of zero length is zero. This inhomogeneous differential equation provides us with a method for calculating the $P(k,t)$ recursively: Because we know $P(0,t)$ from (5.18), we can write for $P(1,t)$

$$\frac{d}{dt}P(1,t) + \lambda P(1,t) = \lambda P(0,t)$$

Using standard methods for solving inhomogeneous linear differential equations with constant coefficients, we obtain

$$P(1,t) = \lambda t\, e^{-\lambda t}, \quad t \geq 0$$

Continuing recursively, having found $P(1,t)$, we can then find $P(2,t)$:

$$P(2,t) = \lambda^2\, t^2/2\, e^{-\lambda t}, \quad t \geq 0$$

Having found $P(2,t)$, we can find $P(3,t)$,

$$P(3,t) = \lambda^3/2\, t^3/3\, e^{-\lambda t}, \quad t \geq 0$$

Finally, we observe the general solution to be

$$P(k,t) = \frac{(\lambda t)^k}{k!}\, e^{-\lambda t} \tag{5.19}$$

These probability mass functions are named **Poisson**.

The Poisson counting process is exceptionally interesting to us because of applications that follow. Therefore, we now take the time to establish some of its features. First, for simplicity, we let

$$b = \lambda t \tag{5.20}$$

Then we write the Poisson pmf (5.19) as

$$P_k = \frac{b^k}{k!} e^{-b} \tag{5.21}$$

A recursion relation between successive P_k is easily observed to be

$$P_k = \frac{b}{k} P_{k-1} \tag{5.22}$$

Using (5.21) we write the Poisson pdf and cdf (and we use the random variable X for time):

$$f_X(x) = \sum_{k=0}^{\infty} P_k \delta(x - k) \tag{5.23}$$

$$F_X(x) = \sum_{k=0}^{\infty} P_k u(x - k) \tag{5.24}$$

The n'th moment about the origin is, using (3.74) and (5.21),

$$E[X^n] = e^{-b} \sum_{k=0}^{\infty} \frac{k^n b^k}{k!} \tag{5.25}$$

Using (5.25) and letting n be zero, we find that all the terms in the pmf sum to one:

$$e^{-b} \sum_{k=0}^{\infty} \frac{b^k}{k!} = e^{-b} e^{b} = 1$$

This is a example of infinite additivity described by Axiom IV in Chapter 2. We find the mean of the Poisson random variable by using (5.25) and letting n be one:

$$\mu_X = e^{-b} \sum_{k=0}^{\infty} \frac{k b^k}{k!}$$

The first term in this series is zero, so k need only start as $k = 1$. Also, k in the numerator cancels a k in the denominator:

$$\mu_X = e^{-b} \sum_{k=1}^{\infty} \frac{b^{k-1}}{(k-1)!}$$

Using the change of variables $j = k - 1$, the series can be summed

$$\mu_X = be^{-b}e^b = b$$

When $n = 2$, (5.25) becomes

$$E[X^2] = e^{-b} \sum_{k=0}^{\infty} \frac{k^2 b^k}{k!}$$

$$= e^{-b} \sum_{k=0}^{\infty} k(k-1+1) \frac{b^k}{k!}$$

$$= e^{-b} \sum_{k=0}^{\infty} \frac{k(k-1) b^k}{k!} + e^{-b} \sum_{k=0}^{\infty} \frac{kb^k}{k!}$$

We have already evaluated the second sum on the right above when we evaluated μ_X. The first sum on the right needs only to start with $k = 2$. Also, the factor $k(k-1)$ in the numerator cancels a corresponding factor in the denominator. Then,

$$E[X^2] = b^2 e^{-b} \sum_{k=2}^{\infty} \frac{b^{k-2}}{(k-2)!} + b$$

Using the change of variables $j = k - 2$, the series can be summed

$$E[X^2] = b^2 e^{-b} e^b = b^2 + b$$

The variance of the Poisson random variable is, therefore, using (3.39):

$$\sigma_X^2 = b^2 + b - b^2 = b$$

Interestingly, the mean and the variance for the Poisson random variable equal each other:

$$\mu_X = \sigma_X^2 = b = \lambda t \tag{5.26}$$

Here we see that λ is an average rate parameter for the Poisson counting process.

Example 5.4   Notice an effect illustrated by the recursion formula (5.22): As long as $b > k$ the coefficients P_k keep increasing. But when k increases to the point where it is greater than b, the coefficients P_k diminish. Two cases illustrate this: the first with $b = 0.8$, and the second with $b = 3$. Table 5.1 lists values for P_k when $b = 0.8$. All values of k are greater than b except for $k = 0$; we therefore see the values of P_k decrease. This is also illustrated in Figure 5.3 where the pdf for this Poisson random variable is shown. Table 5.2 lists values for P_k when $b = 3$. Here we see that P_k increases when $k < b$, and decreases when $k > b$. This is illustrated in Figure 5.4, which shows the pdf for the Poisson random variable when $b = 3$. As a general observation based on these two

Table 5.1   Values, and Cumulative Values, for the Poisson Random Variable pmf P_k when $b = 0.8$

k	P_k	$\sum_{i=0}^{k} P_i$
0	0.4493	0.4493
1	0.3595	0.8088
2	0.1438	0.9526
3	0.0383	0.9909
4	0.0077	0.9986
5	0.0012	0.9998
6	0.0002	1.0000

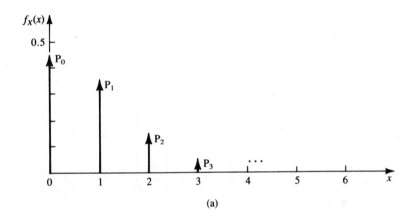

(a)

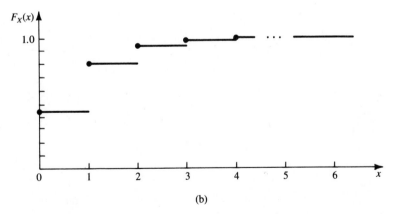

(b)

Figure 5.3   The (a) pdf $f_X(x)$ and (b) the cdf $F_X(x)$ for the Poisson random variable tabulated in Table 5.1; $b = 0.8$.

Table 5.2   Values, and Cumulative Values, for the Poisson Random Variable pmf P_k when $b = 3$

k	P_k	$\sum\limits_{I=0}^{k} P_I$
0	0.0498	0.0498
1	0.1494	0.1992
2	0.2240	0.4232
3	0.2240	0.6472
4	0.1680	0.8152
5	0.1008	0.9160
6	0.0504	0.9664
7	0.0216	0.9880
8	0.0081	0.9961
9	0.0027	0.9988

◆ ◆

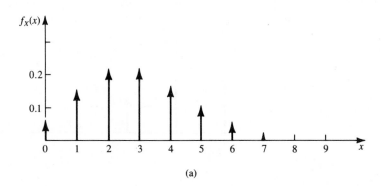

(a)

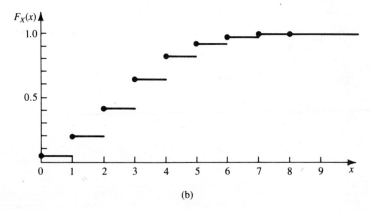

(b)

Figure 5.4   The (a) pdf and $f_X(x)$ and (b) the cdf $F_X(x)$ for the Poisson random variable tabulated in Table 5.2; $b = 3$.

cases, note that the largest value(s) (modes) of the pmf occur where observations of the random variable are equal to or near b, the mean of the random variable.

◆ ◆ ◆ ◆ ◆

An Approximation

While the Poisson and the binomial counting processes are fundamentally different, there is a condition under which they approximate each other. We can see how this works if we compare the means and variances for the two:

	Poisson	Binomial
Mean	b	np
Variance	b	npq

If the two counting processes are approximately equal, their respective means and variances must also be approximately equal. This can happen if q is close to one, say $q = 0.999$, and

$$p = 1 - q$$

is a smaller number. When p is small it is desirable to use a large sample n. Therefore, while p is small, n may be large so that the product $np = b$ may have a reasonable value. Under these conditions it also follows that $np \approx npq$. We illustrate this approximation in the following example.

Example 5.5   Assume a binomial counting process with the parameters $p = 0.001$, $q = 0.999$, and $n = 5000$. Its mean and variance are

$$\mu_X = np = 5 \quad \text{and} \quad \sigma_X^2 = npq \approx 5$$

The binomial pmf is, from (2.47),

$$P_{5000}(k) = \binom{5000}{k} p^k q^{5000-k}$$

Since the mean and variance are nearly equal, we attempt to approximate the binomial counting process with a Poisson counting process. From (5.21),

$$P_k = \frac{5^k}{k!} e^{-5}$$

Here, we used $\mu_X = \sigma_X^2 = b = 5$. Table 5.3 lists the first 15 values of P_k and $P_{5000}(k)$ for the Poissosn and binomial counting processes, respectively. The

Table 5.3   Comparison of the pmfs P_k and $P_{5000}(k)$ for, Respectively, Poisson and Binomial Counting Processes*

k	P_k	$P_{5000}(k)$
0	$0.0067 = e^{-5}$	$0.0067 = q^{5000}$
1	0.0337	0.0336
2	0.0842	0.0841
3	0.1404	0.1403
4	0.1755	0.1755
5	0.1755	0.1755
6	0.1462	0.1463
7	0.1044	0.1045
8	0.0653	0.0653
9	0.0363	0.0362
10	0.0181	0.0181
11	0.0082	0.0082
12	0.0034	0.0034
13	0.0013	0.0013
14	0.0005	0.0005
15	0.0002	0.0002

* When they are approximately equal to each other. This table is discussed in Example 5.5.

recursion formula (5.22) was used to calculate all the Poisson values except the first. We see from the table that the Poisson and binomial counting processes can approximate each other well. Evidently, when the binomial counting process has a mean that is small with respect to the total n ($5 \ll 5000$ in this example), values of k approaching n have as much of an effect as when $k \to \infty$ in the Poisson case. Computational ease is the major reason we choose to use the Poisson over the binomial process when we find that they approximate each other.

♦ ♦ ♦ ♦ ♦

The Erlang Random Variable

Until now we assumed a fixed time interval t, and we determined the probability of a discrete number of events occuring within the interval, as in Example 5.4. Now we change our point of view and seek a description of the random time intervals separating events in the Poisson counting process. Since a time between events may have any value, the random variable we seek is continuous, and is denoted by Y.

The probability that the k'th discrete occurrence appears in the interval between t and $t + \Delta t$ is, using (3.9),

$$P(t < Y \le t + \Delta t) = F_Y(t + \Delta t) - F_Y(t)$$

A different description of this event is that there are exactly $k - 1$ events in the time between zero and t, and exactly one event in the interval between t and $t + \Delta t$. Therefore, using the notation developed with the Poisson random variable,

$$\begin{aligned} P(t < Y \le t + \Delta t) &= P(k-1,t)p \\ &= P(k-1,t)\lambda\Delta t \end{aligned}$$

If we equate these two probabilities for $P(t < Y \le t + \Delta t)$ we find

$$\frac{F_Y(t + \Delta t) - F_Y(t)}{\Delta t} = \lambda P(k-1,t)$$

And, if the limit exists as $\Delta t \to 0$,

$$\frac{d}{dt} F_Y(t) = \lambda P(k-1,t)$$

Using (5.19), and noting that the derivative of the cdf is the pdf, we have

$$f_Y(t) = \frac{\lambda^k t^{k-1}}{(k - 1)!} e^{-\lambda t}, \quad t > 0 \tag{5.27}$$

This is the pdf for the Erlang random variable found in Example 4.10.

Example 5.6 A Poisson counting process has the parameter $\lambda = 2$ per second. This parameter corresponds to the rate at which jobs arrive in a queue for a time-sharing computer. What is the mean time between successive arrivals of the discrete events in this process? Because we are interested in the times between successive events, this question implies that we use the Erlang random variable when k is equal to one. When $k = 1$ the Erlang random variable becomes exponential. From Exercise 3.10, the exponential random variable has a mean of $\mu_Y = 1/\lambda$. Therefore, the mean time between successive occurrences (arrivals) in the given Poisson counting process is 0.5 seconds.

◆ ◆ ◆ ◆ ◆

The Erlang cumulative distribution function is

$$F_Y(t) = P(Y \le t) = \int_0^t f_Y(y)dy$$

where $f_Y(t)$ is the pdf in (5.27). Because $f_Y(t)$ depends on k, $F_Y(t)$ also depends on k. Specifically, the cdf $F_Y(t)$ is the probability that the k'th event occurs within the interval from zero to t. The probability that the k'th event does not occur within zero to t, but rather occurs any time after t, is

$$P(Y > y) = 1 - F_Y(t) = \int_t^\infty f_Y(y)dy$$

Even though t is from a continuous random variable, when a specific t is identified we can use (5.20) and (5.21) to write the discrete Poisson probability

$$P_k = \frac{(\lambda t)^k e^{-\lambda t}}{k!}$$

The probability that the k or more events do not occur in the interval is the complement of the probability that up to $k - 1$ events do occur in the interval. Thus,

$$P(Y > t) = \sum_{j=0}^{k-1} P_j$$

$$= e^{-\lambda t} \sum_{j=0}^{k-1} \frac{(\lambda t)^j}{j!}$$

Combining these two expressions for $P(Y > t)$ leads to an explicit description of the Erlang cdf:

$$F_Y(t) = 1 - e^{-\lambda t} \sum_{j=0}^{k-1} \frac{(\lambda t)^j}{j!} \tag{5.28}$$

Example 5.7　Continuing with the queuing problem introduced in Example 5.6, we consider an Erlang random variable for which the rate parameter is $\lambda = 2$ per second. Let $k = 3$. The Erlang random variable here then describes the time between every third occurrence (the arrival of every third job into the computer's queue). Then, we can perform calculations and find that the Erlang pdf in (5.27) has a mode of $t_{\text{MODE}} = 1$ second, a median of $t_{\text{MEDIAN}} = 1.3370$ seconds, and a mean of $t_{\text{MEAN}} = 1.5$ seconds. Using (5.28), and the values given above, we calculate the following for the cdf:

$$F(t_{\text{MODE}}) = 0.3233$$

$$F(t_{\text{MEDIAN}}) = 0.5000$$

$$F(t_{\text{MEAN}}) = 0.5768$$

◆　◆　◆　◆　◆

The independent variable of time has been used thus far in this discussion of the Poisson counting process. We made this restriction for convenience while introducing this topic. Actually, we can use any continuous independent variable; practical examples are length, area, and volume in addition to time.

Example 5.8   Exhaustive tests on 427 integrated circuit chips revealed that they have an average of 4.3 random defects per chip. While the number of chips is fixed, we have no prior limit on the number of random defects within a chip. Hence, we assume a Poisson model for the defects. If the Poisson model is correct, how many of the chips do we expect to have zero defects? The average for a Poisson random variable is, from (5.26), $\mu_Y = b$. In this example, $b = 4.3$. The probability of a chip with exactly zero defects is

$$P_0 = e^{-b} = e^{-4.3} = 0.014$$

Therefore, we expect $0.014(427) \approx 6$ chips to have exactly zero defects.

If random defects are proportional to the volume a chip contains, what is the average number of defects we expect for another chip that contains 30% more volume? From (5.26), $b = \lambda t$. However, in this example, $b = av$ where v is the volume of the integrated circuit chip and a is a rate parameter with the units of defects per volume. Accordingly, if v increases by 30%, b also increases by 30%. The average number of defects per chip becomes $4.3\,(1 + 0.3) = 5.6$ for the larger chip.

◆   ◆   ◆   ◆   ◆

The Gamma Random Variable

The pdf for the Erlang random variable (5.27) may be generalized such that k is not an integer. To understand this, note first that when k is a positive integer, the factorial of k may be replaced by the gamma function (see Exercise 12 of Chapter 3):

$$(k - 1)! = \Gamma(k)$$

The gamma function is defined for noninteger values of its argument. Formally, then, we can write the pdf in (5.27) as

$$f_Y(y) = \frac{\lambda^v y^{v-1}}{\Gamma(v)}\, e^{-\lambda y}\, u(y) \tag{5.29}$$

where the parameter $v > 0$. Using the change of variables of $x = \lambda y$, and the definition of the gamma function,

$$\int_0^\infty f_Y(y)dy = \frac{1}{\Gamma(v)} \int_0^\infty \lambda^v y^{v-1} e^{-\lambda y} dy$$

$$= \frac{1}{\Gamma(v)} \int_0^\infty x^{v-1} e^{-x} dx = 1$$

Further, the mean and variance of the gamma random variable follow the same form as the mean and variance of the Erlang random variables:

$$\mu_Y = v/\lambda \quad \text{and} \quad \sigma_Y^2 = v/\lambda^2 \tag{5.30}$$

Section 5.4   CONTINUITY CORRECTION TECHNIQUES

• • • • •

An interesting numerical phenomenon can occur with the binomial random variable. Recall from (5.1) that the binomial random variable of order n is the sum of n statistically independent Bernoulli random variables. Then, according to the central limit theorem, as n becomes large the binomial random variable approaches a Gaussian random variable. It is, however, not clear what, if any, correspondence exists between binomial and Gaussian random variables because the former is discrete and the latter is continuous. The following example gives us some insight.

Example 5.9   Consider a binomial random variable for which $n = 40$ and $p = q = 0.5$. The pmf is then

$$P_{40}(k) = \binom{40}{k} (0.5)^{40}$$

This discrete pmf is plotted in Figure 5.5 for values of k between zero and 40.

• •

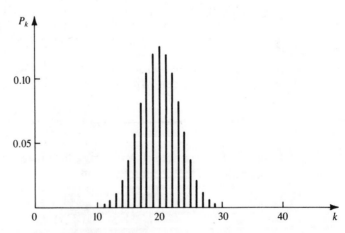

Figure 5.5   A plot of the pmf for a binomial random variable; $n = 40$ and $p = 0.5$.

We observe:

1. The $P_{40}(k)$ with the largest magnitudes cluster about the mean,

$$\mu_X = np = 20$$

2. The variance of the random variable is

$$\sigma_X^2 = npq = 10$$

and the standard deviation is $\sigma_X = \sqrt{10} = 3.16$. Negligible values of $P_{40}(k)$ occur outside of $\mu_X \pm 3\sigma_X$. For values of k less than zero, $P_{40}(k)$ is truncated to zero. For values greater than 40, values of $P_{40}(k)$ are negligible.

3. If an envelope is placed on the pmf connecting all the values on a smooth line, the shape of the envelope is similar to the shape of the Gaussian pdf.

♦   ♦   ♦   ♦   ♦

♦   ♦

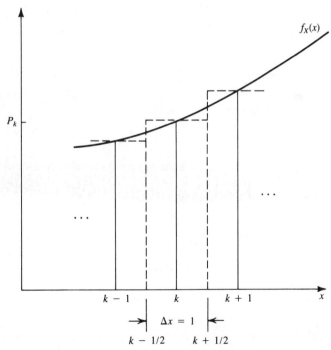

Figure 5.6   Illustrating the numerical technique of continuity correction: The pmf at $x = k$ has the value of P_k.

Figure 5.6 (p. 209) illustrates a portion of a pdf; the discrete values P_k are shown for $k-1$, k, $k+1$. Connecting these values of P_k is a continuous pdf $f_X(x)$. The effect of the pmf at $x = k$ is described two ways. First, there is the probability P_k itself. Second, the area under $f_X(x)$ between $k-1/2$ and $k+1/2$ approximates P_k:

$$\int_{k-1/2}^{k+1/2} f_X(x)dx \approx P_k \Delta x = P_k$$

The increment in his approximation is

$$\Delta x = (k+1/2) - (k-1/2) = 1$$

It then follows that a sum of the P_k may be approximated by an integral of the pdf:

$$\sum_{k=i}^{j} P_k \approx \int_{i-1/2}^{j+1/2} f_X(x)dx = F_X(j+1/2) - F_X(i-1/2) \qquad \textbf{(5.31)}$$

That the pdf tends to be Gaussian can be seen by evaluating both sides of (5.31) and comparing the results. The approximating technique in (5.31) is called **continuity correction.**

Example 5.10   The parameters for the binomial pmf in Figure 5.5 were given as $p = q = 0.5$ and $n = 40$. Assume we are interested in the total effect of $P_{40}(k)$ from $k = 15$ through $k = 21$:

$$P(15 \le X \le 21) = \sum_{k=15}^{21} P_{40}(k)$$

The continuity correction technique (5.31) stipulates that we approximate the sum above with

$$P(14.5 < X < 21.5) = F_X(21.5) - F_X(14.5)$$

where $F_X(x)$ is the cdf for a Gaussian random variable with a mean and variance of

$$\mu_X = np = 20.0 \quad \text{and} \quad \sigma_X^2 = npq = 10.0$$

Therefore,

$$P(14.5 < X < 21.5) = \psi\left(\frac{21.5 - 20.0}{\sqrt{10}}\right) - \psi\left(\frac{14.5 - 20.0}{\sqrt{10}}\right)$$

$$= 0.6414$$

The binomial sum in this example may be evaluated directly; its result is 0.6418, and the two compare rather well. As expected, the Gaussian approximation is best near the mean.

◆ ◆ ◆ ◆ ◆

Continuity correction may also be used with the Poisson random variable.

Example 5.11   A Poisson example is illustrated in Figure 5.7, and the parameter $b = 20$ is used. This makes the mean of this Poisson example equal to the mean of the binomial random variable in Example 5.10:

$$\mu_X = b = 20.0 \quad \text{and} \quad \sigma_X^2 = b = 20.0$$

Again we are interested in the total effect of the Poisson random variable for all values of k from 15 to 21. The desired sum of Poisson contributions is

$$P(15 \le X \le 21) = \sum_{k=15}^{21} P_k$$

Using the continuity correction technique (5.31), the approximate value of the probability is

$$P(14.5 < X < 21.5) = F_X(21.5) - F_X(14.5)$$

In this Poisson example the mean and variance are

$$\mu_X = b = 20.0 \quad \text{and} \quad \sigma_X^2 = b = 20.0$$

Consequently,

$$P(14.5 < X < 21.5) = \psi\left(\frac{21.5 - 20}{\sqrt{20}}\right) - \psi\left(\frac{14.5 - 20}{\sqrt{20}}\right)$$
$$= 0.5220$$

• •

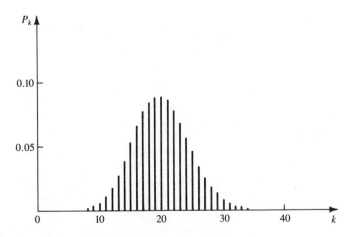

Figure 5.7   A plot of the probability mass function for a Poisson random variable; $b = 20$.

This approximate value is not as close to its correct value (0.5388) as we found in the binomial example. The reasons are apparent: the Poisson pmf in Figure 5.7 has a slight positive skew, and its standard deviation is larger than that found with the binomial example.

◆   ◆   ◆   ◆   ◆

Continuity correction is of interest to us because it illustrates again the effect of the central limit theorem, and because, when it can be applied, it significantly reduces computational labor.

Section 5.5   QUEUES

◆   ◆   ◆   ◆   ◆

Queues[2,3] are interesting applications of probability, and they also provide an example of some of the topics in this chapter. Everyone has experienced being in a queue: waiting in line at a check-out counter, waiting for a telephone circuit as we repeatedly try to place a long-distance call, waiting in traffic as we enter a highway's tollgate, waiting for a time-sharing computer to run our program, etc. The list is almost endless, and the reader can, I am sure, quickly add several more examples from his or her own experiences.

Technically, a study of queues is important for the following reasons:

1. From the user's point of view, a queue, i.e., waiting in line, is a nuisance, and will be tolerated only at some minimal level of inconvenience.

2. From the point of view of a provider of some service, queues are necessary. It is extremely uneconomical to provide a large number of servers to handle the biggest possible rush, only to have many of them idle most of the time.

One motivation to study queues is to find some balance between these two conflicting viewpoints. Probability theory is a useful tool for a study of queues because arrivals into and departures from a queue occur randomly.

Figure 5.8 is a schematic representation of a **queuing system.** A **customer** arives at the input to the queuing system, and if no **server** is free, the customer must wait in a **queue** until it is his or her turn to be served. A **queue discipline** is the name given to a rule by which a customer is selected from a queue for service. Generally, our sense of fairness wants a first-in-first-out (FIFO) queue discipline, but that is not convenient in all cases. For example, if a queue is a stack of boxes in a storage room (here, a "customer" is a box), then it may be more convenient to have a queue discipline of last-in-first-out (LIFO). Or, a customer may be selected from a queue randomly, such as when many people

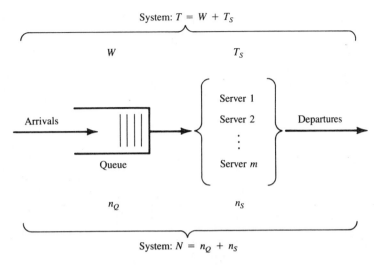

System: $T = W + T_S$

W

T_S

Arrivals

Queue

Server 1

Server 2

$\vdots$

Server m

Departures

n_Q

n_S

System: $N = n_Q + n_S$

Figure 5.8   Illustration of customers arriving at a queue and, after some time, their departure from a server that serves the queue.

♦ ♦

repeatedly dial their telephone, trying to get through a busy long-distance circuit.

The average rate at which customers arrive at a queuing system is λ. In a steady-state situation, the average number of customers in a queuing system is constant. Therefore, the average rate at which customers depart the queuing system is also λ. Departures from the queuing system occur when a server finishes with a customer. The arrivals to a queuing system may be described as a counting process $A(t)$ such as that shown in Figure 5.9. We can, with any amount of sample data, calculate an average rate of arrivals:

$$\bar{\lambda} = \frac{A(t)}{t} \text{ (customers per time)} \tag{5.32}$$

where $A(t) = $ [number of arrivals in $(0,t)$]. Departures from the system $D(t)$ are also described by a counting process, and an example of one is also shown in Figure 5.9. Note that at all times, $A(t) \geq D(t)$. The time each customer spends in the queuing system is the time difference between the customer's arrival and subsequent departure from a server. This waiting time for arrival j is denoted T_j, $j = 1, 2, 3, \ldots$, and is also shown in Figure 5.9, where a FIFO queue discipline is assumed.

It then follows that the average time a customer spends waiting in a queuing system is, for any sample data and at any time t,

$$\bar{T} = \frac{1}{A(t)} \sum_{i=1}^{A(t)} T_i \quad \text{(waiting time per customer)} \tag{5.33}$$

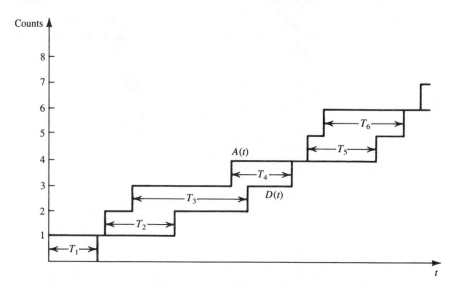

Figure 5.9   Illustration of the arrival and departure counting processes for a queuing system.

The average number of customers in a queuing system, for any sample data and at any time t, is, from (5.30) and (5.33),

$$\overline{N} = \frac{1}{t} \sum_{i=1}^{A(t)} T_i = \overline{\lambda} \overline{T} \quad \text{(dimensionless)} \tag{5.34}$$

If we assume that, with enough data (as j becomes arbitrarily large), sample averages approximate their expected values, then

$$\overline{\lambda} \to \lambda$$
$$\overline{T} \to E[T]$$
$$\overline{N} \to E[N]$$

Hence, (5.34) becomes

$$E[N] = \lambda E[T] \tag{5.35}$$

This relation is known as **Little's formula**; it has a generality much beyond what one might suppose, given the heuristic demonstration leading to (5.35).

A generally accepted notation that is used to name a queuing system is **A/S/m**. Here, A is a description of the dynamics by which arrivals come to the queuing system; S is a description of the dynamics by which a server processes a customer taken from the queue; and m is the number of servers.

We restrict ourselves to the case where the number of servers is $m = 1$. We also assume the time customers arrive at the queuing system is modeled by an exponential random variable with a rate parameter λ. Further, we assume that the time the server takes to service each customer is also modeled by an exponential random variable, with a rate parameter of λ_S. Finally, it is assumed that arrivals and servings are independent random variables, except that the server cannot serve a customer who has not yet arrived in the queue. This exception models the constraint $A(t) \geq D(t)$ in Figure 5.9.

Suppose we define the **state** of a queuing system as the number of customers currently in it, either waiting in the queue or being served. The use of the exponential random variables for times of arrival and for service times means that the queuing system is Markov (see Chapter 2) where each state of a queuing system depends only on its previous state, and not on any state further back in time. Therefore, the conventional name given to the queuing system we are discussing is M/M/1: The arrival dynamics are Markov, the server dynamics are Markov, and there is only one server.

The notation $P(n,t)$ denotes the probability of a queuing system being in state n at time t. For example, if Δt is a small increment of time, the probability of an arrival to the queuing system in the interval Δt is

$$P(A) = \lambda \Delta t \tag{5.36a}$$

Correspondingly, the probability of no arrival in Δt is

$$P(\overline{A}) = 1 - \lambda \Delta t \tag{5.36b}$$

Similarly, the probability of serving (discharging) a customer in the server is

$$P(D) = \lambda_S \Delta t \tag{5.37a}$$

The probability of continuing to serve a customer who is already being served (i.e., to not discharge a customer in the server) is

$$P(\overline{D}) = 1 - \lambda_S \Delta t \tag{5.37b}$$

Then, continuing our assumption that the arrival dynamics are independent of the server dynamics, we write

$$P(n,t+\Delta t) = P(n,t)[P(\overline{A})P(\overline{D}) + P(A)P(D)] \\ + P(n+1,t)P(\overline{A})P(D) + P(n-1,t)P(A)P(\overline{D})$$

The first term on the right of this equation describes two ways for n to remain the same as time increases from t to $t + \Delta t$: either no arrival and no departures occurred, or exactly one arrival and exactly one departure occurred. The second term describes $n + 1$ changing to n by no arrivals and exactly one departure. The third term describes $n - 1$ changing to n by exactly one arrival and no departures. No other possibilities are allowed to happen as $\Delta t \to 0$ using our model (which is based on the assumption of independent increments). If (5.36) and (5.37) are substituted into the expression for $P(n,t+\Delta t)$ given above, we find

$$P(n,t+\Delta t) = P(n,t) - (\lambda + \lambda_S)\Delta t P(n,t) + 2\lambda\lambda_S(\Delta t)^2 P(n,t)$$
$$+ \lambda_S\Delta t P(n+1,t) - \lambda\lambda_S(\Delta t)^2 P(n+1,t)$$
$$+ \lambda\Delta t P(n-1,t) - \lambda\lambda_S(\Delta t)^2 P(n-1,t)$$

If we now assume that the derivative of $P(n,t)$ exists, and we use

$$\lim_{\Delta t \to 0} \frac{P(n,t+\Delta t) - P(n,t)}{\Delta t}$$

we will find

$$\frac{dP(n,t)}{dt} = -(\lambda + \lambda_S)P(n,t) + \lambda_S P(n+1,t) + \lambda P(n-1,t)$$

If the queue has a steady-state condition, it will occur when the derivative above is zero:

$$(\lambda + \lambda_S)P(n,t) = \lambda_S P(n+1,t) + \lambda P(n-1,t) \tag{5.38}$$

When $n = 0$, (5.38) reduces to

$$\lambda P(0,t) = \lambda_S P(1,t) \tag{5.39}$$

We introduce the ratio ρ

$$\rho = \frac{\lambda}{\lambda_S} \tag{5.40}$$

which must be less than one if the queuing system is to be stable. Then, when $n = 0$, we have from (5.39),

$$P(1,t) = \rho P(0,t)$$

When $n = 1$, (5.38) becomes

$$(\lambda + \lambda_S)P(1,t) = \lambda_S P(2,t) + \lambda P(0,t)$$

Combining this with $P(1,t)$, we have

$$(1 + \rho)\rho P(0,t) = P(2,t) + \rho P(0,t)$$

which simplifies to

$$P(2,t) = \rho^2 P(0,t)$$

It follows recursively that

$$P(n,t) = \rho^n P(0,t) \tag{5.41}$$

Since the queuing system can theoretically be in any state $n = 0$, 1,

2, . . . (that is, there can be any non-negative number of customers in the queuing system), we must require that

$$\sum_{n=0}^{\infty} P(n,t) = 1 \qquad (5.42)$$

We can use this with the results of Exercise 28 at the end of this chapter to show that

$$P(0,t) = 1 - \rho \qquad (5.43)$$

$$E[N] = \frac{\rho}{1 - \rho} \qquad (5.44)$$

$$\text{Var}[N] = \frac{\rho}{(1 - \rho)^2} \qquad (5.45)$$

where $P(0,t)$ is the probability of the server not being used. Therefore, from (5.43), ρ is the complementary probability:

$$\rho = 1 - P(0,t) \qquad (5.46)$$

That is, ρ is the probability of the server being busy; hence, ρ is called the **utilization** of the single server system. Note that as $\lambda_s \to \lambda$, then $\rho \to 1$, and both the average number of customers in the queuing system and its variance become unbounded.

Example 5.12   An M/M/1 queuing system has a utilization of $\rho = 0.6$; this means that the server is idle 40% of the time. The average number of customers in the queuing system is, from (5.44),

$$E[N] = \frac{\rho}{1 - \rho} = 1.50$$

The standard deviation for this value is, from (5.45),

$$\sqrt{\text{Var}[N]} = \frac{\sqrt{\rho}}{1 - \rho} = 1.94$$

Realizations of the M/M/1 queuing system with $\rho = 0.6$ should be expected to fluctuate markedly about the mean of 1.50 because of the large standard deviation. A similar behavior occurs with other values of the utilizaton.

◆ ◆ ◆ ◆ ◆

We can use Little's formula (5.35) with (5.44) to write

$$E[N] = \frac{\rho}{1 - \rho} = \lambda E[T] \qquad (5.47)$$

Thus, the average time a customer spends in the queuing system is

$$E[T] = \frac{\rho/\lambda}{1-\rho} = \frac{1/\lambda_S}{1-\rho} \tag{5.48}$$

The average time a customer spends with the server is $1/\lambda_S$. Therefore, the average time spent waiting in the queue, before being served, is

$$
\begin{aligned}
E[W] &= E[T] - \left(\frac{1}{\lambda_S}\right) \\
&= \frac{1/\lambda_S}{1-\rho} - \left(\frac{1}{\lambda_S}\right) \\
&= \frac{\rho}{1-\rho}\left(\frac{1}{\lambda_S}\right)
\end{aligned}
\tag{5.49}
$$

Similarly, with the average number of customers in a queue,

$$
\begin{aligned}
E[n_Q] &= E[N] - \rho \\
&= \frac{\rho}{1-\rho} - \rho \\
&= \frac{\rho^2}{1-\rho}
\end{aligned}
\tag{5.50}
$$

Example 5.13   An M/M/1 queuing system has a utilization of $\rho = 0.6$. The server serves one customer on the average each 45 seconds. This means that

$$\lambda_S = \frac{1}{45} \; (\mathrm{s}^{-1})$$

Using (5.49), customers should expect to spend the following time in the queue before being served:

$$E[W] = \frac{45\rho}{1-\rho} = 1.13 \; (\mathrm{min})$$

At any given time, the expected number of customers in the queue waiting to be served is, using (5.50),

$$E[n_Q] = \frac{\rho^2}{1-\rho} = 0.90$$

◆ ◆ ◆ ◆ ◆

Section 5.6   THE PROPORTION RANDOM VARIABLE

◆ ◆ ◆ ◆ ◆

The **proportion** random variable P is a variation on the binomial random variable. If the binomial random variable Y, in (5.1), is divided by n,

$$P = \frac{Y}{n} \tag{5.51}$$

then, P is the proportion of the total number of outcomes A which are in n. In applications we tend to think of P as a continuous random variable, which is what happens if $n \to \infty$. Nevertheless, P is discrete, and we use (5.3) to find the mean and variance of the proportion random variable,

$$E[P] = \frac{1}{n} E[Y] = \frac{np}{n} = p \tag{5.52}$$

$$\text{Var}[P] = \frac{1}{n^2} \text{Var}[Y] = \frac{np(1-p)}{n^2} = \frac{p(1-p)}{n} \tag{5.53}$$

Now, consider some type of process that makes n independent trials of a Bernoulli experiment. In each trial we say that its outcome is either A or $\bar{A}$. The n independent Bernoulli trials, of course, constitute one binomial experiment. A specific example might be testing a batch of n VLSI chips. Testing each chip, we label it "good" or "bad." These make n independent Bernoulli experiments. However, testing the entire batch is a binomial experiment. Here, we say that $Y = k$ chips were "bad" in the batch of size n. The proportion random variable comes in when we divide k by n, and say that the proportion in the batch of those that are "bad" is k/n. Actually, in practice, as successive batches are tested, observations k/n of the proportion random variable vary from batch to batch. This occurs because the k are observations of the binomial random variable Y with parameters n and p. Note that we are using p as a probability of failure.

Example 5.14   An integrated circuit processing facility makes an application-specific integrated circuit (ASIC) in batches of size $n = 30$. Previous experiments have estimated the binomial parameter p to be 0.047. Data for 50 successive batches of 30 ASICs per batch are listed in Table 5.4. We want to monitor these data to see if p (which is interpreted here as the probability of a single ASIC being defective) changes markedly from its estimated value of 0.047. We do this by plotting sample values of p for each batch and seeing if the result is consistent with the proportion random variable when $p = 0.047$. Using (5.52), the mean of P is

$$E[P] = 0.047$$

Table 5.4   Number of Defective Units Found in Each Batch of 30 ASICs

Batch	Defective	Batch	Defective
1	3	26	0
2	1	27	3
3	0	28	2
4	1	29	1
5	0	30	2
6	4	31	0
7	0	32	0
8	0	33	2
9	2	34	0
10	1	35	3
11	0	36	2
12	1	37	3
13	2	38	2
14	2	39	0
15	1	40	1
16	0	41	5
17	3	42	2
18	2	43	4
19	2	44	5
20	3	45	1
21	0	46	1
22	1	47	5
23	3	48	3
24	1	49	3
25	2	50	3

The standard deviation for P is, using (5.53),

$$\sqrt{\text{Var}[P]} = 0.039$$

We define **upper** and **lower control limits** (UCL, LCL) for the random variable P using plus or minus three standard deviations about the mean:

$$(\text{UCL, LCL}) = E[P] \pm 3\sqrt{\text{Var}[P]}$$
$$= 0.047 \pm 3(0.039)$$
$$= (0.16, -0.07)$$

A negative value for the lower control limit makes no sense in this application, so we choose

$$(\text{UCL, LCL}) = (0.16, 0)$$

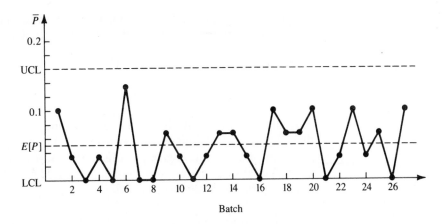

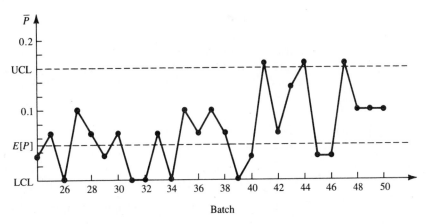

Figure 5.10   A plot of sample values of the parameter p using the data in Table 5.4. See Example 5.14 for a description of this plot.

These upper and lower control limits are plotted in Figure 5.10. Also shown in this figure are the data in Table 5.4; each datum is divided by $n = 30$ before it is plotted:

$$\bar{p} = \frac{k}{30}$$

Studying Figure 5.10, we see that the data are reasonably within their control limits until about batch 40. At that point, there is a marked shift upward in plotted values of $\bar{p}$. This indicates that something has caused the underlying value of p to increase from the assumed value of 0.047. We view this increase as a serious problem because, as we said, p is the probability that an individual ASIC is defective; any increase in p is a great concern.

Changes such as this are very difficult to find without plotting the data and observing trends relative to the control limits. The plot in Figure 5.10 is called a **p chart**.[4,5]

◆ ◆ ◆ ◆ ◆

In the example we just finished, the reader may have found it a little strange that a lower control limit of zero is used when it is clearly impossible for p to be less than zero. Attention given to this lower control limit may be justified by noting that if an excessive number of data should fall in the vicinity of the lower control limit, then either one of two situations has occurred:

1. The number of defects has been significantly reduced.

2. The testing process is not finding all the defects that are present.

Either situation calls for immediate attention. In the first case, the cause for the improvement should be discovered and incorporated into the process. In the second case, the testing process must be repaired.

Exercises

◆ ◆ ◆ ◆ ◆

1. The parameters for a binomial random variable X are $n = 5$ and $p = 0.61$.

   a. Find $P_5(k)$ for $k = 0$ through 5. Plot the pdf and the cdf for X.

   b. Find the probability that $X = 1$ occurs at least four times.

2. Appendix A shows an algorithm for simulating a binomial random variable (BINRNG) based on Eq. (5.1). Operate the algorithm $n = 1000$ times, and find a relative frequency estimate for the probability that $X = 1$ occurs at least four times. Compare this result with the theoretical value in Exercise 1.

3. For a particular solder connection, 1 out of 1000 is defective. A manufactured device contains 76 of these solder joints. If 25,000 of the devices are manufactured, how many of them do you expect to have at least one of these solder defects?

4. With a certain microchip, three good units are found out of evey ten produced.

   a. A microchip is selected at random and tested. If it is good, it is used. If it is not good, it is set aside for an analysis of its failure, and a second microchip is selected at random and tested. This process is continued for however long it takes to find one good microchip. Find n, the length of a sequence for which there is a probability of at least 90% of finding one good microchip.

b. Seven microchips are selected at random. What is the probability that at least one of the seven is good?

Note the difference between the selection processes in parts (a) and (b)?

5. A room contains 10 computer terminals, and each terminal has a network switch to connect it to one of three computers: L, M, or N. Data show that a user randomly selects the L computer with a probability of 33%. What is the minimum number of connections to the L computer that should be supplied to this room such that at least 90% of the time users can successfully be connected to it?

6. A certain rare event, such as an earthquake in a particular locale, is said to occur on the average of once every 50 years. What is the probability of the next earthquake in that locale occurring in the next 1 to 10 years?

7. Use equations (3.73), (4.43), and (5.1) to show that the characteristic function for the binomial random variable with parameters n and p is

$$\Phi_Y(j\omega) = (q + pe^{j\omega})^n$$

8. $Z = X + Y$ where X and Y are independent binomial random variables; X has the parameters n and p; and Y has the parameters m and p. Show that Z is also a binomial random variable and that its parameters are $n + m$ and p.

9. A box of one dozen light bulbs contains two defective bulbs. A sample without replacement of four bulbs is selected for testing. Calculate the probability that the sample contains zero, one, and two defective bulbs.

10. A box of one dozen light bulbs contains four defective bulbs. A sample without replacement of two bulbs is selected for testing. Calculate the probability that the sample contains zero, one, and two defective bulbs.

11. In a lot of $N = 50$ transformers, 2 are defective. If a sample of 5 transformers is selected without replacement, what is the probability that at least 1 of the defective transformers is found?

12. A random variable X is Poisson and is known to have a mean of 5.

a. Plot the pdf and cdf for X.

b. What is the probability that X is within one standard deviation of its mean?

13. Appendix A shows an algorithm for simulating a Poisson random variable (POIRNG). This algorithm is based on counting the number of exponential random numbers occurring in a fixed interval T. Operate the algorithm $n = 1000$ times with the parameter $b = 5$ (e.g., $A = 5$ and $T = 1$). Use a relative frequency technique to estimate the probability that X is within one standard deviation of its mean. Compare this estimated result with the theoretical result of Exercise 12.

14. A random variable X is known to be Poisson and to have a variance of 3.2. Find $P(X=3)$.

15. A random variable X has an average value of 1.20. What is the probability $P(X > 2)$?

16. Defects in the insulation of a cable occur randomly along its length such that there is, on the average, one defect per 1743 m. What length of cable would allow a 50% probability that there is at least one defect?

17. One defect within a microchip is reason enough to reject it, but a rejected microchip may have more than one defect. Assume that the number of defects possible within a microchip has no reasonable upper bound. A pilot production line manufactured a total of 10,812 microchips of which 3791 were free of all defects. The engineer who is designing the production line is interested in knowing if the defects are occurring at random. Tell the engineer how many chips with exactly 1, 2, 3, and 4 defects he or she should expect to find it the defects are occurring randomly.

18. An experimental production process for an integrated circuit will, on the average, produce 2000 defects for each 500 chips manufactured. What is the probability that a given chip will have the following:

    a. No more than two defects?

    b. At least two defects?

    c. How many defects per 500 chips exist if the probability of no defects on a chip is 80%?

19. A light bulb is advertised to have an average lifetime of 1000 h at its rated voltage. Assume that the light bulbs' lifetimes are exponentially distributed so that $\lambda = 1/1000$ h. In a special application, we keep extra light bulbs on hand so that as one burns out another immediately replaces it. How many light bulbs do we need so that over one year (8760 h) we have a 90% probability of keeping a light bulb lit continuously?

20. Y is an Erlang random variable with parameters $n = 10$ and $\lambda = 1$. Compare the area under $f_Y(y)$ between $\mu_Y \pm \sigma_Y$ with the corresponding area under a Gaussian pdf.

21. Use the Poisson approximation in this binomial problem: 5000 devices are manufactured; the probability of a device being defective is 0.0007. Find the probability that more than 3 of the 5000 devices are defective.

22. Use equation (3.73) to show that the characteristic function for the Poisson random variable X is

$$\Phi_X(j\omega) = \exp[b(e^{j\omega} - 1)]$$

23. $Z = X + Y$ where X and Y are independent Poisson random variables; X has the parameter b_X; and Y has the parameter b_Y. Show that Z is a Poisson random variable and that its parameter is $(b_X + b_Y)$.

24. A binomial random variable X has the parameters $n = 30$ and $p = 1/6$. Find the sum:

$$\sum_{k=3}^{7} P_{30}(k)$$

using continuity correction. Compare this result with the exact solution.

25. One thousand devices have been manufactured and are in service over the world. The probability a device will fail within a year is 30%. Assume the failures are independent. What is the probability that between 300 and 320 devices, inclusive, fail in a year?

26. Let $\lambda = 0.07$ be the average occurrence per interval in a Poisson problem. Let $T = 500$ be the number of intervals. Use continuity correction to find the probability

$$P\left(\frac{b}{2} < X \le b\right)$$

where $b = \lambda T$.

27. X is a Poisson random variable with parameter $b = 35$. Find $P(30 \le X \le 40)$.

28. If it is given that $P(n,t) = (1 - p)p^n$ where $0 < P < 1$, show that

a. $\displaystyle\sum_{n=0}^{\infty} P(n,t) = 1$

b. $\displaystyle E[N] = \sum_{n=0}^{\infty} nP(n,t) = \frac{p}{1 - p}$

c. $\displaystyle E[N^2] = \sum_{n=0}^{\infty} n^2 P(n,t) = \frac{p(1 + p)}{(1 - p)^2}$

d. $\displaystyle \text{Var}[N] = \frac{p}{(1 - p)^2}$

29. An efficient manager wants to hire only one server for a queue (M/M/1) and wants to have a utilization ratio of 0.8. If people appear at the input to the queue at the rate of ten per hour:

    a. What is the rate at which the server must process the customers?

    b. What is the average number of people waiting for the server in the queue?

    c. How long is it expected that people will have to wait in the queue before being served?

    d. On the average, how long does it take for a person to go through the entire system?

30. A large number of remote terminals are connected to one central computer that can process instructions at the rate of 12 MIPS (millions of instructions per second). It is estimated that the utilization ratio will be relatively small, say 0.35.

    a. How much time per instruction in the system should a user expect to wait?

    b. How many instructions are expected to be in the queue to the computer on the average?

    c. What do the answers of parts (a) and (b) become if the utilization ratio goes to 0.95?

31. A portion of a manufacturing process is measured, and is found to produce, on the average, 17 units every 3 min. If it takes 1 min and 23 s for an item to go through this process, what is the expected number of units within the process being worked on (by a server) or waiting to be worked on (in a queue)? (In manufacturing, **work in process** is called WIP.)

32. For the M/M/1 queue, derive a relation for the probability that a server has m or more customers in the queue.

33. Assume that each batch in Table 5.5 contains 15 VLSI chips.

    a. Make a plot of $\bar{p} = k/15$ for the 20 batches.

    b. Since there is a total of 31 defects listed in Table 5.5, estimate that

$$p = \frac{31}{(20)(15)} = 0.103$$

    Use this value of p to plot the UCL, and LCL, and $E[P]$ on the plot in part (a).

Table 5.5 Data Used in Exercise 5.33

Batch	Defects	Batch	Defects
1	0	11	3
2	1	12	1
3	2	13	4
4	1	14	2
5	2	15	0
6	2	16	1
7	1	17	4
8	1	18	2
9	1	19	0
10	2	20	1

34. This exercise uses only the first 20 batches in Table 5.4. Assume that each batch, 1 through 20, contains 25 ASICs.

a. Make a plot of $\bar{p} = k/25$ for the 20 batches.

b. Since there is a total of 28 defects listed in these 20 batches, estimate that

$$p = \frac{28}{(20)(25)} = 0.056$$

Use this value of p to plot the UCL, the LCL, and $E[P]$ on the plot in part (a).

References

◆   ◆   ◆   ◆   ◆

1. Larson, Harold J., and Bruno O. Shubert. *Probabilistic Models in Engineering Sciences, Volume I: Random Variables and Stochastic Processes.* New York: John Wiley and Sons, 1979.

2. Leon-Garcia, Alberto. *Probability and Random Processes for Electrical Engineering.* Reading, Mass.: Addison-Wesley Publishing Company, 1989.

3. Asmussen, Soren. *Applied Probability and Queues.* Chichester, UK: John Wiley and Sons, 1987.

4. Montgomery, Douglas C. *Introduction to Statistical Quality Control.* 2d ed. New York: John Wiley and Sons, 1985.

5. Grant, Eugene L., and Richard S. Leavenworth, *Statistical Quality Control.* 6th ed. New York: McGraw-Hill Book Company, 1988.

6 Statistical Inferences and Confidence

One never knows, do one?

Fats Waller

Introduction   In previous chapters, we introduced several probabilistic models of randomness; uniform, Gaussian, exponential, binomial, Poisson, and others. Typically, it is to our advantage to specify one of these models because then we know some generally useful features: a pdf, a cdf, a mean and a variance, and a characteristic function. In practice, however, we may not know a probabilistic model completely. For example, we might know that a random variable X in a reliability study is exponential:

$$f_X(x) = \lambda.e^{-\lambda x}u(x)$$

but not know the value of its parameter λ Likewise, we might know that a random variable Y in a measurement process is Gaussian, but not know the values of its mean μ_Y or its standard deviation σ_Y. Usually, in these practical instances, we use data to estimate a value of an unknown parameter.

   A function of several random variables, where the random variables represent sample data, is called a **statistic.** In this chapter we examine statistics obtained from some selected probability models. Then we show how sample data are used with a statistic to estimate a parameter used in a probability model.

Only part of statistics is devoted to finding formulas for estimating parameters. The other part addresses the quality of the estimate. Merely to estimate a parameter without a statement of its goodness is not generally helpful in engineering.

Let θ_0 denote some parameter in which we are interested (such as an exponential parameter λ); and let θ be an estimated value of θ_0 calculated using available data in some appropriate formula:

$$\theta = g(x_1, x_2, \ldots, x_n) \tag{6.1}$$

Here, the x_i, $i = 1, 2, \ldots, n$, are data, and the function of n variables $g(x_1, x_2, \ldots, x_n)$ is some specific formula we have selected. Examples of the formula are (1.1) and (1.4). If we replace the data x_i with the random variables X_i, the formula becomes a statistic, a function of n identically distributed random variables. The result of this is

$$\hat{\theta} = g(X_1, X_2, \ldots, X_n) \tag{6.2}$$

where $\hat{\theta}$ is a random variable called an **estimator.** We use three tests of goodness with this estimator.

1. The **bias** B of an estimator is the difference between the expected value of the estimator and the parameter of interest:

$$B = E[\hat{\theta}] - \theta_0 \tag{6.3}$$

   If the bias is zero, then the estimator is **unbiased.** Bias is a measure of the systematic error (see Chapter 1) of an estimator.

2. The **variance** of an estimator is

$$\text{Var}[\hat{\theta}] = E[(\hat{\theta} - E[\hat{\theta}])^2] \tag{6.4}$$

   Variance is a measure of the imprecision of an estimator.

3. It is possible that an estimator will have a small bias and a large variance. The reverse is also true such that we can choose an estimator that has a small variance and a large bias. To alleviate this difficulty, we combine bias and variance together in one statement called the **mean squared error** (MSE):

$$\text{MSE} = E[(\hat{\theta} - \theta_0)^2]$$

Introducing the mean of the estimator, we have

$$\text{MSE} = E[((\hat{\theta} - E[\hat{\theta}]) - (\theta_0 - E[\hat{\theta}]))^2]$$

Expanding the square leads to

$$\text{MSE} = E[(\hat{\theta} - E[\hat{\theta}])^2] - 2E[\hat{\theta} - E[\hat{\theta}]](\theta_0 - E[\hat{\theta}]) + (\theta_0 - E[\hat{\theta}])^2$$

The first term in this expansion is the variance (6.4). The second term vanishes as the expectation operator is applied to it. The third term is the square of the bias (6.3). Therefore,

$$\text{MSE} = \text{Var}[\hat{\theta}] + B^2 \tag{6.5}$$

The mean squared error is an inverse measure of the accuracy of an estimator. We say that an estimator is **consistent** if, as the number of data increases, both the variance and the bias go to zero. Then the MSE also goes to zero, and a consistent estimator is an accurate estimator.

Example 6.1   Suppose we used the random variable Y in (4.46) as an estimator of the mean for some random variable X. The random variables X_i are assumed to be IID. Then

$$\hat{\mu}_x = \frac{1}{n} \sum_{i=1}^{n} X_i$$

Using (4.47) and (6.3),

$$E[\hat{\mu}_x] = \mu_x$$

The estimator $\hat{\mu}_x$ is therefore unbiased. Using (4.47),

$$\text{Var}[\hat{\mu}_x] = \frac{\sigma_x^2}{n}$$

This variance vanishes as $n \to \infty$. Therefore, the estimator $\hat{\mu}_x$ is consistent — a "good" quality for an estimator to have.

◆ ◆ ◆ ◆ ◆

The criteria related to goodness used in (6.3) through (6.5) are very useful. However, as an example of another criterion of goodness, some statistics are insensitive to **outliers**. Outliers are data remarkably different from the typical grouping of sample data. An outlier often suggests a bad datum. Statistics insensitive to outliers are called **robust**.[1] The median is a robust statistic, as is illustrated in the next example.

If an odd number of data are arranged in ascending order, then the median is the center datum. If an even number of data are arranged in ascending order, the median is defined as the arithmetic average of the two center data.

Example 6.2   Suppose the distribution of measured currents in 39 examples of an integrated circuit is

> 10 samples have currents between 3 and 5 μA
> 20 samples have currents between 5 and 7 μA
> 8 samples have currents between 7 and 9 μA
> 1 sample has a current at 200 μA

The mean of the current using these sample data is

$$\frac{10(4\ \mu A) + 20(6\ \mu A) + 8(8\ \mu A) + 200\ \mu A}{39} = 10.9\ \mu A$$

But, if the intent of the sample mean is to present a representative value for the current, then the sample mean has not done its job. A better statistic is the median, which in this case is 6 μA. The median is robust because it is insensitive to the value of the 200 μA outlier; any value greater than the median has the same effect.

◆ ◆ ◆ ◆ ◆

Section 6.1   THE MAXIMUM LIKELIHOOD TECHNIQUE

◆ ◆ ◆ ◆ ◆

Defining a statistic can be straightforward, as with the estimate for the mean in Example 6.1, or it can be artful, motivated by practical exigencies, as with *Exploratory Data Analysis*.[1] Here, we present one method, called the **maximum likelihood** (ML) technique, which has been helpful in applications where the form of a pdf is known, but values of parameters in the pdf are not.

The pdf of a random variable X is $f(x, \theta_0)$; the unknown parameter is θ_0. The joint pdf for n independent observations of X is

$$f(x_1, x_2, \ldots, x_n, \theta_0) = f(x_1, \theta_0)f(x_2, \theta_0) \ldots f(x_n, \theta_0) \qquad \textbf{(6.6)}$$

The same unknown parameter appears in each marginal pdf. After substituting n specific data x_i, $i = 1, 2, \ldots, n$ into (6.6), we then vary the parameter θ_0 until the joint pdf (6.6) is a maximum. When this happens, the parameter is denoted by θ, and this value is used as an estimate of θ_0. What we are saying is that the data are observations—measurements—that have taken place. Since they have already occurred, we choose the parameter in the pdf so that the occurrence of these data is "most likely." The joint pdf (6.6) in the ML process is called a **likelihood function**[2,3] and is denoted by L:

$$L = \prod_{i=1}^{n} f(x_i, \theta) \qquad \textbf{(6.7)}$$

To maximize L, differentiate L with respect to θ, and set the result equal to zero. Then solve this equation for θ. In the ML technique, however, we do not maximize L directly; we maximize the natural logarithm of L. This does not change the maximizing process because

$$\frac{d}{d\theta}\ln L = \frac{1}{L}\cdot\frac{dL}{d\theta} = 0$$

An example illustrates this.

Example 6.3 The pdf for an exponential random variable used in a study of the reliability of integrated circuits is

$$f_X(x) = \lambda e^{-\lambda x}u(x)$$

Here, the parameter θ_0 is λ. We use $\bar{\lambda}$ as the estimated value of the unknown parameter λ. Using the exponential pdf, the likelihood function (6.7) is

$$L = \prod_{i=1}^{n}\bar{\lambda}\exp(-\bar{\lambda}x_i)$$

$$L = (\bar{\lambda})^n\exp\left(-\bar{\lambda}\sum_{i=1}^{n}x_i\right)$$

The natural logarithm of the likelihood function is

$$\ln L = n\ln\bar{\lambda} - \bar{\lambda}\sum_{i=1}^{n}x_i$$

Maximizing the log-likelihood function with respect to $\bar{\lambda}$ leads directly to

$$1/\bar{\lambda} = \frac{1}{n}\sum_{i=1}^{n}x_i$$

Note that $\bar{\lambda}$ is an estimated value obtained using the n data x_i. The estimator corresponding to (6.2) is

$$1/\hat{\lambda} = \frac{1}{n}\sum_{i=1}^{n}X_i$$

We recall that $1/\lambda$ is the mean of an exponential random variable. This, and the results in Example 6.1, show that the estimator

$$\hat{\mu}_X = 1/\hat{\lambda}$$

is consistent.

$\blacklozenge$ $\blacklozenge$ $\blacklozenge$ $\blacklozenge$ $\blacklozenge$

Section 6.2   ESTIMATION OF A MEAN

◆ ◆ ◆ ◆ ◆

An estimator for a mean, shown in Example 6.1, is

$$\hat{\mu}_X = \frac{1}{n} \sum_{i=1}^{n} X_i \tag{6.8}$$

where the X_i are IID. In that example, (4.47) was used to demonstrate that

$$E[\hat{\mu}_X] = \mu_X \tag{6.9}$$

$$\text{Var}[\hat{\mu}_X] = \frac{\sigma_X^2}{n} \tag{6.10}$$

The estimator (6.8) is therefore consistent. We can combine these expectations in (6.8) and introduce a new random variable Z as follows:

$$Z = \frac{\hat{\mu}_X - \mu_X}{\sigma_X/\sqrt{n}} \tag{6.11}$$

Z is normalized because its mean is zero and its variance is one. Also, because of the central limit theorem, we assume that n is large enough that, for all practical purposes, Z is Gaussian.

Figure 6.1 illustrates the pdf of the normalized Gaussian random variable. Centered about zero in this figure is an interval where $|z| < z_c$; z_c is a positive number we select. The probability of Z being in this interval is

$$P(-z_c < Z < z_c) = 1 - \alpha \tag{6.12}$$

Here, $(1 - \alpha)$ is a probability conventionally called a **confidence level**. We say we have a confidence level (a probability) of $(1 - \alpha)$ that the random variable Z is in the interval between $\pm z_c$.

Next, we use (6.11) to write (6.12) as

$$P\left(-z_c < \frac{\hat{\mu}_X - \mu_X}{\sigma_X/\sqrt{n}} < z_c\right) = 1 - \alpha$$

Rearranging,

$$P\left(-\frac{z_c\sigma_X}{\sqrt{n}} < \hat{\mu}_X - \mu_X < \frac{z_c\sigma_X}{\sqrt{n}}\right) = 1 - \alpha$$

$$P\left(\frac{z_c\sigma_X}{\sqrt{n}} > -\hat{\mu}_X + \mu_X > -\frac{z_c\sigma_X}{\sqrt{n}}\right) = 1 - \alpha$$

$$P\left(\hat{\mu}_X + \frac{z_c\sigma_X}{\sqrt{n}} > \mu_X > \hat{\mu}_X - \frac{z_c\sigma_X}{\sqrt{n}}\right) = 1 - \alpha \tag{6.13}$$

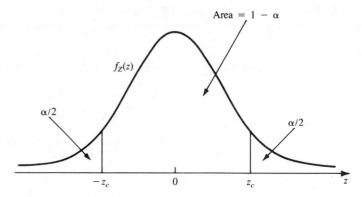

Figure 6.1   The pdf for a normalized Gaussian random variable. The area $1 - \alpha$ is the confidence level.

• •

This statement is general because it uses the random variable $\hat{\mu}_X$. However, this statement is also true for any particular observation of $\hat{\mu}_X$. The sample mean in (1.1) is such an observation:

$$\bar{x} = \frac{1}{n} \sum_{i=1}^{n} x_i$$

Therefore, we can replace $\hat{\mu}_X$ in (6.13) with $\bar{x}$, and write the expression for the **confidence interval** in terms of known data:

$$\mu_X = \bar{x} \pm \frac{z_c \sigma_X}{\sqrt{n}} \tag{6.14}$$

Here, z_c is selected with the confidence level is chosen; Table 6.1 lists some representative values of z_c versus $(1 - \alpha)$. In using (6.14), we also assume that we know the standard deviation σ_X. This is the weak link in our development thus far. Frequently, if the mean is not known neither is the standard deviation. In a subsequent section we will show how this difficulty is removed.

Example 6.4   The following data x_k (in ohms) were collected from 12 independent measurements of the input resistance of an antenna, which, by design, is supposed to have a value of 70 Ω.

69.71	71.56
77.31	73.33
69.05	66.98
68.66	71.72
72.84	70.77
75.32	71.36

Table 6.1   Confidence Levels
$(1-\alpha)$ as a Function of
the Parameter z_c for the
Normalized Gaussian
Random Variable.

z_c	$1-\alpha(\%)$
1.645	90.00
1.960	95.00
2.326	98.00
2.576	99.00
3.291	99.90
3.891	99.99

It is known that these data are samples of a random variable X which has a variance of 13. The mean of X is not known, so we calculate a sample mean using (1.1) with the result

$$\bar{x} = 71.55 \ \Omega$$

What are the confidence limits on this estimate of μ_X if we require a confidence level of 95%? From Table 6.1, if $(1-\alpha)$ is 95%, then $z_c = 1.960$. Using (6.14),

$$\mu_X = \bar{x} \pm \frac{z_c \sigma_X}{\sqrt{n}}$$

$$= 71.55 \pm \frac{1.960\sqrt{13}}{\sqrt{12}}$$

$$= 71.55 \pm 2.04 \ \Omega$$

Therefore, we have a confidence level (a probability) of 95% that the mean of X is in the interval

$$69.51 < \mu_X < 73.59 \ \Omega$$

♦ ♦ ♦ ♦ ♦

An estimated value, such as the sample mean $\bar{x}$, is called a **point estimate;** a confidence interval, such as the expression in (6.14), is called an **interval estimate.**

Section 6.3   ESTIMATION OF A VARIANCE

♦ ♦ ♦ ♦ ♦

The generality we were able to assume when we estimated a mean cannot be carried forward to the estimation of a variance. Formally, we must assume we are working with a Gaussian random variable, although the following results are useful with pdfs that are similar to a Gaussian pdf. In this section, we assume that the mean μ_X of a Gaussian random variable is known. In the next section, we show how a mean and a variance are both estimated from one set of data.

In seeking an estimator for a variance, we first apply the ML technique to see what guidance it gives us. For the Gaussian random variable, the likelihood function (6.7) is

$$L = \prod_{i=1}^{n} f(x_i, s_1)$$

The parameter θ_0 is σ_X and the estimated parameter θ in (6.1) is denoted as s_1. Substituting the Gaussian pdf into the likelihood function,

$$L = \prod_{i=1}^{n} \frac{1}{\sqrt{2\pi} s_1} \exp[-(x_i - \mu_X)^2 / 2s_1^2]$$

$$L = (2\pi)^{-n/2} s_1^{-n} \prod_{i=1}^{n} \exp[-(x_i - \mu_X)^2 / 2s_1^2]$$

$$L = (2\pi)^{-n/2} s_1^{-n} \exp\left[\frac{-1}{2s_1^2} \sum_{i=1}^{n} (x_i - \mu_X)^2 \right]$$

The natural logarithm of the likelihood function is

$$\ln L = -\frac{n}{2} \ln(2\pi) - n \ln s_1 - \frac{1}{2s_1^2} \sum_{i=1}^{n} (x_i - \mu_X)^2 \qquad (6.15)$$

Taking the derivative of (6.15) with respect to s_1 and setting the resulting equation equal to zero leads directly to

$$s_1^2 = \frac{1}{n} \sum_{i=1}^{n} (x_i - \mu_X)^2 \qquad (6.16)$$

where s_1 is the value of the standard deviation that maximizes the likelihood function for the sample data x_i. This suggests the following estimator for the variance when the mean μ_X is known:

$$S_1^2 = \frac{1}{n} \sum_{i=1}^{n} (X_i - \mu_X)^2 \qquad (6.17)$$

where S_1 is an estimator and corresponds to $\hat{\theta}$ in (6.2).

A new random variable V is introduced to bring out some properties of the estimator for the variance in (6.17):

$$V = n \frac{S_1^2}{\sigma_X^2} = \sum_{i=1}^{n} \left(\frac{X_i - \mu_X}{\sigma_X} \right)^2 \qquad (6.18)$$

If the X_i are independent Gaussian random variables, V is the sum of the square of n independent normalized Gaussian random variables Z:

$$V = \sum_{i=1}^{n} Z_i^2$$

According to Example 4.11, V is a chi-square random variable of order n. It is common practice in this instance to call n the number of **degrees of freedom**. (The number of degrees of freedom in a problem is a measure of the number of independent data used in a problem.) Using results presented in Example 4.11,

$$E[V] = n \quad \text{and} \quad \text{Var}[V] = 2n$$

Combining these with (6.18), we find that the estimator in (6.17) is unbiased:

$$E[S_1^2] = E\left[\frac{\sigma_X^2 V}{n}\right]$$

$$= \sigma_X^2 \frac{E[V]}{n}$$

$$= \sigma_X^2 \tag{6.19}$$

We also find the variance of the estimator in (6.17):

$$\text{Var}[S_1^2] = \text{Var}\left[\frac{\sigma_X^2 V}{n}\right]$$

$$= \sigma_X^4 \frac{\text{Var}[V]}{n^2}$$

$$= \frac{2\sigma_X^4}{n} \tag{6.20}$$

Since the estimator is unbiased, and its variance vanishes as $n \to \infty$, it follows that the estimator (6.17) is consistent.

A typical chi-square pdf is plotted in Figure 6.2. Even though this pdf is skewed to the right, we divide it into regions similar to the manner in which we divided the Gaussian pdf in Figure 6.1. Appendix E presents a table useful in finding the abscissa values of v_a and v_b in Figure 6.2. Then, using the center region of the pdf in Figure 6.2,

$$P(v_a < V < v_b) = 1 - \alpha$$

where, as before, $1 - \alpha$ is called a confidence level. Using (6.18), this relation is

$$P\left(v_a < \frac{nS_1^2}{\sigma_X^2} < v_b\right) = 1 - \alpha$$

Rearranging the inequalities leads to

$$P\left(\frac{nS_1^2}{v_b} < \sigma_X^2 < \frac{nS_1^2}{v_a}\right) = 1 - \alpha$$

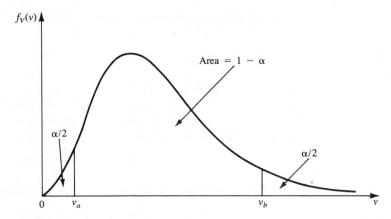

Figure 6.2   A typical chi-square pdf. The area $1 - \alpha$ is the confidence level. While the pdf is not symmetrical, we designate the areas on either side of the confidence level to be equal: $\alpha/2$.

• •

The relation is valid for the random variable S_1, and is therefore also valid for s_1, an observation of the random variable S_1:

$$P\left(\frac{ns_1^2}{v_b} < \sigma_X^2 < \frac{ns_1^2}{v_a}\right) = 1 - \alpha \qquad (6.21)$$

We use (6.21) to make an interval estimate of the variance of a Gaussian random variable when its mean is known. We illustrate with an example.

Example 6.5   Use the same data from an antenna's input resistance that are given in Example 6.4. Now, however, assume the mean is known: $\mu_X = 70\ \Omega$. The data, in ohms, are repeated:

69.71	71.56
77.31	73.33
69.05	66.98
68.66	71.72
72.84	70.77
75.32	71.36

Using these 12 data and (6.16), to estimate the variance, we find

$$s_1^2 = \frac{1}{12}\sum_{i=1}^{12}(x_i - 70)^2 = \frac{120.63}{12} = 10.05\ \Omega^2$$

The point estimate for the variance is therefore $10.05 \; \Omega^2$. A confidence level of, say, 95% is chosen. Then $\alpha/2 = 0.025$. Using Table E.1 for $n = 12$ degrees of freedom,

1. $P(V > v_b) = 0.025$, $v_b = 23.337$.
2. $P(V > v_a) = 1 - 0.025 = 0.975$, $v_a = 4.404$.

Then, using (6.21),

$$\frac{12(10.05)}{23.337} < \sigma_x^2 < \frac{12(10.05)}{4.404}$$

$$5.17 < \sigma_x^2 < 27.39 \; \Omega^2$$

We now have a confidence level of $(1 - \alpha) = 95\%$ that the unknown variance is within the interval from 5.17 to $27.39 \; \Omega^2$ (or that the standard deviation is between 2.27 and $5.23 \; \Omega$).

◆ ◆ ◆ ◆ ◆

Section 6.4   MORE ON ESTIMATORS

◆ ◆ ◆ ◆ ◆

We have introduced two estimators in this chapter: One is for the mean when the variance is known; the other is for the variance when the mean is known. In each case the estimator was used to obtain both point and interval estimates. Each interval estimate is associated with a confidence level.

Assume we have n independent data x_i that are Gaussian. We should, if it is at all possible, verify the Gaussian assumption by plotting the data on probability paper. Neither the mean nor the variance of the random variable is known. For ease of reference, we repeat the sample calculations for the mean (1.1) and the variance (1.4):

$$\bar{x} = \frac{1}{n} \sum_{i=1}^{n} x_i \tag{1.1}$$

$$s_x^2 = \frac{1}{n-1} \sum_{i=1}^{n} (x_i - \bar{x})^2 \tag{1.4}$$

The first thing we do, of course, is calculate values of $\bar{x}$ and s_x using the data x_i. Estimated values calculated this way suggest the following estimators:

$$\hat{\mu}_x = \frac{1}{n} \sum_{i=1}^{n} X_i \tag{6.22}$$

$$\hat{\sigma}_x^2 = \frac{1}{n-1} \sum_{i=1}^{n} (X_i - \hat{\mu}_x)^2 \tag{6.23}$$

The estimator for the mean (6.22) has already been examined in Example 6.1, and has been found to be consistent. The estimator for the variance (6.23), however, is new. It is not the same as (6.17). The new estimator (6.23) uses the random variable $\hat{\mu}_X$ instead of the parameter μ_X.

There is an important relation between the estimators of the mean and the variance in (6.22) and (6.23). We can see this by rearranging (6.22):

$$\sum_{i=1}^{n} X_i - n\hat{\mu}_X = 0$$

$$\sum_{i=1}^{n} (X_i - \hat{\mu}_X) = 0 \tag{6.24}$$

Similar to the results of the sample data in (1.3), only $(n-1)$ of the terms $(X_i - \hat{\mu}_X)$ in (6.24) are independent; the sum of any $(n-1)$ terms determines the one remaining.

We introduce a new random variable W using (6.23), similar to V in (6.18),

$$W = (n-1)\frac{\hat{\sigma}_X^2}{\sigma_X^2} = \sum_{i=1}^{n} \left(\frac{X_i - \hat{\mu}_X}{\sigma_X}\right)^2 \tag{6.25}$$

Because of (6.25), the random variable W is chi-square of order $(n-1)$. In other words, W is a chi-square random variable with $(n-1)$ degrees of freedom, as opposed to V, which has n degrees of freedom. This result can be established more carefully using methods from mathematical statistics.[4] It also follows, from results in Example 4.11, that

$$E[W] = (n-1) \quad \text{and} \quad \text{Var}[W] = 2(n-1)$$

Using these and (6.25), we find that the estimator for the variance in (6.23) is consistent:

$$E[\hat{\sigma}_X^2] = E\left[\frac{\sigma_X^2 W}{n-1}\right]$$

$$= \frac{\sigma_X^2}{n-1} E[W]$$

$$= \sigma_X^2 \tag{6.26}$$

$$\text{Var}[\hat{\sigma}_X^2] = \text{Var}\left[\frac{\sigma_X^2 W}{n-1}\right]$$

$$= \frac{\sigma_X^4}{(n-1)^2} \text{Var}[W]$$

$$= \frac{2\sigma_X^4}{n-1} \tag{6.27}$$

With reference to Figure 6.2 again, the confidence level is described by

$$P(v_a < W < v_b) = 1 - \alpha$$

Using (6.25), this is equivalent to

$$P\left[\frac{(n-1)\hat{\sigma}_X^2}{v_b} < \sigma_X^2 < \frac{(n-1)\hat{\sigma}_X^2}{v_a}\right] = 1 - \alpha$$

Since this is true for the random variable $\hat{\sigma}_X^2$, it is also true for s, one of its observations:

$$P\left[\frac{(n-1)s_X^2}{v_b} < \sigma_X^2 < \frac{(n-1)s_X^2}{v_a}\right] = 1 - \alpha \qquad \textbf{(6.28)}$$

This is the interval estimate for the variance when neither the mean nor the variance is known.

Example 6.6 The resistance data, in ohms, used in Examples 6.4 and 6.5 are

69.71	71.56
77.31	73.33
69.05	66.98
68.66	71.72
72.84	70.77
75.32	71.36

Using (1.1) and (1.4), the point estimates of the sample mean and sample variance are

$$\bar{x} = 71.55 \ \Omega \quad \text{and} \quad s_X^2 = 8.34 \ \Omega^2$$

Using (6.28) and Table E.1, we find for $(n-1) = 11$ degrees of freedom, and a confidence level of, say, 95%,

1. $P(W > v_b) = 0.025$, $v_b = 21.920$.

2. $P(W > v_a) = 1 - 0.025 = 0.975$, $v_a = 3.816$.

$$\frac{11(8.34)}{21.920} < \sigma_X^2 < \frac{11(8.34)}{3.816}$$

$$4.19 < \sigma_X^2 < 24.04 \ \Omega^2$$

We have a confidence level of 95% that the unknown variance is within the range from 4.19 to 24.04 Ω^2 (or that the standard deviation is between 2.05 and 4.90 Ω).

◆ ◆ ◆ ◆ ◆

Regarding a confidence level for the mean, previously we assumed we knew the value of the parameter σ_X, and, because of that, we could use (6.11) to introduce the normalized Gaussian random variable Z. Not knowing the value of σ_X, we replace it with the estimated standard deviation in (6.23). When we do that, we do not have the Gaussian random variable Z anymore, as the following development shows. We have to introduce a new random variable T:

$$T = \frac{\hat{\mu}_X - \mu_X}{\hat{\sigma}_X / \sqrt{n}} \tag{6.29}$$

Using (6.25), T becomes

$$T = (\hat{\mu}_X - \mu_X)\left(\frac{1}{\sigma_X \sqrt{\dfrac{W}{n-1}} \Big/ \sqrt{n}}\right)$$

$$T = \left(\frac{\hat{\mu}_X - \mu_X}{\sigma_X / \sqrt{n}}\right)\left(\frac{1}{\sqrt{\dfrac{W}{n-1}}}\right)$$

$$T = \frac{Z}{\sqrt{W/(n-1)}} \tag{6.30}$$

where the numerator Z is the normalized Gaussian random variable and W is a chi-square random variable of order $(n-1)$. Mathematical statistics shows that $\hat{\mu}_X$ and $\hat{\sigma}_X$ are independent.[2] This is a rather remarkable result because both estimators use the same random variables X_i. Its significance to us is that if $\hat{\mu}_X$ and $\hat{\sigma}_X$ are independent, then Z and W are also independent. Therefore, it follows that the random variable T is Student's t, which we studied in Example 4.16. A plot of a typical Student's t pdf is shown in Figure 6.3. This figure also illustrates the area of the confidence level $(1 - \alpha)$. Data relating Student's t pdf to confidence levels are tabulated in Appendix E.

From Figure 6.3 we see

$$P(-t_c < T < t_c) = 1 - \alpha$$

Using (6.29), this becomes

$$P\left(-t_c < \frac{\hat{\mu}_X - \mu_X}{\hat{\sigma}_X / \sqrt{n}} < t_c\right) = 1 - \alpha$$

This is equivalent to

$$\mu_X = \hat{\mu}_X \pm t_c \hat{\sigma}_X / \sqrt{n}$$

Since this is true for the random variables $\hat{\mu}_X$ and $\hat{\sigma}_X$, it is also true for their observations $\bar{x}$ and s_X:

$$\mu_X = \bar{x} \pm t_c s_X / \sqrt{n} \tag{6.31}$$

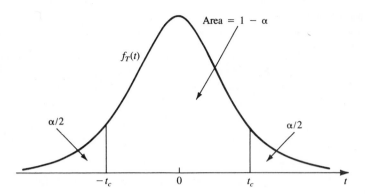

Figure 6.3   A typical Student's t pdf. The area $1 - \alpha$ is the confidence level.

◆ ◆

with a probability of $(1 - \alpha)$. Equation (6.31) is the interval estimate of the mean when we have to estimate both the mean and the variance.

Example 6.7   If we use the same 12 independent data used in Examples 6.4 through 6.6, we find

$$\bar{x} = 71.55 \ \Omega \quad \text{and} \quad s_X = \sqrt{8.34} = 2.89 \ \Omega$$

We want to calculate confidence limits for the mean using a confidence level of, say, $1 - \alpha = 0.95$. Refer to Table E.2, and find $t_c = 2.202$ when $\alpha/2 = 0.025$, and $n - 1 = 11$ degrees of freedom. Therefore, using (6.31),

$$\mu_X = \bar{x} \pm \frac{t_c s_x}{\sqrt{n}}$$

$$\mu_X = 71.55 \pm 2.202(2.89)/\sqrt{12}$$

$$\mu = 71.55 \pm 1.84 \ \Omega$$

with a confidence level of 95%.

◆ ◆ ◆ ◆ ◆

This chapter is a brief introduction to a selected portion of statistics. This selection was made because the confidence limits used with estimated parameters will certainly be encountered by engineers many times in their practice.

The reader is strongly encouraged to continue with a serious study of statistics, particularly as it relates to the design of experiments—a topic exceedingly important to practicing engineers, but beyond the scope of this book.

Exercises

❖   ❖   ❖   ❖   ❖

1. The sample covariance (1.13) suggests the following estimator for the covariance $Cov[XY]$ in (4.20):

$$\hat{Cov}[XY] = \frac{n \sum_{i=1}^{n} X_i Y_i - \sum_{i=1}^{n} X_i \sum_{j=1}^{n} Y_j}{n(n-1)}$$

Assuming independence between data when $i \neq j$, show that this estimator is unbiased.

2. **a.** Find the median of the data in Example 6.4. Compare the median with the mean of these data.

   b. Assume, because of some noise, that the value of 71.36 in Example 6.4 was actually recorded as 1071.36. Further, assume that the computer processing these data is incapable of recognizing that the value of 1071.36 is an outlier. Calculate the median and the mean of these data using the outlier in place of 71.36.

3. Given the following data:

986.0	1187.4
1076.5	1075.6
1050.6	911.3
1011.3	1147.8
1061.7	1038.0

   a. Find the median and the mean of the data.

   b. Assume that a flaw in an automatic recording system caused the value of 1050.6 to be recorded as zero, and that the computer processing these data is incapable of recognizing that this datum is an outlier. Calculate the median and the mean of these data using the outlier in place of 1050.6.

4. A small prosperous company pays the following salaries:

   20 clerks and assemblers at $13,000 each
     3 professional employees at $50,000 each
       1 owner at $500,000

   a. Find the median salary in the company.

b. Find the average salary in the company.

c. If the owner is to publish a "typical" salary for the company, which value should he or she use, the median or the mean?

5. Use the maximum likelihood technique to find an estimator for a^2, the parameter in the Rayleigh pdf in Example 3.4. What is the bias of the resulting estimator?

6. Define the likelihood function for the discrete binomial random variable as

$$L = \prod_{i=1}^{m} P_n(k_i)$$

where the outcomes of m independent binomial trials are the integers k_i.

a. Find a maximum likelihood estimator for the binomial parameter p.

b. Find the bias of the estimator obtained in part (a).

7. Ten independent observations of a time delay, in microseconds, are

56.3	52.9
51.4	55.6
50.5	55.7
53.0	55.6
50.8	55.8

It is known that the mean and the variance of the random variable Y (time) from which these observations were obtained are

$$\mu_Y = 53.75 \ \mu s \quad \text{and} \quad \sigma_Y^2 = 4.69 \ \mu s^2$$

a. Calculate the sample mean for the given data.

b. The mean calculated in part (a) is one observation of the estimator

$$\hat{Y} = \frac{1}{10} \sum_{i=1}^{10} Y_i$$

What are $E[\hat{Y}]$ and the standard deviation of $\hat{Y}$?

8. The following data were measured from 10 separate resistors, each of which is marked as 1000 Ω. The fabrication process for the resistors is known to have a standard deviation of $\sigma_X = 100 \ \Omega$.

986.0	1187.4
1076.5	1075.6
1050.6	911.3
1011.3	1147.8
1061.7	1038.0

a. Estimate the mean of these resistance values.

b. Find the confidence limits for the estimated mean when the confidence level is 95%.

c. Find the confidence limits for the estimated mean when the confidence level is 99.9%.

9. Thirty sample measurements are obtained from a random variable X, which has a standard deviation of $\sigma X = 120$; $\Sigma x_i = 30{,}016.07$.

a. Find the sample mean.

b. Find the confidence limits for a confidence level of 90%.

c. Find the confidence limits for a confidence level of 98%.

10. The dielectric strength of air is measured 20 times with an instrument that has a standard deviation of 300 V/mm in its readings. The data, when averaged, estimate the dielectric strength of air as 2.9 kV/mm. Find the interval estimate of the air's dielectric strength using a confidence level of 95%.

11. This computer experiment examines the mean (6.9) and the variance (6.10) of the estimator $\hat{\mu}_X$ in (6.8). To do this experiment, let a computer generate 120 observations of a Gaussian random variable X that has a mean of 100 and a variance of 10 (using GRNG in Appendix A for example). Separate these 120 independent observations into 12 groups of 10 each. For each group of ten, calculate

$$\bar{x} = \frac{1}{10} \sum_{i=1}^{10} x_i$$

so that you will have the 12 values $(\bar{x})_j$, $j = 1, 2, \ldots, 12$.

a. Calculate the mean and the standard deviation of the 12 values $(\bar{x})_j$.

b. Compare the values calculated in part (a) with the theoretical values of $E[\hat{\mu}_X]$ and $\sqrt{\mathrm{Var}[\hat{\mu}_X]}$ where

$$\hat{\mu}_X = \frac{1}{10} \sum_{i=1}^{10} X_i$$

12. A sample variance is $s_1^2 = 150.0$ for $n = 15$ degrees of freedom. Estimate the standard deviation σ_X using a confidence level of 90%.

13. A sample standard deviation $s_1 = 92$ for $n = 17$ degrees of freedom. Estimate the standard deviation σ_X with a confidence level of 99%.

14. In this computer experiment, we examine the estimator (6.17), its mean (6.19), and its variance (6.20). To do this experiment, let a computer generate 120 independent observations of a Gaussian random variable that has a mean of 100 and a variance of 10 (using GRNG in Appendix A for example). Separate these 120 observations into 12 groups of 10 each. For each group, calculate

$$s_1^2 = \frac{1}{10} \sum_{i=1}^{10} (x_i - 100)^2$$

so that you will have the 12 values $(s_1^2)_j$, $j = 1, 2, \ldots, 12$.

a. Calculate the mean and the standard deviation of the 12 values $(s_1^2)_j$.

b. Compare the values calculated in part (a) with the theoretical values of $E[S_1^2]$ and $\sqrt{\text{Var}[S_1^2]}$ where

$$S_1^2 = \frac{1}{10} \sum_{i=1}^{10} (X_i - 100)^2$$

15. An experiment is performed in which neither the mean nor the standard deviation is known.

a. Assume that 6 data are measured, and that $s_X^2 = 5.00$. Find an interval estimate of the variance with a confidence level of 95%.

b. Repeat part (a), but assume that $n = 20$ data are measured.

16. Suppose that $n = 10$ independent measurements of the random variable X are made. Using these measurements, we find

$$\sum_{i=1}^{n} x_i = 828.28 \quad \text{and} \quad \sum_{i=1}^{n} x_i^2 = 68{,}715.10$$

Further, suppose that X is a Gaussian random variable.

a. Find an interval estimate of the variance using a 90% confidence interval.

b. Find an interval estimate of the mean using a 90% confidence interval.

17. Given the following data obtained from independent measurements of a random variable X, find the sample mean and standard deviation, and

their confidence intervals, when a confidence level of 95% has been selected.

848.3	1044.9
1131.2	898.1
980.4	1056.6
949.1	923.7
990.3	1002.3

18. Given the following data obtained from independent measurements of a random variable X, find the sample mean and standard deviation, and their confidence intervals, when a confidence level of 90% has been selected.

986.0	1187.4
1076.5	1075.6
1050.6	911.3
1011.3	1147.8
1061.7	1038.0

References

♦   ♦   ♦   ♦   ♦

1. Tukey, J. W. *Exploratory Data Analysis.* Reading, Mass.: Addison-Wesley Publishing Company, 1977.

2. Mann, Nancy R., Ray E. Schafer, and Nozer D. Singpurwalla. *Methods for Statistical Analysis of Reliability and Life Data.* New York: John Wiley and Sons, 1974.

3. Nelson, Wayne. *Applied Life Data Analysis.* New York: John Wiley and Sons, 1982.

4. Hogg, R. V. and A. T. Craig. *Introduction to Mathematical Statistics.* 4th ed. New York: Macmillan Publishing Company, 1978.

7 Reliability

Expenses happen; revenues don't.

T. H. (Tommy) Thompson

Introduction   Reliability is a measure of how well an item works. Specifically:

> Reliability is the probability that an item will perform a required function under stated conditions for a stated period of time.[1]

Customers who use an item are the ones concerned about its reliability. The manufacturer has done what he believes to be his part: The item has been designed, fabricated, tested, distributed, and now a customer has it. Will the item work as intended? We hope so, but all too often it does not and the consequences of its malfunction can be severe: safety hazards, financial loss, and customer dissatisfaction and frustration. Therefore, in responsible engineering practice, reliability must be concurrent with manufacturability, testability, and function; it must never be introduced as an afterthought when everything else is done.

249

This chapter is a brief introduction to reliability, failure rates, and the reliability of a system of interconnected components. We conclude with examples of specific models (Weibull and lognormal), which are useful with practical data. This chapter is not all-inclusive; references 2 through 5 can assist you to further your skills in reliability theory and practice.

When an item fails, human nature makes us want to discard it or fix it immediately. The disciplined enginer will, on the contrary, want to study carefully each and every item that has failed before it is trashed or repaired. Through such study, the engineer can expand his or her knowledge, reliability can be improved, and fewer expenses and more revenues result.

Section 7.1   RELIABILITY

◆ ◆ ◆ ◆ ◆

In our theory of reliability, a device is put into service at time zero, and then we follow it until it fails. T is the random variable we use for the time of failure. The cumulative distribution function[a] is therefore the probability of a device failing between time zero and some non-negative time t:

$$F(t) = P(T \le t) = P(0 \le T \le t) \tag{7.1}$$

We stipulate that the independent parameter time t is non-negative, which will save us from repeatedly saying so in the remainder of this chapter.

Reliability $R(t)$ is defined as the probability that a device will fail *after* time t:

$$R(t) = P(T > t) \tag{7.2}$$

Therefore, using (7.1),

$$R(t) = 1 - F(t) \tag{7.3}$$

Then, with (3.5), reliability may also be written as

$$R(t) = 1 - \int_0^t f(\tau)d\tau \tag{7.4}$$

We can interpret reliability in two ways:

1. When we have one device and put it into service at time zero, we can say that the probability the device will last more than t units of time is $R(t)$. Or, the probability the device will fail before t is $1 - R(t)$.

---

[a] For convenience, we drop the subscript T on the cdf $F_T(t)$ and on the pdf $f_T(t)$.

2. When we have many of the same devices and put them all into service at time zero, we can say that a fraction $R(t)$ of them will continue to function after t units of time. Or, that a fraction $1 - R(t)$ of the devices will fail before time t.

The **mean time to failure** (MTTF) for the random variable T is (3.27):

$$\text{MTTF} = E[T] = \int_0^\infty tf(t)dt \tag{7.5}$$

Example 7.1   Commonly, but not universally, we find that the failure of electrical components is modeled by the exponential random variable. Specifically, for reliability studies, we write the exponential pdf and cdf as

$$f(t) = \lambda e^{-\lambda t} \quad \text{and} \quad F(t) = 1 - e^{-\lambda t}$$

where λ is called a **rate parameter** because it has the units of inverse time. Reliability for an exponential random variable is (7.3)

$$R(t) = e^{-\lambda t}$$

This reliability decreases exponentially toward zero as the time of service increases.

The mean time to failure (MTTF) of Eq. (7.5) for the exponential random variable is the exponential time constant:

$$\text{MTTF} = \int_0^\infty t\lambda e^{-\lambda t}dt = 1/\lambda$$

If, for example, a light bulb is rated with an average life of 1000 h, and if the time to failure for the light bulb is an exponential random variable, then the probability that the light bulb will provide at least 1000 h of use (before burning out) is

$$R(1/\lambda) = e^{-1} = 0.368$$

♦ ♦ ♦ ♦ ♦

Reliability is, in general, a strictly monotone decreasing function as shown in Figure 7.1. Therefore, the inverse of $y = R(t)$, which is $t = R^{-1}(y)$, is also a function. $R(t)$ is defined such that $0 \le t < \infty$ and $y = R(t)$ is defined such that $0 \le R \le 1$. Therefore, the area under the reliability plot may be described in two ways:

$$\int_0^\infty R(t)dt = \int_0^1 R^{-1}(y)dy$$

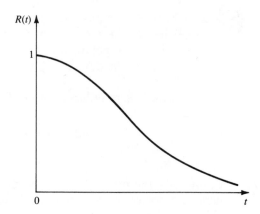

Figure 7.1   A plot of an arbitrary reliability showing that it decreases with increasing time.

From (7.4),

$$\frac{dR}{dt} = \frac{dy}{dt} = -f(t)$$

Using this as a change of variables in the second integral:

$$t = R^{-1}(y), \quad dy = -f(t)dt$$
$$y = 0 \Rightarrow t = \infty$$
$$y = 1 \Rightarrow t = 0$$

$$\int_0^1 R^{-1}(y)dy = -\int_\infty^0 tf(t)dt$$

Therefore, using (7.5),

$$\text{MTTF} = \int_0^\infty R(t)dt = \int_0^\infty tf(t)dt \qquad (7.6)$$

This result shows that the area under the reliability plot is the MTTF.

Example 7.2   If the time to failure T is an exponential random variable, then, using results from Example 7.1,

$$R(t) = e^{-\lambda t}$$

Substituting this into (7.6),

$$\text{MTTF} = \int_0^\infty R(t)dt = \int_0^\infty e^{-\lambda t}dt = 1/\lambda$$

Finding the MTTF using this approach is, of course, consistent with the more direct way (7.5) that was used in Example 7.1.

♦ ♦ ♦ ♦ ♦

Section 7.2   **FAILURE RATES**

♦ ♦ ♦ ♦ ♦

When dealing with the reliability of manufactured devices, we prefer to discuss a rate of failure rather than instances of failure. The failure rate conventionally used is also called a hazard rate or hazard function, and is related to the probability of a device failing within the interval $t < T < t + dt$ given that the *device is operating properly at time t.* This conditional probability may be expressed in two ways.

First, using the concept of relative frequency from Chapter 2,

$$P[(t < T \le t+dt)|(T > t)] = \frac{dn}{n(t)} \tag{7.7}$$

where $n(t)$ is the number of devices that are operating properly at time t and where dn is the number that fail in the interval between t and $t+dt$.

A second description uses the definition (2.22) of the conditional probability:

$$P[(t < T \le t+dt)|(T > t)] = \frac{P[(t < T \le t+dt) \cap (T > t)]}{P(T > t)}$$

The joint probability in this relation is evaluated by noting that the event $(t < T \le t+dt)$ is contained within $(T > t)$, so that the intersection of the two events is $(t < T \le t+dt)$. Then, using (3.16) and (7.2),

$$P[(t < T \le t+dt)|(T > t)] = \frac{f(t)dt}{R(t)} \tag{7.8}$$

Combining (7.7) and (7.8), we have

$$\frac{dn}{n(t)} = \frac{f(t)dt}{R(t)}$$

This relation is then rearranged, and the **failure rate** $h(t)$ is defined as

$$h(t) = \frac{1}{n(t)} \frac{dn}{dt} = \frac{f(t)}{R(t)} \tag{7.9}$$

Some general features of failure rates are illustrated in Figure 7.2. The plot in this figure is idealized, and is picturesquely called the **bathtub curve.** Initially, a

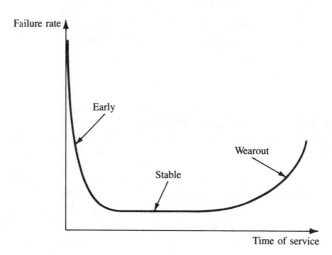

Figure 7.2   An idealized plot of the failure rates of a manufactured device.

• •

failure rate tends to be high because of manufacturing flaws (such as loose screws, cold solder joints, etc.) that escaped inspection. These flaws often reveal themselves early in the life of a device — in the period of **early failures.**[b]

When the flaws of the early failure period no longer appear, a device goes into its **stable,** or **steady-state,** period. During this period, a failure rate becomes as low as it is going to get for a given design, manufacturing process, and testing protocol. It is a period when the failure rate becomes a constant, or nearly so. Ultimately, the cumulative effects of wear appear, and the failure rate begins to increase. This process is referred to as **wearout.**

Example 7.3   Assume that failures of a relay are described by an exponential pdf with a parameter $\lambda = 0.002$ per year:

$$f(t) = \lambda e^{-\lambda t}$$

The reliability (7.4) is

$$R(t) = e^{-\lambda t}$$

Therefore, according to (7.9), the failure rate is

$$h(t) = \frac{f(t)}{R(t)} = \lambda = 0.002 \text{ failures/yr}$$

_____

[b] Reflecting the interest of actuaries, engineers sometimes refer to the early failure period as **infant mortality.**

Note that the failure rate associated with an exponential random variable is the constant λ. Therefore, when a device has times-to-failure that have an exponential pdf, it has a stable, or steady-state, failure rate (see Figure 7.2).

◆ ◆ ◆ ◆ ◆

Example 7.4   Early work with failure rates was done by actuaries. Of course, they dealt with people instead of devices, but the same principles apply.

Actuarial data for $n_0 = 100,000$ people living at age 10, for ages 30 to 34, are given in Table 7.1. Using (7.9) (with $dt = 1$ year), sample values of the human failure rate are calculated, as listed in the fourth column of Table 7.1. Note that these data indicate that the human failure rate increases with age between ages 30 to 34. This suggests the "wearout" failure period. The data in Table 7.1 are typical. To be more realistic, these data should account for the difference between males and females, and the differences among the various social structures found in the world, as shown in Table 7.5 in the exercises at the end of this chapter.[6]

◆ ◆ ◆ ◆ ◆

The derivative of the reliability function (7.4) is

$$\frac{d}{dt}R(t) = -f(t)$$

Substituting this into (7.9) leads to

$$h(t) = -\frac{\dfrac{d}{dt}R(t)}{R(t)}$$

$$h(t) = -\frac{d}{dt}\ln R(t) \tag{7.10}$$

Table 7.1   Actuarial Data for People Ages 30 to 34 Years as Discussed in Example 7.4

Year	Number Living at the Start of the Year	Number of Deaths in the Year	$\bar{h}(t)$ per Year
30	62,029	611	0.0099
31	61,418	646	0.0105
32	60,772	681	0.0112
33	60,091	717	0.0119
34	59,374	754	0.0127

The **cumulative failure rate** $H(t)$ is obtained by integrating $h(t)$ from time zero to t:

$$H(t) = \int_0^t h(\tau)d\tau = -\ln R(t) \tag{7.11}$$

The cumulative failure rate is useful for calculating the expected number of failures in an interval of time. An average failure rate (AFR, see Ref. 3) for some interval of time, say time zero to t_1 is

$$\text{AFR} = \frac{1}{t_1} \int_0^{t_1} h(t)dt$$

Using (7.11), the average failure rate is

$$\text{AFR} = \frac{H(t_1)}{t_1} = \frac{-\ln R(t_1)}{t_1} \tag{7.12}$$

It then follows from (7.12) that the average, or expected, number of failures in the interval for time zero to t_1 is

$$(\text{AFR})t_1 = H(t_1) = -\ln R(t_1) \tag{7.13}$$

Example 7.5   The relay in Example 7.3 has the constant failure rate $\lambda = 0.002$ failures/yr. The manufacturer of the relay wants to estimate the number of relays that will fail in the first six months of use. Therefore, using (7.13) with the exponential random variable,

$$H(0.5 \text{ y}) = -\ln R(0.5)$$
$$= -\ln e^{-\lambda 0.5}$$
$$= 0.5\lambda = 0.001 \text{ failures}$$

The manufacturer should therefore expect that one out of each 1000 relays will fail in the first six months of use.

This result is fairly obvious because of the assumed constant failure rate, but the method used here will be helpful in more complicated examples in which the failure rate is not a constant.

◆ ◆ ◆ ◆ ◆

Taking the inverse of the logarithm in (7.11), we have a relation for the reliability in terms of the failure rate:

$$R(t) = \exp\left[-\int_0^t h(\tau)d\tau\right] \tag{7.14}$$

Example 7.6   Assume a constant failure rate C for a device. Then (7.14) gives the reliability as

$$R(t) = \exp\left[-C\int_0^t d\tau\right]$$
$$= e^{-Ct}$$

Using the results of Example 7.3, the constant C is, in fact, the parameter λ for the exponential random variable. This example points out that the constant failure rate of the stable failure period is a unique feature of the exponential random variable.

◆ ◆ ◆ ◆ ◆

Conventionally, the units for a failure rate are either $\%/K$ or PPM/K. A failure rate of $\%/K$ means 1 failure in 100 devices when they are operated for 1000 h. This is the same as multiplying 1 failure/h by 10^5. Similarly, PPM/K means one failure per one million devices operated for 1000 h. This is the same as multiplying 1 failure/h by 10^9. The failure rate called FIT **(failures in time)** is the same as PPM/K.

Example 7.7   The sample failure rate for a 30-year-old person in Table 7.1 is

$$\bar{h}(30 \text{ years}) = 0.0099 \text{ failures/yr}$$

In terms of failures per hour

$$\bar{h}(30 \text{ yr}) = \frac{0.0099}{(365)(24)} = 11.3 \times 10^{-7}$$

Or,

$$\bar{h}(30 \text{ yr}) = 1130 \text{ PPM}/K = 1130 \text{ FIT}.$$

◆ ◆ ◆ ◆ ◆

Section 7.3   RELIABILITY OF SYSTEMS

◆ ◆ ◆ ◆ ◆

When several components are connected to form a system, the reliability of the system depends on the functional relations among the components. As far as their tendency to fail is concerned, we assume that all components within a system are **independent**[c]; a more general treatment[7] is beyond the scope of this book. Three cases are considered: a series system, a parallel system, and a standby system.

A Series System

A **series system** has the characteristic that if any one of its component fails, then the entire system fails. This continues the idea expressed in (2.37) in which a series arrangement of switches is used. A series system does not require that all component physically be in series as shown in Figure 2.7. All that is required, as the definition says, is that the system will fail when the first component fails.

Let T_i, $i = 1, 2, \ldots, n$, be the random variable for failure times of the n components. Also, let T_S be the random variable for the series system time to failure. It then follows that if the system is operating properly at time t, then each component is also operating properly at time t. We can describe this situation, using probabilities, with

$$P(T_S > t) = P\{(T_1 > t) \cap (T_2 > t) \cap \cdots \cap (T_n > t)\} \qquad \textbf{(7.15)}$$

We read $(T > t)$ as the event when the time to failure is greater than time t. Because of the assumed independence of the components, we can use (2.36) to write (7.15) as

$$P(T_S > t) = \prod_{i=1}^{n} P(T_i > t)$$

Introducing reliability through (7.2),

$$R_S(t) = \prod_{i=1}^{n} R_i(t) \qquad \textbf{(7.16)}$$

If we take the natural logarithm of this, we find

$$\ln[R_S(t)] = \sum_{i=1}^{n} \ln[R_i(t)]$$

Differentiating both sides of this equation with respect to time, and using (7.10),

---

[c] Many times independence is assumed without determining whether there might not be some reason that could cause two or more subsystems to fail at the same time. If, for example, two subsystems share a common power supply and the power supply fails, both subsystems would fail. The reader must therefore recognize that the assumption of independence must never be a "casual" assumption; it must be justified by a careful study in each application.

we obtain

$$h_S(t) = \sum_{i=1}^{n} h_i(t) \qquad (7.17)$$

This rather remarkable result places no restriction on the components in a series system other than that they be independent.

If, as a special case, the n components have constant failure rates corresponding to exponential random variables, we then have

$$h_S(t) = \sum_{i=1}^{n} \lambda_i = \lambda_S \qquad (7.18)$$

And, the system reliability (7.16) becomes

$$R_S(t) = e^{-\lambda_S t} \qquad (7.19)$$

Using results for the exponential random variable contained in Example 7.1,

$$\text{MTTF} = \frac{1}{\lambda_S} \qquad (7.20)$$

If it happens that all of the components in a series system follow an exponential failure behavior, then each has a constant failure rate, and according to (7.18), the series system has a constant failure rate. If a component fails and is replaced by a similar good unit, then its failure rate is constant, and the series system's failure rate continues to be constant. It is in this case, when all the components have exponential failure rates, that a series system has **zero memory** with respect to past failures. If, however, the components in a series system have failure rates varying with time, then the phenomenon of zero memory with respect to past failures cannot be assumed.

Example 7.8   In an electrical power application, a distribution system consists of (1) a transmission line, (2) a step-down transformer, and (3) a disconnect relay. These three components form a series system because a failure of any one component causes the entire system to fail. Data for these components assumes exponential failure rates:

Transmission line: $\lambda_{\text{TL}} = 0.02$ failures/yr
Transformer: $\lambda_{\text{XR}} = 0.001$ failures/yr
Disconnect relay: $\lambda_{\text{DR}} = 0.007$ failures/yr

The failure rate for the distribution system (7.18) is

$$\lambda_S = 0.028 \text{ failures/yr}$$

The reliability of the distribution system (7.19) is

$$R_S(t) = e^{-0.028t}$$

From this we conclude that the probability of the distribution system performing one year without a failure is

$$R_S(1 \text{ yr}) = e^{-0.028} = 0.97$$

The distribution system's mean time to failure (7.20) is

$$\text{MTTF} = \frac{1}{\lambda_S} = 35.7 \text{ yr}$$

◆   ◆   ◆   ◆   ◆

A Parallel System

A **parallel system** is composed of redundant components and has the characteristic that the system will fail only if all the components fail. This contains the idea expressed in (2.38) in which a parallel arrangement of switches is used.

As before, we let T_i, $i = 1, 2, \ldots, n$, be the random variable for the failure times of the n components. We let T_P be the random variable for the parallel system's time to failure. It then follows that if the parallel system has failed at time t, then each component in the system has also failed by time t. Using probabilities, we write

$$P(T_P \le t) = P\{(T_1 \le t) \cap (T_2 \le t) \cap \cdots \cap (T_n \le t)\} \qquad (7.21)$$

We read $(T \le t)$ as the event a failure occurs on or before time t. The probability of the event $(T \le t)$ is recognized as the cdf of the random variable T. Therefore, using this, and using the assumption of independence, (7.21) becomes

$$F_P(t) = \prod_{i=1}^{n} F_i(t) \qquad (7.22)$$

Using (7.3), this is written as

$$R_P(t) = 1 - \prod_{i=1}^{n} [1 - R_i(t)] \qquad (7.23)$$

It will greatly simplify our discussion if it is restricted to the case where $n = 2$. Then, (7.23) becomes

$$R_P(t) = R_1(t) + R_2(t) - R_1(t)R_2(t) \qquad (7.24)$$

This, of course, is (2.20) rewritten for this application. Also, for the case when $n = 2$, (7.22) is

$$F_P(t) = F_1(t)F_2(t) \qquad (7.25)$$

The pdf for the random variable T_P is obtained by differentiating (7.25) with respect to time:

$$f_P(t) = f_1(t)F_2(t) + F_1(t)f_2(t) \tag{7.26}$$

The failure rate for the parallel system is generally most easily obtained directly from definition (7.9) using (7.24) and (7.26).

It is difficult to go beyond this point without making further assumptions. For example, suppose we assume that T_1 and T_2 are exponential random variable with parameters λ_1 and λ_2. Then (7.24) becomes

$$R_P(t) = e^{-\lambda_1 t} + e^{-\lambda_2 t} - e^{-(\lambda_1 + \lambda_2)t} \tag{7.27}$$

Using (7.6), we have the mean time to failure for the parallel system:

$$\text{MTTF} = \int_0^\infty R_P(t)dt$$

Substituting (7.27) into this,

$$\text{MTTF} = \int_0^\infty e^{-\lambda_1 t}dt + \int_0^\infty e^{-\lambda_2 t}dt - \int_0^\infty e^{-(\lambda_1+\lambda_2)t}dt$$

Integrating, we find that

$$\text{MTTF} = \frac{1}{\lambda_P} = \frac{1}{\lambda_1} + \frac{1}{\lambda_2} - \frac{1}{\lambda_1 + \lambda_2} \tag{7.28}$$

where λ_P is the failure rate for the parallel system.

Further, we use (7.26) to write

$$f_P(t) = \lambda_1 e^{-\lambda_1 t} + \lambda_2 e^{-\lambda_2 t} - (\lambda_1 + \lambda_2)e^{-(\lambda_1+\lambda_2)t}$$

and, with (7.27), we use (7.9) to obtain

$$h_P(t) = \frac{\lambda_1 e^{-\lambda_1 t} + \lambda_2 e^{-\lambda_2 t} - (\lambda_1 + \lambda_2)e^{-(\lambda_1+\lambda_2)t}}{e^{-\lambda_1 t} + e^{-\lambda_2 t} - e^{-(\lambda_1+\lambda_2)t}} \tag{7.29}$$

Example 7.9   Suppose the electrical power distribution to a city is obtained from two independent transmission lines. The lines are connected in parallel at the city so that if one line is interrupted the other will continue to supply the city with power. The failure (interruption) rates for the lines are assumed to be exponential:

Transmission line A: $\lambda_A = 0.02$ failures/yr
Transmission line B: $\lambda_B = 0.015$ failures/yr

The parallel system of transmission lines has the reliability (7.27):

$$R_P(t) = e^{-0.02t} + e^{-0.015t} - e^{-0.035t}$$

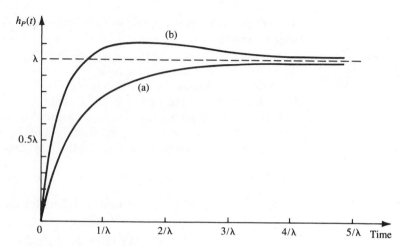

Figure 7.3   Plots of the failure rates for parallel systems. In (a) $\lambda_2 = \lambda_1 = \lambda$, and in (b) $\lambda_2 = 2\lambda_1 = 2\lambda$.

The cdf for this redundant system is $F_P(t) = 1 - R_P(t)$, therefore its pdf is

$$f_P(t) = 0.02e^{-0.02t} + 0.015e^{-0.015t} - 0.035e^{-0.035t}$$

Using these relations and (7.4), we can calculate that the reliability at one year is $R_P(1 \text{ year}) = 0.9997$. The pdf at one year is $f_P(1 \text{ year}) = 0.000584$. Therefore, using (7.29), the failure rate at one year is $h_P(1 \text{ year}) = 0.000585$ failures/year. We also use (7.28) to find the mean time to failure of the parallel system:

$$\text{MTTF} = \frac{1}{0.02} + \frac{1}{0.015} - \frac{1}{0.035} = 88.1 \text{ years}$$

The failure rate in (7.29) is plotted in Figure 7.3. Interestingly, we see in Figure 7.3 that in a parallel system, little is gained if the failure rates of the two components are significantly different. For example, if $\lambda_2 = 2\lambda_1$, then — except for a short time at the beginning of the system's operation — the failure rate is always better using only component 1.

A Standby System

A standby component differs from a parallel (redundant) component in that a parallel component is used in service while the standby component is held in reserve until it is needed. The random variable T_B for the time to failure for a **standby system** is therefore $T_B = T_1 + T_2$, where T_1 is the random variable for the time to failure for a primary component and T_2 is the random variable for the time to failure for the standby component. When the primary component fails, the standby component is pressed into service. Then, when the standby component fails, the system must fail (assuming that the primary component had not been repaired or replaced by then).

The mean time to failure will, in this case, always be the sum of the mean times to failure for the primary and the standby components:

$$\text{MTTF} = E[T_B] = E[T_1] + E[T_2] \tag{7.30}$$

Typically, a standby component is identical to its primary component. Assuming independence, the pdf for T_B is the result of the convolution in (4.33). Therefore,

$$f_B(t) = \int_0^t f(x)f(t-x)dx \tag{7.31}$$

Substituting an exponential pdf with parameter λ in (7.31) and integrating, we find

$$f_B(t) = \lambda^2 t e^{-\lambda t} \tag{7.32}$$

This is the same as (5.27), the pdf for an Erlang random variable when $k = 2$. Integration of (7.32) using (3.5) leads to the cdf,

$$F_B(t) = 1 - (1 + \lambda t)e^{-\lambda t} \tag{7.33}$$

From (7.3), we can write the reliability

$$R_B(t) = (1 + \lambda t)e^{-\lambda t} \tag{7.34}$$

Finally, using (7.9), we find the failure rate when there is one identical, exponential, and independent standby component:

$$h_B(t) = \frac{\lambda^2 t}{1 + \lambda t} \tag{7.35}$$

Example 7.10 A motor has an exponential failure rate of $\lambda = 2.3\%/K$. If a second motor is bought and used as a standby unit for the first, what mean time to failure is expected for the system? What is the reliability and the failure rate when $t = 1$ year? Independence is assumed.

$$\lambda = 2.3\%/K = 2.3 \times 10^{-5} \text{ failures/h} = 0.20 \text{ failures/yr}$$

From (7.30),

$$\text{MTTF} = \frac{2}{\lambda} = \frac{2}{0.2} = 10 \text{ yr}$$

From (7.34),

$$R_B(t) = (1 + 0.2t)e^{-0.2t}$$

and when $t = 1$ yr

$$R_B(1 \text{ yr}) = 0.98$$

From (7.35),

$$h_B(t) = \frac{(0.2)^2 t}{1 + 0.2t}$$

and when $t = 1$ yr

$$h_B(1 \text{ yr}) = 0.03 \text{ failures/yr}$$

◆   ◆   ◆   ◆   ◆

In Exercise 7.16 we ask the reader to show that if the primary and standby components have exponential failure rates of λ_1 and λ_2, respectively, where $\lambda_2 > \lambda_1$, then the standby system failure rate is

$$h_B(t) = \frac{\lambda_1 \lambda_2 (e^{-\lambda_1 t} - e^{-\lambda_2 t})}{\lambda_2 e^{-\lambda_1 t} - \lambda_1 e^{-\lambda_2 t}} \tag{7.36}$$

Figure 7.4 shows plots of (7.35) and (7.36) when $\lambda_2 = 2\lambda_1 = 2\lambda$. Similar to the parallel system, the standby system failure rate increases markedly when the reliability of the standby component is much poorer than the reliability of the primary component.

◆ ◆

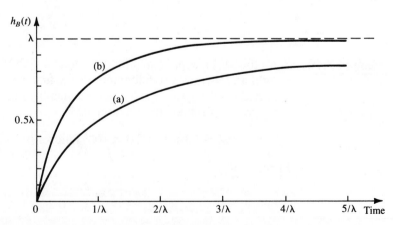

Figure 7.4   Plots of the failure rates for standby systems. In (a) $\lambda_2 = \lambda_1 = \lambda$, and in (b) $\lambda_2 = 2\lambda_1 = 2\lambda$.

Section 7.4   THE WEIBULL MODEL

◆ ◆ ◆ ◆ ◆

In 1951, the Swedish engineer Waloddi Weibull[8] introduced what he called "a statistical distribution function of wide applicability." He was right. The cdf he introduced is widely accepted[2-5,9,10] because of its versatility in modeling data obtained from random variables with unknown parameters.

To achieve this versatility, Weibull used a cdf that is an extension of the exponential cdf: Instead of a simple variable in the exponent, Weibull chose a polynomial term,

$$F(t) = 1 - \exp\left[-\left(\frac{t}{c}\right)^m\right], \quad t \geq 0 \tag{7.37}$$

The parameters m and c must be positive, but are otherwise arbitrary. Therefore, they may be chosen to best fit data.

If we differentiate the cdf in (7.37), we find its pdf to be

$$f(t) = \left(\frac{m}{c}\right)\left(\frac{t}{c}\right)^{m-1} \exp\left[-\left(\frac{t}{c}\right)^m\right] \tag{7.38}$$

The Weibull mean and variance are

$$E[T] = c\Gamma\left(1 + \frac{1}{m}\right) \tag{7.39}$$

$$\text{Var}[T] = c^2\left[\Gamma\left(1 + \frac{2}{m}\right) - \Gamma^2\left(1 + \frac{1}{m}\right)\right] \tag{7.40}$$

where $\Gamma(x)$ is the gamma function (see Exercise 12 in Chapter 3). Verification of (7.39) and (7.40) is left as an exercise. The reliability (7.3) of the Weibull random variable is

$$R(t) = \exp\left[-\left(\frac{t}{c}\right)^m\right] \tag{7.41}$$

Its failure rate is obtained by combining (7.9), (7.38), and (7.41):

$$h(t) = \left(\frac{m}{c}\right)\left(\frac{t}{c}\right)^{m-1} \tag{7.42}$$

and its cumulative failure rate (7.11) is

$$H(t) = \left(\frac{t}{c}\right)^m \tag{7.43}$$

Figure 7.5 shows the versatility possible with a failure rate using the Weibull random variable. When $m < 1$, the failure rate is decreasing, as it does in the

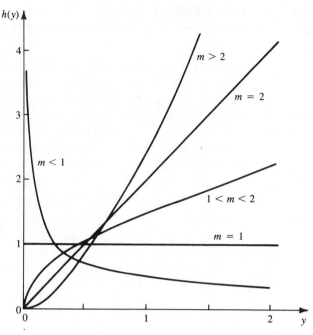

Figure 7.5   Behavior of the Weibull failure rate versus time as a function of the Weibull shape parameter m.

• •

early failure period. When $m = 1$, the Weibull pdf becomes an exponential pdf, and the failure rate is a constant, as we discussed in Examples 7.3 and 7.6. When $m > 1$, the failure rate increases, as in the wearout failure period. It is for these reasons that the Weibull parameter m is called the **shape parameter.**

Regardless of the value of m, when $t = c$, the cdf (7.37) is 0.632. This means, of course, if the random variable T represents times of failures, 63.2% of the failures occur before time $t = c$. Correspondingly, the reliability at time $t = c$ is 36.8%. For these reasons, the parameter c in the Weibull pdf is called the **time parameter,** or the **characteristic time.**

Example 7.11   The manufacturer of a sonar system used by fishermen wants to know how many sonar systems will, on the average, fail in their first 9000 h of normal use (9000 h is approximately 1 yr). Experience with the sonar system indicates that its failure rate can be modeled with a Weibull random variable having a shape parameter of $m = 0.3$ and a time parameter of $c = 90.5 \times 10^6$ h. Because $m < 1$, this model takes into account the early failure period following manufacture.

The cumulative failure rate for the Weibull model is given in (7.43). Using this, the number of failures in the first 9000 h is

$$H(9000 \text{ h}) = \left(\frac{9000}{90.5 \times 10^6} \right)^{0.3}$$
$$= 0.063$$

The manufacturer of the sonar system should expect that 6 out of each 100 units sold will, with normal use, fail in the first year.

◆ ◆ ◆ ◆ ◆

Estimation Using Regression

In this section, we use the Weibull pdf empirically[d]; we merely choose the parameters m and c to best fit some given data. A method of estimating the Weibull parameters uses the regression technique discussed in Chapter 1. To examine this, we begin with (7.37):

$$F(t) = 1 - \exp\left[-\left(\frac{t}{c} \right)^m \right]$$

Rearranging, and using the natural logarithm, we have

$$-\ln[1 - F(t)] = \left(\frac{t}{c} \right)^m$$

Then, using the natural logarithm again,

$$\ln\{-\ln[1 - F(t)]\} = m\ln(t) - m\ln(c) \tag{7.44}$$

This is identified as the linear relation

$$y = mx + b \tag{7.45a}$$

where

$$y = \ln\{-\ln[1 - F(t)]\} \tag{7.45b}$$
$$x = \ln(t) \tag{7.45c}$$
$$b = -m\ln(c) \tag{7.45d}$$

---

[d] The reader should note that Gumbel, in his classic study of the statistics of extreme values,[11] was able to derive the Weibull probability model.

To calculate values of y in (7.45b) we need an estimate for the cdf $F(t)$. Therefore, using the mean ranking technique (1.27),

$$F(t_k) \approx \overline{F}(t_k) = N_k/n = \frac{k}{n+1} \qquad (7.46)$$

With x,y data suggested by (7.45b) and (7.45c), the regression technique summarized in (1.14) will give the shape parameter m directly, and the characteristic time is obtained from (7.45d):

$$c = \exp\left(-\frac{b}{m}\right) \qquad (7.47)$$

Table 7.2 Times of Failures t_k (in hours) of 26 Items*

Rank k	t_k	x_k	y_k
1	7	1.9459	−4.3373
2	7	1.9459	−3.6375
3	24	3.1781	−3.2254
4	28	3.3322	−2.9310
5	38	3.6376	−2.7010
6	46	3.8286	−2.5118
7	66	4.1897	−2.3506
8	139	4.9345	−2.2100
9	159	5.0689	−2.0851
10	172	5.1475	−1.9725
11	231	5.4424	−1.8698
12	236	5.4638	−1.7754
13	247	5.5094	−1.6878
14	375	5.9269	−1.6061
15	391	5.9687	−1.5294
16	407	6.0088	−1.4570
17	480	6.1738	−1.3885
18	714	6.5709	−1.3233
19	859	6.7558	−1.2610
20	911	6.8145	−1.2015
21	940	6.8459	−1.1443
22	1034	6.9412	−1.0892
23	1324	7.1884	−1.0361
24	1388	7.2356	−0.9848
25	1439	7.2717	−0.9351
26	1444	7.2752	−0.8868

* Listed in rank order. Seventy-six items were tested. The remaining 50 items were removed from testing at 1460 h. Also tabulated are values for x_k and y_k used with the regression technique in Example 7.12.

Example 7.12   We use the regression technique with the data in Table 7.2. Because we are approximating the cdf using the mean ranking technique (7.46), and because $n = 76$, we have

$$F(t_k) \approx \frac{k}{n+1} = \frac{k}{77}$$

and, using (7.45b),

$$y_k = \ln\left[-\ln\left(1 - \frac{k}{77}\right)\right]$$

From (7.45c),

$$x_k = \ln(t_k)$$

Values of x_k and y_k are listed with k and t_k in Table 7.2. Applying the regression technique to the data in this table leads to $m = 0.5432$ and $b = -4.8277$. (Figure 7.6 shows a plot of the data y_k versus x_k from Table 7.2 together with the regression line $y = 0.5432x - 4.8277$.) Using (7.47), we find the characteristic time $c = 7240$ h. The value of $m < 1$ indicates an early failure process for the data in Table 7.2. (A plot of the estimated failure rate is shown subsequently in Figure 7.9.)

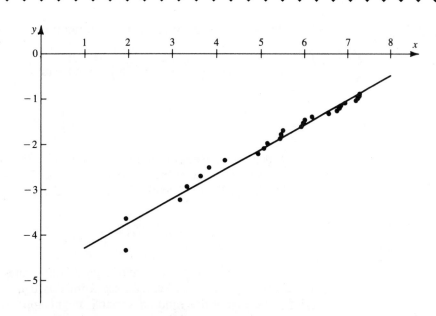

Figure 7.6   A plot of the data y_k versus x_k in Table 7.2 together with the regression line $y = 0.5432x - 4.8277$ calculated in Example 7.12.

The Weibull parameters calculated in this example are estimated values. Confidence limits for these estimations are available in more advanced texts.[9,10]

◆ ◆ ◆ ◆ ◆

Section 7.5   THE LOGNORMAL MODEL

◆ ◆ ◆ ◆ ◆

Various authors[2-4,7,8,9] introduce the **lognormal model** as a useful companion to the Weibull model for the analysis and prediction of failure rates. The lognormal random variable was introduced in Example 3.15. Adapting the notation used there: If X is a Gaussian random variable with mean μ_X and a standard deviation σ_X, then $T = e^X$ is a lognormal random variable for times to failure. While the mean and variance of the lognormal random variable are readily available (see Exercise 3.36), it is common practice to refer to the lognormal random variable in terms of μ_X and σ_X, the parameters of the underlying Gaussian random variable. Since μ_X is the **median** of the Gaussian random variable, it follows that the median of the lognormal random variable, denoted t_{50}, is

$$t_{50} = e^{\mu_X} \tag{7.48}$$

Using this, the pdf and cdf of a lognormal random variable are

$$f(t) = \left(\frac{t}{t_{50}} \sigma_X e^{\mu_X} \sqrt{2\pi} \right)^{-1} \exp\left[-\ln^2\left(\frac{t}{t_{50}} \right) \middle| \sigma_X^2 \right] \tag{7.49}$$

$$F(t) = \psi\left[\ln\left(\frac{t}{t_{50}} \right) \middle| \sigma_X \right] \tag{7.50}$$

These expressions are important for us because, first, the independent variable t is normalized: t/t_{50}. Secondly, it is necessary to use (7.49) and (7.50) directly in the defining relation (7.9) to obtain the lognormal failure rate:

$$h(t) = \frac{f(t)}{1 - F(t)} \tag{7.51}$$

Figure 7.7 illustrates the nature of typical failure rates modeled with a lognormal random variable. We can see from this figure that, within certain regions, the lognormal random variable might approximate the early, the stable, and the wearout failure rates as shown in Figure 7.2.

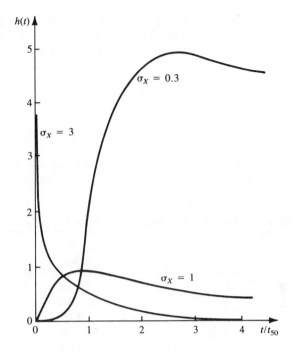

Figure 7.7   Plots of typical failure rates for the lognormal random variable. (In each plot, $\mu_X = 0$.)

Estimation Using Regression

A method of estimating the lognormal parameters σ_X and t_{50} uses the regression technique discussed in Chapter 1. To apply this technique, we begin with the cdf in (7.50). Since the cdf is strictly monotone, we can write the inverse relation for (7.50) as

$$\ln t = \sigma_X \psi^{-1}[F(t)] + \ln t_{50} \tag{7.52}$$

This is identified as the linear relation

$$y = mx + b \tag{7.53a}$$

where

$$y = \ln t \tag{7.53b}$$

$$x = \psi^{-1}[F(t)] \tag{7.53c}$$

$$m = \sigma_X \tag{7.53d}$$

$$b = \ln t_{50} = \mu_X \tag{7.53e}$$

We again use the mean ranking approximation (7.46) for the cdf. The inverse function in (7.53c) is evaluated using Table C.1 in Appendix C. For example, if $f(t) = 0.889$, then using Table C.1 we find that

$$\psi^{-1}[F(t)] = 1.22$$

Also, if $(F1t) = 0.111 = 1 - 0.889$, then

$$\psi^{-1}[F(t)] = -1.22$$

How the regression technique is aplied to (7.52) is illustrated in the next example.

Table 7.3   Times of Failures t_k (in hours) of 26 Items*

Rank k	t_k	y_k Int$_k$	$F_Y(t_k) = \dfrac{k}{77}$	x_k $\psi^{-1}[F_y(t_k)]$
1	7	1.946	0.013	-2.23
2	7	1.946	0.026	-1.94
3	24	3.178	0.039	-1.76
4	28	3.332	0.052	-1.626
5	38	3.638	0.065	-1.514
6	46	3.829	0.078	-1.42
7	66	4.190	0.091	-1.335
8	139	4.934	0.104	-1.26
9	159	5.069	0.117	-1.19
10	172	5.147	0.130	-1.126
11	231	5.442	0.143	-1.1067
12	236	5.464	0.156	-1.01
13	247	5.509	0.169	-0.96
14	375	5.927	0.182	-0.908
15	391	5.969	0.195	-0.86
16	407	6.009	0.208	-0.813
17	480	6.174	0.221	-0.77
18	714	6.571	0.234	-0.725
19	859	6.756	0.247	-0.683
20	911	6.815	0.260	-0.643
21	940	6.846	0.273	-0.603
22	1034	6.941	0.286	-0.565
23	1324	7.188	0.299	-0.527
24	1388	7.236	0.312	-0.49
25	1439	7.272	0.325	-0.454
26	1444	7.275	0.338	-0.418

* Listed in rank order. Seventy-six items were tested. The remaining 50 items were removed from testing at 1460 h. Also tabulated in columns 3 and 5 are data used in the regression technique in Example 7.13.

Example 7.13   Table 7.2 presents the times to failure in rank order for 26 items. These data are repeated in the first two columns of Table 7.3 for use in this example. The third column in Table 7.3 is calculated directly using (7.53b). The fourth column is the mean ranking estimate of the cdf calculated using (7.46). The fifth column is calculated by combining the fourth column with (7.53c), and using Table C.1 in Appendix C.

Next, we use the data in the third and fifth columns of Table 7.3 (which are y_k and x_k, respectively) in a regression technique discussed in Chapter 1. The results are

$$\sigma_X = 3.3 \quad \text{and} \quad \mu_X = \ln t_{50} = 8.83$$

(Figure 7.8 shows a plot of the data y_k versus x_k from Table 7.3 together with the regression line $y = 3.3x + 8.83$.)

Using (7.48), $t_{50} = 6800$ h. A plot of $h(t)$ when $\sigma_X = 3.3$ would not be too different from the plot of $h(t)$ when $\sigma_X = 3$ (shown in Figure 7.7). Therefore,

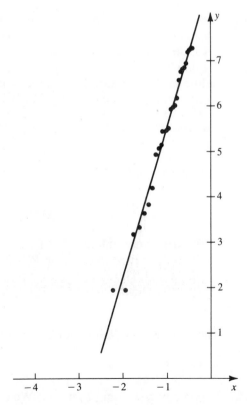

Figure 7.8   A plot of the data y_k versus x_k in Table 7.3 together with the regression line $y = 3.3x + 8.83$ calculated in Example 7.13.

the lognormal model of the data in Table 7.3 indicates an early failure period, just as the Weibull model did in Example 7.12. A plot of the estimated failure rate is shown in Figure 7.9. Confidence intervals for estimated values of the lognormal parameters are available.[9,10]

◆ ◆ ◆ ◆ ◆

Section 7.6   COMPARISONS OF THE WEIBULL AND LOGNORMAL MODELS

◆ ◆ ◆ ◆ ◆

It is open to discussion, with a given set of data, whether to use the Weibull or the lognormal model for estimating failure rates. Typically, if these two models are used to interpolate experimental data, there is little practical difference between the two. Most significantly, it is when we extrapolate experimental data that the greatest difference between the two models occurs. We illustrate this in the two examples that follow.

Example 7.14   Figure 7.9 shows a plot of the estimated failure rates for the Weibull model calculated in Example 7.12 and the lognormal model calculated in Example 7.13. Both models were, of course, calculated from the same data in Tables 7.2 and 7.3. Values from the models may be used to estimate an average failure rate at the start of a product's life, and they may be useful to estimate warranty and service costs. For the Weibull model, using (7.12) and (7.41),

$$\text{AFR} = \frac{1}{t_1}\left(\frac{t_1}{c}\right)^m$$

For the data in Example 7.12 ($m = 0.54$ and $c = 7240$ h), the average failure rate for the first 100 h is

$$\text{AFR}_W = 99.0\%/K$$

For the lognormal model in Example 7.13, ($\ln t_{50} = 8.83$, $\sigma_X = 3.3$), (7.3) and (7.50) are used to calculate $R(100 \text{ h}) = 0.8998$. Then, using (7.12),

$$\text{AFR}_L = \frac{-1}{t_1}\ln R(t_1) = 105.6\%/K$$

These two average failure rates are, in practical terms, not very different.

◆ ◆ ◆ ◆ ◆

Example 7.15   Suppose now we want to use the Weibull and lognormal models discussed in Example 7.14 to find the failure rate at 10,000 h. This time (very roughly 1 yr) is frequently used to estimate the failure rate in the stable failure pe-

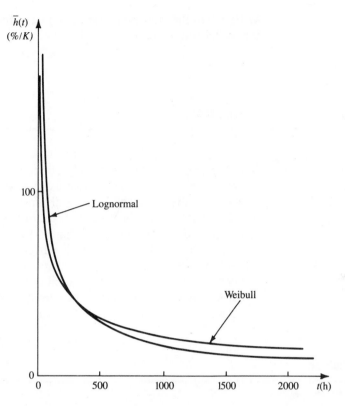

Figure 7.9 Plots of sample (estimated) failure rates for Weibull and lognormal models using the data in Tables 7.2 and 7.3.

◆ ◆

riod following the decline of the early failure period. Using data from Example 7.12, ($m = 0.54$, $c = 7240$ h) and (7.42), the Weibull model predicts

$$\bar{h}(10,000 \text{ h})_W = 6.43\%/K$$

To calculate a failure rate at 10,000 h for the lognormal random variable in Example 7.13 ($\ln t_{50} = 8.83$, $\sigma_X = 3.3$), we first substitute the given values in (7.49) and calculate

$$f(10,000 \text{ h}) = 1.193 \times 10^{-5}$$

Then, using the given values in (7.50), we find

$$F(10,000 \text{ h}) = 0.5459$$

When these are substituted in (7.51), the sample failure rate is found to be

$$\bar{h}(10,000 \text{ h})_L = 2.63\%/K$$

At 10,000 h, the failure rate estimated from the Weibull model is approximately 2.4 times greater than the value from the lognormal model.

◆ ◆ ◆ ◆ ◆

Section 7.7   CONCLUSION

◆ ◆ ◆ ◆ ◆

This chapter on reliability is merely a brief introduction to a large and growing discipline. Engineers of the future must give constant attention to product and service reliability as part of the general effort to improve quality for customers. A predicton is "that by the turn of the century microchips will have 100 million transistors and failure rates of less than 10 FIT." [12] Advances in complexity and reliability of this order of magnitude will continue to require new engineering design strategies. Certainly these strategies will argue for greater use of concurrent engineering, meaning that reliability is incorporated into the design process at the beginning along with function, manufacturability, testability, and serviceability.

Exercises

◆ ◆ ◆ ◆ ◆

1. A brand of light bulbs is advertised to have an average lifetime of 1000 h. Assume the light bulbs are in a stable failure period. What is the time at which the reliability is 50%?

2. A type of battery is assumed to have an exponential failure rate. What value should λ have if 90% of the batteries are to fail after their 36-month warranty period?

3. The pdf and cdf for the Erlang random variable are given in (5.27) and (5.28). Find the failure rate of the Erlang random variable when $k = 2$. What is the failure rate when $t = 1/\lambda$?

4. If times to failure of a power supply in an adverse environment are described by the Raleigh random variable, then the pdf is

$$f(t) = \frac{t}{a} e^{-t^2/2a}, \quad t \geq 0$$

   a. Find the falure rate.

   b. What is the value of the parameter a if the reliability of the power supply is 50% at 5000 h?

5. Show that the cumulative failure rate (7.11) for the exponential random variable is

$$H(t) = \lambda t$$

As the following exercise shows, this observation can be used to estimate λ from data.

6. The cumulative failure rate (7.11) is the integrated effect of the failure rate $h(t)$. Using (7.9), this may be approximated by adding the effects of $h(t)dt$:

$$H(t_k) \approx \sum_{j=1}^{k} h(t_j)dt = \sum_{j=1}^{k} \frac{dn}{n(t_j)}$$

If we run a life test on several devices, then each time a device fails $dn = 1$ and $n(t_k)$ is the number of devices operating properly at the instant before t_k. Therefore,

$$H(t_k) \approx \sum_{j=1}^{k} \frac{1}{n(t_k)}$$

Measured times to failure t_k for a certain device are listed in Table 7.4 (p. 278) in rank order. The number of devices working before each failure is the reverse of the rank order, and is listed in the third column. The fourth column is $1/n(t_k)$. The last column is the cumulative sum of the values in the fourth column, and is approximately $H(t_k)$ as shown above. Calculated values of the first two entries in the fourth and fifth columns are illustrated.

Complete columns four and five for ranks 3 through 17 in Table 7.4. Plot $H(t_k)$ versus t_k on linear graph paper. According to the previous exercise, this should be a straight line if the data are samples of an exponential random variable. Use regression to:

a. Fit a straight line to the data in the plot.

b. Estimate the parameter λ.

7. Use the actuarial data in Table 7.5 (p. 278) to estimate the failure rate for males ages 0 through 100. Plot the results on linear graph paper.

8. Use the actuarial data in Table 7.5 to estimate the human failure rate for females ages 0 through 100. Plot the results on linear graph paper.

9. The times to failure for a product in a stable failure period may be simulated using an exponential random number generator such as EXPRNG in Appendix A. For example, suppose a product, say a light bulb, is advertised to have a mean lifetime (MTTF) of 1000 h. Then, the exponential parameter is $\lambda = 1/1000$ ($\lambda = A$ in EXPRNG).

Table 7.4 Measured Times to Failure Listed in Rank Order and Used in Exercise 7.6

Rank k	t_k(h)	$n(t_k)$	$1/n(t_k)$	$H(t_k)$
1	60.2	17	0.059	0.059
2	84.3	16	0.063	0.121
3	95.5	15		
4	113.6	14		
5	139.4	13		
6	170.0	12		
7	208.3	11		
8	238.2	10		
9	585.6	9		
10	658.7	8		
11	755.7	7		
12	900.7	6		
13	1291.4	5		
14	1732.9	4		
15	1851.6	3		
16	2653.4	2		
17	2950.2	1		

Table 7.5 Life Tables Typical of U.S. Males and Females*

Age	Males	Females	Age	Males	Females
0	100000	100000			
1	81049	83807	45	49982	52906
2	76601	79276	50	45385	49249
3	74654	77246	55	39986	44787
4	73378	75933	60	33953	39519
5	72430	74940	65	26945	32774
10	70315	72654	70	19498	25138
15	68827	70924	75	12183	16752
20	66790	68678	80	5997	9030
25	63989	65932	85	2092	3503
30	61021	62965	90	415	794
35	57767	59759	95	35	77
40	54137	56389	100	1	2

* Shown at each age are the number alive out of an initial 100,000 males and females.

The data given here are reported in Ref. 6, page 12, to be "from the United States (1901–1958)." The data from ages 0 through 5 are "Model West, Level 10," page 37. The remaining data are "Model West, Level 10," page 46.

Use an exponential random number generator for $n = 12$ times, and print its output in the format #####.#. Use as a starting seed any number of four or more digits in length. The exponential random numbers you print simulate typical lifetimes, in hours, of a dozen light bulbs with MTTFs of 1000 h.

Find the median of your 12 data and comment on the variability you find in the data.

10. Suppose a system is composed of 15,000 components, each of which is in a stable failure period. The failure rate of each component is $\lambda = 10$ FITS. Suppose, further, that a failure of any one component causes the system to fail. What is the predicted number of system failures per month?

11. A circuit board consists of 250 medium-scale ICs (each $\lambda_{MSIC} = 10$ FITS), 12 linear ICs (each $\lambda_{LIC} = 35$ FITS), 125 silicon transistors (each $\lambda_T = 20$ FITs), 350 carbon resistors (each $\lambda_R = 1$ FIT), and 300 ceramic capacitors (each $\lambda_C = 1$ FIT). Each of these components must work for the circuit board to work properly. At some time t_0 the circuit board is known to be working. What is the probability it is working 10,000 h later? Assume independence.

12. A computer system for a manned space vehicle actually consists of three independent subsystems. The computer system works properly if any two of the subsystems work. If the failure rate for each subsystem is λ, what is the reliability for the computer system? What is the computer system's mean time to failure in terms of λ? Comment on the worth of this design compared to using only two independent subsystems.

13. A telephone system requires the availability of two trunk lines. A system is designed that has three independent trunk lines available and is considered to be working if any two of the trunk lines work. Assume that the failure rate for a trunk line is λ. What is the reliability of the system? What is the mean time to failure in terms of λ? Comment on the system's worth compared to having only two independent trunk lines.

14. A power supply is found to be too unreliable for its intended application; its failure rate is two per year. To improve the reliability of the system using the power supply, it is decided to put three of the power supplies in parallel on a bus along with relays that will disconnect a failed power supply from the bus. Assume that the disconnect relays are very much more reliable than the power supplies, and that the three power supplies are independent as far as their failures are concerned. What is the MTTF of the parallel system?

15. The mean time to failure of a certain high-intensity lamp is three months. Assuming independence, and an exponential failure rate, how

many of the bulbs should be kept in standby for us to be at least 90% sure that a high-intensity lamp will be kept on for a year?

16. Verify the derivation for (7.36), the failure rate for a standby system of two independent components with exponential parameters λ_1 and λ_2.

17. Verify the derivation for the mean $E[T]$ for the Weibull random variable in (7.39).

18. Verify the derivation for the variance $Var[T]$ for the Weibull random variable in (7.40). [You may use the mean of T as it is given in (7.39) without having to derive it in this exercise.]

19. Use the data in Exercise 6 to find a Weibull model (i.e., find m and c) using the regression technique. Find the failure rate when $t = 5000$ h. How many devices are expected to fail in the first 100 h of operation following manufacture?

20. Use the data in Exercise 6 to find the lognormal model (i.e., find t_{50} and σ_x) using the regression technique. Find the failure rate when $t = 5000$ h. How many devices are expected to fail in the first 100 h of operation following manufacture?

21. Seventy-six ($n = 76$) devices were put through a life test. At the end of 1460 h, 12 out of 76 devices had failed, and the life test was stopped (censored). The time to failure data are listed in Table 7.6. Find a Weibull model for these data (i.e., find m and c) using the regression

Table 7.6   Data for Use in Exercises 7.21 and 7.22

Rank k	Time to Failure (h)
1	3.3
2	7.1
3	8.0
4	50.8
5	92.4
6	331.1
7	464.9
8	592.7
9	784.0
10	929.1
11	1011.1
12	1451.6

technique. Find the failure rate at $t = 5000$ h. How many devices are expected to fail in the first 100 h of operation following manufacture?

22. Seventy-six ($n = 76$) devices were put through a life test. At the end of 1460 h, 12 out of 76 devices had failed, and the life test was stopped (censored). The time to failure data are listed in Table 7.6. Find a lognormal model for these data (i.e., find t_{50} and σ_X) using the regression technique. Find the failure rate at $t = 5000$ h. How many devices are expected to fail in the first 100 h of operation following manufacture?

References

◆ ◆ ◆ ◆ ◆

1. "IEEE Standard 100-1977." *IEEE Standard Dictionary of Electrical and Electronic Terms.* New York: The Institute of Electrical and Electronics Engineers Press, 1977.

2. O'Connor, Patrick D. T. *Practical Reliability Engineering.* 2d ed. Chichester: John Wiley and Sons, Ltd., 1985.

3. Tobias, Paul A. and David C. Trinidade. *Applied Reliability.* New York: Van Nostrand Reinhold Company, 1986.

4. Klinger, David J., Yoshinao Nakada, and Maria A. Menendez. *AT&T Reliability Manual.* New York: Van Nostrand Reinhold Company, 1990.

5. Musa, John D., Anthoney Iannino, and Kazuhira Okumoto. *Software Reliability Measurement, Prediction, and Application.* New York: McGraw-Hill Book Company, 1987.

6. Coale, Ansley J., Paul Demeny, with Barbara Vaughan. *Regional Model Life Tables and Stable Populations* 2d. ed. New York: Academic Press, 1983.

7. Klaassen, Hlaas B. and Jack C. L. van Peppen. *System Reliability, Concepts and Applications.* London: Edward Arnold, A Division of Hodder & Stoughton, 1989.

8. Weibull, Waloddi. "A Statistical Distribution Function of Wide Applicability." *J. Appl. Mech.,* 18, 293–297, September 1951.

9. Mann, Nancy R., Ray E. Schafer, and Nozer D. Singpurwallia. *Methods for Statistical Analysis of Reliability and Life Data.* New York: John Wiley and Sons, 1974.

10. Nelson, Wane. *Applied Life Data Analysis.* New York: John Wiley and Sons, 1982.

11. Gumbel, Emil J. *Statistics of Extremes.* New York: Columbia University Press, 1958.

12. Crook, D. L. "Evolution of VLSI Reliability Engineering." *Proceedings of the 28th Reliability Physics Symposium.* New York: Institute of Electrical and Electronics Engineers, pp. 2–11, 1990.

8 Random Processes: Correlation, Spectral Densities, and Systems

* *

Times go by turns, and chances change by course . . .

Robert Southwell 1561?–1595

Introduction   Linear and nonlinear systems, such as filters, modulators, and demodulators, are important to electrical engineers who process information and data. We assume that only time-invariant systems are used in these applications. When the input to a time-invariant system is random, its output will, in general, also be random. However, it is an impossible design task to study each one of the many random signals that might be used as an input to a system. Instead we decide on some average characteristics of an **ensemble** (a collection or grouping) of signals, and then design a time-invariant system for these average characteristics. We begin by defining a **random process (a stochastic process)**[1-7] as a random variable that is a function of time. This definition is an extension to the concept of a random variable described in the introduction to Chapter 3. We then illustrate random processes in a discussion using the three different ensembles of random signals shown in Figures 8.1, 8.2, and 8.3.

   Figure 8.1 shows an ensemble of Gaussian noise recordings. We assume that each **sample function** in this ensemble exists for all time. As shown in Figure 8.1,

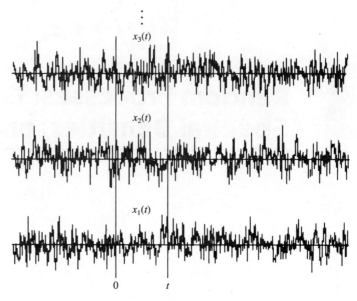

Figure 8.1 An ensemble of noise recordings. Each record extends (theoretically) for all time: from $-\infty$ to $+\infty$. The ensemble contains all possible zero-mean Gaussian noise recordings of the type being studied; this is suggested by the ellipses (. . .) at the top of the figure.

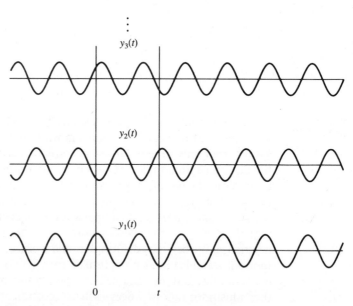

Figure 8.2 An ensemble consisting of sinusoids with random phase angles. Each record extends (theoretically) for all time: from $-\infty$ to $+\infty$. The ensemble contains sinusoids with all possible phase angles uniformly distributed between $\pm \pi$; this is suggested by the ellipses (. . .) at the top of the figure.

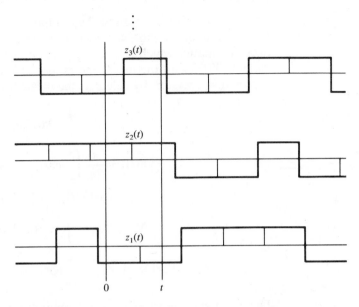

Figure 8.3   An ensemble of a random sequence of unsynchronized pulses. Each record extends (theoretically) for all time: from $-\infty$ to $+\infty$. The ensemble contains all possible pulse-sequence recordings of the type being studied; this is suggested by the ellipses (. . .) at the top of the figure.

the value of each Gaussian noise sample function at an arbitrary but fixed time t is $x_j(t), j = 1, 2, \ldots$. The random values $x_j(t)$ are, therefore, measurements of a time-varying random variable $X(t)$, and together, they form the sample space of $X(t)$.

In general, a random variable $X(t)$ has a probability density function $f_{X(t)}(x,t)$ which is a function of time as well as the measurements $x_j(t)$. We assume that the noise in Figure 8.1 is an example of a special case in which a random variable is time-varying, but its pdf measured across its ensemble at any fixed time t is independent of time:

$$f_{X(t)}(x,t) = \frac{1}{\sqrt{2\pi}\sigma_X} \exp(-x^2/2\sigma_X^2) \tag{8.1}$$

Any time could be selected in Figure 8.1, and the values measured from this ensemble will be Gaussian with a mean of zero and a constant variance:

$$E[X(t)] = 0 \quad \text{and} \quad \text{Var}[X(t)] = \sigma_X^2 \tag{8.2}$$

Another random process is shown in Figure 8.2 where the ensemble is

$$Y(t) = A\cos(\omega_0 t + \Phi) \tag{8.3}$$

Each sinusoid in this ensemble has a phase ϕ, which is an observation taken from the random variable Φ. Observations of Φ occur randomly between $\pm \pi$. It does not matter which specific time is chosen, (8.3) expresses the random variable $Y(t)$ as a function of the random variable Φ: $Y = g(\Phi)$. Using the expectation operator, we calculate the mean and the variance of $Y(t)$:

$$E[Y(t)] = \int_{-\infty}^{\infty} y(t,\phi) f_{\Phi}(\phi) d\phi$$

$$E[Y(t)] = \frac{A}{2\pi} \int_{-\pi}^{\pi} \cos(\omega_0 t + \phi) d\phi = 0 \tag{8.4}$$

$$\mathrm{Var}[Y(t)] = E[Y^2(t)]$$

$$\mathrm{Var}[Y(t)] = \int_{-\infty}^{\infty} y^2(t,\phi) f_{\Phi}(\phi) d\phi$$

$$\mathrm{Var}[Y(t)] = \frac{A^2}{2\pi} \int_{-\pi}^{\pi} \cos^2(\omega_0 t + \phi) d\phi = \frac{A^2}{2} \tag{8.5}$$

The mean and the variance of the random process $Y(t)$ are independent of time.[a]

A third example of a random process is shown in Figure 8.3. Each sample function of this ensemble is a sequence of equally likely positive and negative pulses. The duration of each pulse is T seconds. The times at which the pulses change are not synchronized among the members of the ensemble. Values from the random process at an arbitrary time t are equally likely to be $\pm V$. Therefore, the pdf is independent of time:

$$f_{Z(t)}(z,t) = 0.5 \, \delta(z + V) + 0.5 \, \delta(z - V) \tag{8.6}$$

Using (8.6), we find

$$E(Z(t)] = 0 \quad \text{and} \quad \mathrm{Var}[Z(t)] = V^2 \tag{8.7}$$

If, in general, a random process $X(t)$ is a random variable varying in time, its randomness needs to be described by more than a pdf. A pdf, by itself, can only be used to find the mean and the variance. These two expectations are not able to characterize the significant differences that occur among different random

---

[a] One could in fact show that, for any fixed time t, the random variable $Y(t)$ has the arcsine pdf

$$f_{Y(t)}(y) = \frac{1}{\pi\sqrt{A^2 - y^2}}$$

where $|y| \leq A$. The mean and variance of this pdf are the same as those shown in (8.4) and (8.5). The arcsine pdf is independent of time.

processes. For example, consider again the three random processes in Figures 8.1, 8.2, and 8.3. Each has a mean of zero and a constant variance, yet they are very different from each other. Sample functions of the Gaussian noise in Figure 8.1 are "extremely" random. Each sample function in Figure 8.2 is a sinusoid, and is determinate except for its phase. The sequence of pulses in Figure 8.3 is certainly not determinate because in any sample function the pulses occur in a sequence that is equally likely to be positive or negative. However, because any pulse is a constant over a finite interval of time T, this random process does not exhibit as much randomness as the noise in Figure 8.1. It is clear that the pdf for a single random variable is not adequate to describe data as complicated as a random process.

To describe a random process more completely, we introduce **joint** probability density functions. To illustrate, a second-order joint pdf is

$$f_{X(t)}[x(t_1),x(t_2)], \quad -\infty < t_1, t_2 < \infty \tag{8.8}$$

In this joint pdf, $X(t)$ denotes a random process; $x(t_1)$ and $x(t_2)$ are observations of a sample function contained in $X(t)$ at times t_1 and t_2. Another joint pdf is

$$f_{X(t)Y(t)}[x(t_1),y(t_2)], \quad -\infty < t_1, t_2 < \infty \tag{8.9}$$

Here, $X(t)$ and $Y(t)$ are different random processes. The $x(t_1)$ is an observation of a sample function contained in $X(t)$ at time t_1, and $y(t_2)$ is an observation of a sample function contained in $Y(t)$ at time t_2. With (8.8), we can use correlation (introduced in Chapter 4) to compare a signal with itself at two different times. With (8.9), we can use correlation to compare two different signals at two different times, a process that is developed in the next section.

Section 8.1   CORRELATION

◆ ◆ ◆ ◆ ◆

Correlation describes a random process in a way that is impossible for the mean and the variance to do. Both the mean and variance depend on a pdf, which includes time at only one instant. Correlation, on the other hand, is a bivariate parameter, and uses a bivariate pdf such as (8.8) or (8.9), which includes two different times: t_1 and t_2. We therefore define an **autocorrelation function:**

$$R_X(t_1,t_2) = E[X(t_1)X(t_2)] \tag{8.10}$$

In making this definition, we used (8.8) and (4.19). To illustrate how the autocorrelation function characterizes a random process, we return to the ensembles illustrated in Figures 8.1, 8.2, and 8.3.

Figure 8.1 illustrates an ensemble of noise. Sample functions in this ensemble fluctuate so rapidly and randomly that values at different times are uncorrelated. That is, the products

$$x_1(t_1)x_1(t_2)$$
$$x_2(t_1)x_2(t_2)$$
$$x_3(t_1)x_3(t_2)$$

.

.

.

when averaged over the ensemble, are zero. This happens because of (8.2), and because when $t_1 \neq t_2$, $X(t_1)$ is uncorrelated with $X(t_2)$:

$$\begin{aligned} R_X(t_1,t_2) &= E[X(t_1)X(t_2)] \\ &= E[X(t_1)]E[X(t_2)] \\ &= \mu_X^2 = 0 \end{aligned}$$

Of course, when $t_2 = t_1$, the autocorrelation function does not vanish:

$$\begin{aligned} R_X(t_1,t_1) &= E[X(t_1)X(t_1)] \\ &= E[X^2(t_1)] = \sigma_X^2 \end{aligned}$$

The final result, a variance, is independent of time.

In practice, as t_1 and t_2 approach each other, there is a transition as the autocorrelation function changes from zero to the value of the variance.

We define an **ideal noise,** however, as one in which the transition region is arbitrarily small:

$$\begin{aligned} R_X(t_1,t_2) = E[X(t_1)X(t_2)] &= \sigma_X^2 \quad t_2 = t_1 \\ &= 0, \quad t_1 \neq t_2 \end{aligned} \tag{8.11}$$

Because t_1 and t_2 are arbitrary, we can let $t_1 = t$ and $t_2 = t + \tau$. Then (8.11) becomes

$$\begin{aligned} R_X(\tau) = E[X(t)X(t + \tau)] &= \sigma_X^2 \quad \tau = 0 \\ &= 0, \quad \tau \neq 0 \end{aligned} \tag{8.12}$$

A plot of (8.12) is shown in Figure 8.4(a). The autocorrelation function in this example does not depend on the location of the time origin; it depends only on the difference $t_2 - t_1 = \tau$.

Wide-sense stationary (WSS) is a name given to a random process for which the following is true:

1. The mean and the variance[b] are independent of time:

$$E[X(t)] = \mu_X \quad \text{and} \quad \text{Var}[X(t)] = \sigma_X^2 \tag{8.13}$$

---

[b] Equations (8.13) and (8.14) contain some redudancy: Later we show that $R_X(0) = E[X^2(t)]$, and that we can write the variance using this with the mean and (3.39). We do not concern ourselves with the redundancy at this step in our development.

2. The autocorrelation function is independent of the time origin:

$$E[X(t)X(t + \tau)] = R_X(\tau) \qquad (8.14)$$

The random process in Figure 8.1 satisfies both these conditions and therefore is WSS. Note that the definition for wide-sense stationarity is determined by the expectations of mean, variance, and autocorrelation function. Any constraint wide-sense stationarity places on the pdfs from which these expectations are derived is not discussed.

The autocorrelation function (8.10) applied to the ensemble in Figure 8.2 produces results very different from that of noise. Using a sample function from (8.3),

$$y_j(t_1)y_j(t_2) = A \cos(\omega_0 t_1 + \phi_j) \, A \cos(\omega_0 t_2 + \phi_j), \quad j = 1, 2, \ldots$$

While the phase is determined randomly, it has the same value in both sinusoids in the product. The expected value of these products may be calculated using the pdf for the single random variable Φ:

$$R_Y(t_1, t_2) = E[Y(t_1)Y(t_2)]$$

$$R_Y(t_1, t_2) = \int_{-\pi}^{\pi} y(t_1, \phi_j) y(t_2, \phi_j) \frac{1}{2\pi} \, d\phi_j$$

$$R_Y(t_1, t_2) = \frac{A^2}{2\pi} \int_{-\pi}^{\pi} \cos(\omega_0 t_1 + \phi_j) \cos(\omega_0 t_2 + \phi_j) d\phi_j$$

$$R_Y(t_1, t_2) = \frac{A^2}{2} \cos[\omega_0(t_2 - t_1)]$$

The autocorrelation function in this example is independent of the time origin and depends only on the time difference $t_2 - t_1 = \tau$:

$$R_Y(\tau) = E[Y(t)Y(t + \tau)] = \frac{A^2}{2} \cos \omega_0 \tau \qquad (8.15)$$

Note that the mean and variance of this random variable are given in (8.4) and (8.5), and are independent of time. Therefore, the random process in Figure 8.2 is WSS. The autocorrelation function (8.15) is plotted in Figure 8.4(b).

Next, we find the autocorrelation function of the ensemble of random pulses in Figure 8.3. To do this, we examine two separate cases.

1. *When* $|t_2 - t_1| > T$: The values of the sample function $z(t_1)$ and $z(t_2)$ must be obtained from different pulses if $|t_2 - t_1|$ is greater than T, the width of one pulse. When this ensemble was described, different pulses within a given sample function were specified to be uncorrelated. It then follows that

$$R_Z(t_1, t_2) = E[Z(t_1)Z(t_2)]$$
$$= E[Z(t_1)]E[Z(t_2)]$$
$$= \mu_Z^2 = 0, \quad |t_2 - t_1| > T$$

2. *When* $|t_2 - t_1| \leq T$: The values of the sample function may be obtained from different pulses or from the same pulse. Let A be the event two values of a sample function are obtained from the same pulse. Then, because different sample functions are not synchronized, we let the probability of A be

$$P(A) = 1 - \frac{|t_2 - t_1|}{T}, \quad |t_2 - t_1| \leq T$$

The probability that two values of a sample function are obtained from different (uncorrelated) pulses is

$$P(\overline{A}) = 1 - P(A)$$
$$= \frac{|t_2 - t_1|}{T}, \quad |t_2 - t_1| \leq T$$

Then, using conditional expectation (3.86), and the total probability theorem (2.28),

$$R_Z(t_1, t_2) = E[Z(t_1)Z(t_2)|A]P(A) + E[Z(t_1)Z(t_2)|\overline{A}]P(\overline{A})$$

If t_1 and t_2 are on the same pulse,

$$E[Z(t_1)Z(t_2)|A] = (\pm V)^2 = V^2$$

On the other hand, if t_1 and t_2 are on different pulses,

$$E[Z(t_1)Z(t_2)|\overline{A}] = E[Z(t_1)]E[Z(t_2)] = 0$$

Combining the above relations for both $\overline{A}$ and A,

$$R_Z(t_1, t_2) = V^2 \left(1 - \frac{|t_2 - t_1|}{T} \right), \quad |t_2 - t_1| \leq T$$

These results show that the autocorrelation function $R_Z(t_1, t_2)$ is independent of the time origin. The random process $Z(t)$ is WSS. Therefore,

$$R_Z(\tau) = E[Z(t)Z(T + \tau)] = V^2 \left(\frac{1 - |\tau|}{T} \right), \quad |\tau| \leq T$$
$$= 0, \quad\quad\quad\quad |\tau| > T \quad\quad\quad \textbf{(8.16)}$$

This autocorrelation function is plotted in Figure 8.4(c).

We can now observe how the autocorrelation function characterizes a random process. The autocorrelation function for ideal noise, in Figure 8.4(a), shows that for $|\tau| > 0$ values of sample functions are uncorrelated. The autocorrelation function for the cosine functions with random phase, in Figure 8.4(b), is periodic: As different values of the sample functions repeat periodically the autocorrelation function also repeats periodically. The autocorrelation func-

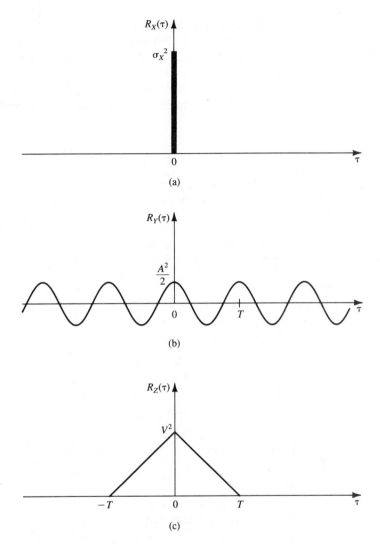

Figure 8.4   Autocorrelation functions for the random processes illustrated (a) in Figure 8.1, (b) in
Figure 8.2, and (c) in Figure 8.3.

◆ ◆

tion for the sequence of random pulses in Figure 8.4(c) is zero if $|\tau|$ is greater
than the pulse width, but it is not zero when the finite width of the pulses is taken
into account.

All three of the ensembles used as examples are WSS. There are many
practical applications for which this limited theory serves very well. It is also
quite adequate as a foundation for more general applications. *We therefore
restrict our introduction to random processes that are wide-sense stationary.*

The autocorrelation function (8.14) correlates a random process with itself at two different times. There are other cases in which two different random process are compared with each other, for example, $X(t)$ and $Y(t)$ where $X(t)$ is an input to a system and $Y(t)$ is the system's output. In these cases the joint pdf (8.9) applies. Then, $X(t)$ and $Y(t)$ are **jointly wide-sense stationary** so that (8.13) and (8.14) apply to $Y(t)$ too. **Crosscorrelation** functions are defined as follows:

$$R_{XY}(\tau) = E[X(t)Y(t + \tau)] \qquad \textbf{(8.17a)}$$

$$R_{YX}(\tau) = E[Y(t)X(t + \tau)] \qquad \textbf{(8.17b)}$$

Assuming the random processes $X(t)$ and $Y(t)$ are jointly WSS, correlation functions have several important properties.

Symmetry Properties

The autocorrelation function is even:

$$R_X(-\tau) = R_X(\tau) \qquad \textbf{(8.18)}$$

To see this, let

$$R_X(-\tau) = E(X(t)X(t - \tau))$$

The change of variable $w = t - \tau$ leads to

$$R_X(-\tau) = E[X(w + \tau)X(w)]$$

The commutative property of multiplication then leads to

$$R_X(-\tau) = E[X(w)X(w + \tau)] = R_X(\tau)$$

The three autocorrelation functions in Figure 8.4 are clearly even. A similar process for crosscorrelation functions leads to

$$R_{XY}(-\tau) = R_{YX}(\tau) \qquad \textbf{(8.19)}$$

Note that the crosscorrelation function is not even; the order of its subscripts in (8.19) is important.

Bounding Relations for Correlation Functions

The mean-square of a WSS random process is a constant,

$$R_X(0) = E[X^2(t)] = \sigma_X^2 + \mu_X^2 \qquad \textbf{(8.20)}$$

If $X(t)$ is a zero-mean random process, the mean-square is the variance. The three zero-mean autocorrelation functions in Figure 8.4 illustrate this.

The mean-square bounds an autocorrelation function:

$$|R_X(\tau)| \le R_X(0) \tag{8.21}$$

This is also illustrated in Figure 8.4. To show (8.21), we start with

$$E[(X(t) \pm X(t+\tau))^2] \ge 0$$

This expectation is non-negative because of the squared function. The inequality remains valid after the square is expanded:

$$E[X^2(t) \pm 2X(t)X(t+\tau) + X^2(t+\tau)] \ge 0$$

Performing the expectations,

$$R_X(0) \pm 2R_X(\tau) + R_X(0) \ge 0$$

which leads directly to (8.21).

The arithmetic mean of the mean-squares $R_X(0)$ and $R_Y(0)$ bounds the crosscorrelation function:

$$|R_{XY}(\tau)| \le \frac{1}{2}[R_X(0) + R_Y(0)] \tag{8.22}$$

Similarly, the geometric mean of the mean-squares $R_X(0)$ and $R_Y(0)$ also bounds the crosscorrelation function:

$$|R_{XY}(\tau)| \le \sqrt{R_X(0)R_Y(0)} \tag{8.23}$$

That these two bounds on the crosscorrelation function are true can be seen using the following development. We start with a relation involving two random processes $X(t)$ and $Y(t)$:

$$E[(X(t) \pm kY(t+\tau))^2] \ge 0$$

where k is an arbitrary real constant. Expanding the square,

$$E[X^2(t) \pm 2kX(t)Y(t+\tau) + k^2Y^2(t+\tau)] \ge 0$$

and, performing the expectations,

$$R_X(0) \pm 2kR_{XY}(\tau) + k^2R_Y(0) \ge 0 \tag{8.24}$$

If $k = 1$, then

$$R_X(0) + R_Y(0) \pm 2R_{XY}(\tau) \ge 0$$

which leads directly to (8.22).

Now, return to (8.24), and assume that k is a positive real constant:

$$k^2R_Y(0) + 2kR_{XY}(\tau) + R_X(0) \ge 0$$

If this relation is viewed as a quadratic function of k, the quadratic function can never be negative if its discriminant is non-positive; i.e., the quadratic cannot be negative if it does not have real roots:

$$4R_{XY}^2(\tau) - 4R_X(0)R_Y(0) \le 0$$

which leads directly to (8.23).

Incidentally, the geometric mean in (8.23) is stronger than the arithmetic mean in (8.22). That is,

$$\sqrt{R_X(0)R_Y(0)} \le \frac{1}{2}[R_X(0) + R_Y(0)]$$

Periodicity Relations

If a random process is periodic with a period T, then the autocorrelation function is also periodic with period T:

$$R_X(\tau + T) = R_X(\tau) \tag{8.25}$$

This is illustrated in Figure 8.4(b). To show (8.25), let

$$R_X(\tau + T) = E[X(t)X(t + \tau + T)]$$
$$= E[X(t)X(t + \tau)] = R_X(\tau)$$

Similar relations hold for the crosscorrelations in (8.17):

$$R_{XY}(\tau + T) = R_{XY}(\tau) \tag{8.26}$$

Covariance

If $X(t)$ and $Y(t)$ are random processes with non-zero means:

$$E[X(t)] = \mu_x \quad \text{and} \quad E[Y(t)] = \mu_Y$$

then it may be convenient to define **covariance functions**. The **autocovariance function** is

$$C_X(\tau) = E[(X(t) - \mu_X)(X(t + \tau) - \mu_X)]$$
$$= R_X(\tau) - \mu_X^2 \tag{8.27}$$

{Since $R_X(0) = E[X^2]$, it follows that $C_X(0) = \text{Var}[X]$.}
The **crosscovariance function** is

$$C_{XY}(\tau) = E[(X(t) - \mu_X)(Y(t + \tau) - \mu_Y)]$$
$$= R_{XY}(\tau) - \mu_X\mu_Y \tag{8.28}$$

Similar relations can be written for $C_Y(\tau)$ and $C_{YX}(\tau)$.

The autocovariance and crosscovariance functions are merely autocorrelation and crosscorrelation functions when their respective random processes have means of zero. All of the properties of correlation functions mentioned above apply equally to covariance functions. We prefer to use correlation functions in the following—even if the mean of a random process is not zero—because the word **correlation** conveys more directly the physical meaning of the expectations we are discussing.

Sum of Two WSS Random Processes

Suppose a random process $Z(t)$ is the sum of two WSS random processes:

$$Z(t) = X(t) + Y(t) \tag{8.29}$$

Then,

$$R_Z(\tau) = E[Z(t)Z(t+\tau)]$$
$$R_Z(\tau) = E[(X(t) + Y(t))(X(t+\tau) + Y(t+\tau))]$$
$$R_Z(\tau) = R_X(\tau) + R_{XY}(\tau) + R_{YX}(\tau) + R_Y(\tau) \tag{8.30}$$

If $X(t)$ and $Y(t)$ are orthogonal, $R_{XY}(\tau) = 0 = R_{YX}(\tau)$, and (8.30) becomes

$$R_Z(\tau) = R_X(\tau) + R_Y(\tau) \tag{8.31}$$

This result is important because of the many practical instances where two orthogonal random processes (say, signal and noise) combine additively.

Constant and Periodic Terms in a Random Process

Suppose a random process $Y(t)$ contains only constant and periodic terms. Then, because of (8.18) and (8.25),

$$R_Y(\tau) = \mu_Y^2 + \sum_{k=1}^{\infty} C_k \cos(2\pi kt/T) \tag{8.32}$$

Suppose a random process $X(t)$ contains *no* constant or periodic terms. Then, contrary to (8.32), the autocorrelation function vanishes as the time difference $|\tau|$ becomes large:

$$\lim_{|\tau|\to\infty} R_X(\tau) = 0 \tag{8.33}$$

Autocorrelation functions with this property are shown in Figures 8.4(a) and 8.4(c). We conclude that as $\tau \to \infty$, the effects of constant values and periodicities dominate in the autocorrelation function $R_Z(\tau)$.

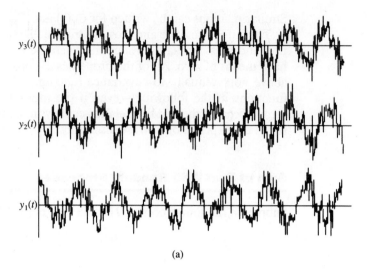

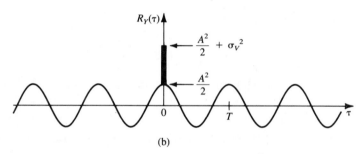

(b)

Figure 8.5   (a) Sample functions from the ensemble $Y(t)$ and (b) the autocorrelation function of $Y(t)$.

• •

Example 8.1   The ensemble of data in Figure 8.5(a) is typical of the sum of a periodic signal and a random noise. You can see this by looking at the data, although the noise is too great for you to determine what the periodic signal is. Suppose the autocorrelation function of the random process $Y(t)$ is calculated, and the result is shown in Figure 8.5(b). (We will show techniques for calculating autocorrelation functions in another section.) Examination of the autocorrelation function shows that it is periodic except at the origin where it has a singular point. The nature of the autocorrelation function shows that $Y(t)$ is the sum of a periodic signal — as in Figure 8.2 — and a noise — as in Figure 8.1:

$$Y(t) = S(t) + N(t)$$

The autocorrelation function in Figure 8.5(b) shows that the mean of $Y(t)$ is zero. We therefore assume that the means of both the signal and the noise random processes are zero. Then, assuming the random processes $S(t)$ and $N(t)$ are uncorrelated, they are also orthogonal; $R_{SN}(\tau) = R_{NS}(\tau) = 0$. The autocorrelation function in Figure 8.5(b) is therefore the sum of two more basic autocorrelation functions as in (8.31):

$$R_Y(\tau) = R_S(\tau) + R_N(\tau)$$

We associate $R_N(\tau)$ with the noise, similar to the autocorrelation function shown in Figure 8.4(a). We associate $R_S(\tau)$ with a periodic signal, similar to the autocorrelation function graph shown in Figure 8.4(b). Then, using the autocorrelation function for $Y(t)$ in Figure 8.5(b), we find the period of the signal, the variance of the signal, and the variance of the noise. Thus, the autocorrelation function extracts this information from the random process $Y(t)$; this information is not apparent from the random process in Figure 8.5(a).

◆ ◆ ◆ ◆ ◆

Product of Uncorrelated WSS Random Processes

If $Z(\tau)$ is the product of two uncorrelated WSS random processes:

$$Z(t) = X(t)Y(t) \tag{8.34}$$

the autocorrelation function of the product is

$$
\begin{aligned}
R_Z(\tau) &= E[Z(t)Z(t + \tau)] \\
&= E[X(t)Y(t)X(t + \tau)Y(t + \tau)] \\
&= E[X(t)X(t + \tau)]E[Y(t)Y(t + \tau)] \\
&= R_X(\tau)R_Y(\tau) \tag{8.35}
\end{aligned}
$$

This can be useful in nonlinear operations found in some modulation and demodulation applications.

Integrability of the Autocorrelation Function

In the next section, where we introduce the Fourier transform of an autocorrelation function, we will find that it must be non-negative:

$$\int_{-\infty}^{\infty} R_X(\tau)e^{-j\omega\tau}d\tau \geq 0 \text{ for all } \omega \tag{8.36}$$

We mention this relation because we are discussing and listing all the important properties of autocorrelation functions; we will establish the reason for (8.36) in the next section.

Section 8.2   **POWER SPECTRAL DENSITY**

◆   ◆   ◆   ◆   ◆

As we saw in the last section, WSS random processes are described using correlation functions. These random processes contain signals found in a variety of systems (transducers, filters, modems, channels, codecs, to name a few) which are described in terms of their frequency characteristics. We find it necessary, therefore, to include a spectral description of WSS random processes. The Fourier transform is the vehicle we use to do this.

By their very nature, Fourier transforms cannot be applied directly to WSS signals. The Fourier transform requires a function[c] $x(t)$ to be absolutely integrable before its transform $X(\omega)$ has meaning. A sample function from a WSS random process exists for all time with a constant mean and variance. Therefore, the requirement

$$\int_{-\infty}^{\infty} |x(t)| dt < \infty$$

cannot be satisfied with a sample function from a WSS random process.

To overcome this difficulty, we devise a **window**:

$$x_T(t) = x(t), \quad |t| \le T/2$$
$$= 0, \qquad |t| > T/2 \tag{8.37}$$

This window is illustrated in Figure 8.6. The width T of the window is arbitrary provided it is "large enough." We denote this by letting $T \to \infty$. The window, however, is realistic because data can only be measured over finite intervals of time.

As long as T is finite, the Fourier transform can be applied to the windowed sample function of time $x_T(t)$ in (8.37). The resulting Fourier transform pair is

$$X_T(\omega) = \int_{-\infty}^{\infty} x_T(t) e^{-j\omega t} dt \tag{8.38}$$

$$x_T(t) = \frac{1}{2\pi} \int_{-\infty}^{\infty} X_T(\omega) e^{j\omega t} d\omega \tag{8.39}$$

The **power** of a signal is its square. Power used in this way is a generalization; it will not have the units of watts unless the signal is a voltage or current and a one ohm resistance is absorbing the power. This generalization of power is a convention long used in signal processing, and we use it here: Averaging the power of the signal $x(t)$ within a window of width T, we find

$$P_T = \frac{1}{T} \int_{-T/2}^{T/2} x^2(t) dt$$

---

[c] We are here excluding generalized functions, such as the Dirac-delta function.

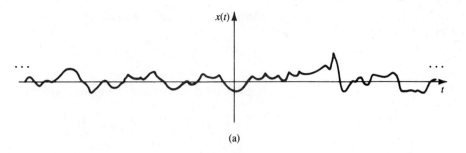

(a)

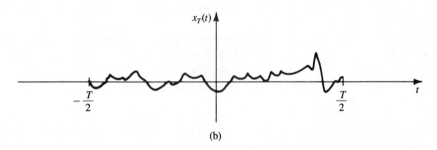

(b)

Figure 8.6   A sample function $x(t)$ from a random process $X(t)$ is illustrated in (a). In (b), a window of width T allows us to view $x(t)$ during $|t| < T/2$. The windowed portion of $x(t)$ is called $x_T(t)$.

• •

Using the windowed sample function (8.37),

$$P_T = \frac{1}{T} \int_{-\infty}^{\infty} x_T^2(t)\, dt$$

Then, using (8.39) for only one of the factors in the integrand,

$$P_T = \frac{1}{T} \int_{-\infty}^{\infty} x_T(t) \frac{1}{2\pi} \int_{-\infty}^{\infty} X_T(\omega) e^{j\omega t}\, d\omega\, dt$$

Interchanging the order of integration,

$$P_T = \frac{1}{2\pi T} \int_{-\infty}^{\infty} X_T(\omega) \int_{-\infty}^{\infty} x_T(t) e^{j\omega t}\, dt\, d\omega$$

Using the transform in (8.38),

$$P_T = \frac{1}{2\pi T} \int_{-\infty}^{\infty} X_T(\omega) X_T(-\omega)\, d\omega$$

where $x_T(t)$ is a real function of time. Therefore, using (8.38),

$$X_T(-\omega) = X_T^*(\omega) \tag{8.40}$$

where the complex conjugate is indicated by the $*$. Then,

$$P_T = \frac{1}{2\pi T} \int_{-\infty}^{\infty} |X_T(\omega)|^2 d\omega$$

Summarizing this sequence of equations, we have **Parseval's theorem:**

$$T \cdot P_T = \int_{-T/2}^{T/2} x^2(t)dt = \frac{1}{2\pi} \int_{-\infty}^{\infty} |X_T(\omega)|^2 d\omega \tag{8.41}$$

Here, the width of the window T cannot increase without bound. If that happens, Parseval's theorem has no meaning; $x_T(t)$ would no longer be absolutely integrable.

Parseval's theorem applies to arbitrary sample functions taken from an ensemble of a random process. We now extend Parseval's theorem to the entire ensemble. To do this, we use the boldface $\mathbf{X}_T(\omega)$ to denote the Fourier transform of the windowed random process, $X_T(t)$. Thus,

$$\int_{-T/2}^{T/2} X^2(t)dt = \frac{1}{2\pi} \int_{-\infty}^{\infty} |\mathbf{X}_T(\omega)|^2 d\omega \tag{8.42}$$

The sample function relation in (8.41) is contained in random process relation (8.42).

Now, taking the expected value of (8.42),

$$E\left[\int_{-T/2}^{T/2} X^2(t)dt \right] = \frac{1}{2\pi} E\left[\int_{-\infty}^{\infty} |\mathbf{X}_T(\omega)|^2 d\omega \right]$$

Interchanging the expectation with the integration,

$$\int_{-T/2}^{T/2} E[X^2(t)]dt = \frac{1}{2\pi} \int_{-\infty}^{\infty} E[|\mathbf{X}_T(\omega)|^2]d\omega$$

Since $E[X^2(t)]$ is a constant for a WSS random process, the integral on the left can be evaluated, and

$$T \cdot E[X^2(t)] = \frac{1}{2\pi} \int_{-\infty}^{\infty} E[|\mathbf{X}_T(\omega)|^2]d\omega$$

Then using (8.20),

$$T \cdot R_X(0) = \frac{1}{2\pi} \int_{-\infty}^{\infty} E[|\mathbf{X}_T(\omega)|^2]d\omega$$

Now it is possible to take the limit as $T \rightarrow \infty$ and to arrive at an expression for the average power in a WSS random process:

$$R_X(0) = \frac{1}{2\pi} \int_{-\infty}^{\infty} \lim_{T \rightarrow \infty} \frac{1}{T} E[|\mathbf{X}_T(\omega)|^2]d\omega$$

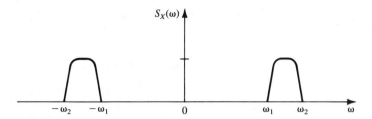

Figure 8.7   A band-limited power spectral density. It is non-zero for the band of frequencies $\omega_1 <$ $|\omega| < \omega_2$.

• •

This is separated into two simpler relations. In doing this we define the **power spectral density** (PSD) $S_X(\omega)$ for the WSS random process $X(t)$:

$$R_X(0) = \frac{1}{2\pi} \int_{-\infty}^{\infty} S_X(\omega)d\omega \qquad (8.43)$$

where

$$S_X(\omega) = \lim_{T \to \infty} \frac{1}{T} E[|\mathbf{X}_T(\omega)|^2] \qquad (8.44)$$

While the PSD is defined in (8.44), the manner in which it is used is shown in (8.43). The spectral description in a PSD specifies how much of an average power is in any range of frequencies. If a WSS random process $X(t)$ is band-limited, that is shown in its PSD; see Figure 8.7 for an example.

The defining relation for $S_X(\omega)$ in (8.44) looks rather formidable. Estimating $S_X(\omega)$ in specific applications is a technical specialty in its own right and we will not attempt it here. Nevertheless, some properties or characteristics of the PSD can be deduced directly from (8.44).

Note the expectation operator in (8.44). Attempts to estimate a PSD without the averaging implied by the expectation lead to estimators that may be unstable (additional data will cause the variance of the estimator to *increase*). Estimators with this potential instability are called **periodograms** to distinguish them from (8.44).

Symmetry Properties

Because of the magnitude in (8.44), a PSD can never be negative:

$$S_X(\omega) \geq 0, \text{ for all } \omega \qquad (8.45)$$

If the PSD were to be negative for some frequencies, it would imply a negative power for those frequencies. That is not allowed for the signals we study; it would imply a contradiction with the assumptions used to develop (8.44).

Again, because of the magnitude in (8.44), a PSD is a real function of ω,

$$S_X^*(\omega) = S_X(\omega) \tag{8.46}$$

Not only is a PSD real, but it is also an even function of ω:

$$S_X(-\omega) = S_X(\omega) \tag{8.47}$$

This evenness is proved as follows: Because each $x_T(t)$ is real, then (8.40) applies to the Fourier transform of each sample function in the ensemble. It then follows that

$$\mathbf{X}_T(-\omega) = \mathbf{X}_T^*(\omega)$$

Using this in (8.44) directly establishes (8.47).

Wiener-Khinchin Relations

The **Wiener-Khinchin relations** are established in Appendix F. They state that the PSD and autocorrelation function for a WSS random process are a Fourier transform pair:

$$S_X(\omega) = \int_{-\infty}^{\infty} R_X(\tau) e^{-j\omega\tau} d\tau \tag{8.48}$$

$$R_X(\tau) = \frac{1}{2\pi} \int_{-\infty}^{\infty} S_X(\omega) e^{j\omega\tau} d\omega \tag{8.49}$$

Note that when $\tau = 0$, (8.49) is the same as (8.43).

The fact that the PSD cannot be negative (8.45) when combined with (8.48) verifies an inequality introduced in the last section (8.36).

Example 8.2   Let a rectangular function of time $x(\tau)$ be

$$x(\tau) = A, \quad |\tau| < T/2$$
$$= 0, \quad \text{otherwise}$$

and $x(\tau)$ is illustrated in Figure 8.8(a). The Fourier transform of $x(\tau)$ is

$$X(\omega) = AT \frac{\sin(\omega T/2)}{\omega T/2}$$

as shown in Figure 8.8(b). Because $x(\tau)$ is even (8.18), it satisfies the mean-square bound in (8.21) and is absolutely integrable. However, the transform of $x(\tau)$, as shown in Figure 8.8(b), does not satisfy (8.36), which is the same as (8.45); it is negative for some intervals of ω. Hence, $x(\tau)$ cannot be an autocorrelation function for a WSS random process.

◆ ◆ ◆ ◆ ◆

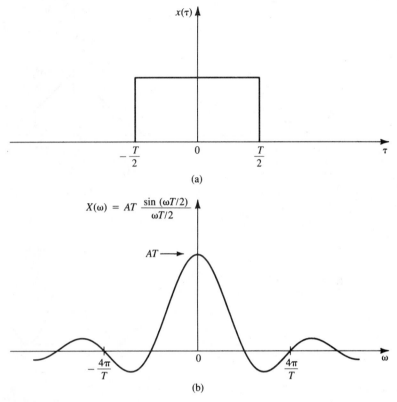

Figure 8.8   (a) A rectangular function of time and (b) its Fourier transform. This Fourier transform pair cannot represent an autocorrelation and its PSD because a PSD can never be negative, as demonstrated by (8.45).

◆ ◆

Example 8.3   The transform pair $x(\tau)$ and $X(\omega)$ in Example 8.2 cannot be an autocorrelation function and a PSD. However, suppose the rectangular function $x(\tau)$ is convolved with itself:

$$y(\tau) = x(\tau) * x(\tau)$$

where the asterisk signifies convolution. The result of this convolution is the triangular function shown in Figure 8.9(a). It follows immediately, from the properties of the Fourier transform, that

$$Y(\omega) = X^2(\omega) = (AT)^2 \left(\frac{\sin(\omega T/2)}{\omega T/2} \right)^2$$

This transform is illustrated in Figure 8.9(b). This Fourier transform pair is able to represent an autocorrelation function and its PSD. In fact, the trian-

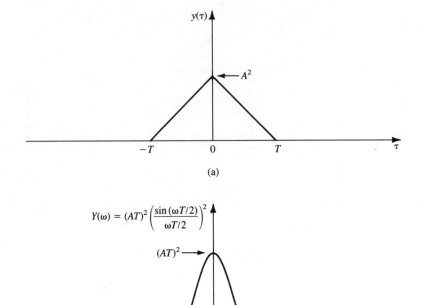

Figure 8.9   (a) A triangular function of time and (b) its Fourier transform. This Fourier transform pair could be an autocorrelation function and its PSD because the inequality in (8.45) is satisfied.

◆ ◆

gular function in Figure 8.9(a) is the same as the autocorrelation function we found in Figure 8.4(c) for the WSS random process in Figure 8.3.

◆ ◆ ◆ ◆ ◆

Example 8.4   Suppose a PSD is idealized to represent a signal with the spectrum in Figure 8.10(b). This, for example, could approximate a low-frequency signal; all frequencies above W radians per second are filtered out. The correlation function of this signal is obtained using (8.49):

$$R_X(\tau) = \frac{AW}{\pi}\left(\frac{\sin W\tau}{W\tau}\right)$$

and is illustrated in Figure 8.10(a). This is essentially the same Fourier transform pair used in Example 8.2, except that the roles of ω and τ have been reversed. The result in this example will be useful when we study noise.

◆ ◆ ◆ ◆ ◆

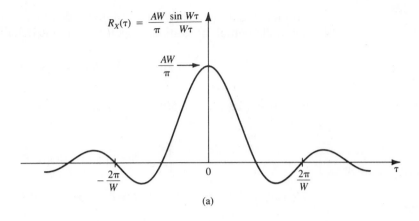

$$R_X(\tau) = \frac{AW}{\pi} \frac{\sin W\tau}{W\tau}$$

(a)

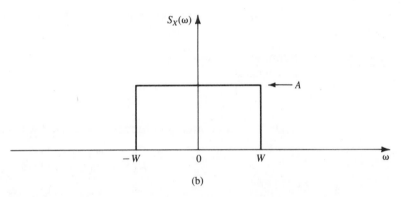

(b)

Figure 8.10   (a) A correlation function and (b) its PSD for a signal containing a uniform spectrum when $|\omega| < W$.

Combine the Fourier transform pair (8.48) and (8.49) so that the PSD is eliminated:

$$R_X(\tau) = \frac{1}{2\pi} \int_{-\infty}^{\infty} \int_{-\infty}^{\infty} R_X(\alpha) e^{-j\omega\alpha} d\alpha e^{j\omega\tau} d\omega$$

This integral relation is an identity for the autocorrelation function[d] $R_X(\tau)$; α is a dummy of integration and is not to be connected with τ, which is a parameter in the outer integral. Interchanging the order of integration,

$$R_X(\tau) = \frac{1}{2\pi} \int_{-\infty}^{\infty} R_X(\alpha) \int_{-\infty}^{\infty} e^{-j\omega(\alpha-\tau)} d\omega d\alpha \qquad \textbf{(8.50)}$$

---

[d] The statement is written here for an autocorrelation function in particular, but it is a valid identity for any function $f(t)$.

This relation is an **identity** for any autocorrelation function $R_X(\tau)$. Then, using the fundamental integration property of a Dirac-delta function $\delta(t)$, namely,

$$\int g(x - x_0)\delta(x)dx = g(x_0)$$

we can extract from (8.50) the following expression for the Dirac-delta function:

$$\int_{-\infty}^{\infty} e^{-j\omega(\alpha - \tau)}d\omega = 2\pi\delta(\alpha - \tau) \qquad (8.51)$$

We can generalize (8.51) as follows

$$\int_{-\infty}^{\infty} e^{\pm jxy}dx = 2\pi\delta(y) \qquad (8.52)$$

The usefulness of (8.52) is illustrated in the following two examples.[e]

Example 8.5   Suppose, as an idealization, we assume the PSD $S_X(\omega)$ is a constant A for all frequencies,

$$S_X(\omega) = A, \quad |\omega| < \infty$$

Then, the autocorrelation function associated with this is, using (8.49), is

$$R_X(\tau) = \frac{A}{2\pi}\int_{-\infty}^{\infty} e^{j\omega\tau}d\omega$$

This integral has no meaning in the conventional sense. But, using (8.52), we can write

$$R_X(\tau) = A\delta(\tau)$$

This is a description of idealized noise. We assume when the noise in Figure 8.1 becomes completely random, the Fourier transform in this example applies. The singular value of the autocorrelation function in Figure 8.4(a) becomes

$$R_X(\tau) = \sigma_X^2\delta(\tau)$$

Therefore, ideal noise contains all frequencies equally, so that its spectrum is constant for all frequencies,

$$S_X(\omega) = \sigma_X^2$$

---

[e] The statement in (8.52) is general, and y can stand for either τ or ω depending on the needs of an application.

This idealization is, by convention, called **white noise.**[f] Note that for white noise, the average power $R_X(0)$ in (8.43) has no meaning.

◆　◆　◆　◆　◆

Example 8.6   Let us examine the autocorrelation function for the periodic signal shown in Figure 8.4(b):

$$R_X(\tau) = \frac{A^2}{2} \cos \omega_0 \tau$$

The PSD for this is obtained using (8.48):

$$S_X(\omega) = \frac{A^2}{2} \int_{-\infty}^{\infty} \cos \omega_0 \tau \; e^{-j\omega\tau} d\tau$$

Using exponential functions for the cosine, this becomes

$$S_X(\omega) = \frac{A^2}{4} \int_{-\infty}^{\infty} \exp[-j(\omega - \omega_0)\tau] d\tau + \frac{A^2}{4} \int_{-\infty}^{\infty} \exp[-j(\omega + \omega_0)\tau] d\tau$$

Then, using (8.52),

$$S_X(\omega) = \frac{\pi A^2}{2} \delta(\omega - \omega_0) + \frac{\pi A^2}{2} \delta(\omega + \omega_0)$$

This result can be used in (8.43) to obtain the average power; the result is, of course,

$$R_X(0) = \frac{A^2}{2}$$

We accept these highly idealized results because they are easily interpreted. The random process we are discussing is the sinusoid with random phase angle in (8.3), and illustrated in Figure 8.2. Clearly, the average power of this random process is localized at $\omega = \pm\omega_0$. This is what the Dirac-delta function is interpreted to be doing.

◆　◆　◆　◆　◆

Sum and Product of Two WSS Random Processes

We saw in (8.31) that if $X(t)$ and $Y(t)$ are uncorrelated WSS random processes, and if they have zero means, then the autocorrelation of their sum is the sum of

---

[f] White light is made up of uniform power contributions at all visible wavelengths. By analogy, white noise is made up of uniform power contributions at all frequencies.

their autocorrelations. Because of the linearity of the Fourier transform, it follows from (8.31) that the PSD of the sum is the sum of the PSDs:

$$S_Z(\omega) = S_X(\omega) + S_Y(\omega) \qquad (8.53)$$

Further, when two uncorrelated WSS random processes $X(t)$ and $Y(t)$ are multiplied, then, according to (8.35),

$$R_Z(\tau) = R_X(\tau)R_Y(\tau)$$

Using the Wiener-Khinchin relation (8.48) to obtain $S_Z(\omega)$,

$$S_Z(\omega) = \int_{-\infty}^{\infty} R_X(\tau)R_Y(\tau)e^{-j\omega\tau}d\tau$$

Using (8.49),

$$S_Z(\omega) = \int_{-\infty}^{\infty} R_X(\tau)\frac{1}{2\pi}\int_{-\infty}^{\infty} S_Y(\omega)e^{j\alpha\tau}d\alpha e^{-j\omega\tau}d\tau$$

Interchanging the order of integration,

$$S_Z(\omega) = \frac{1}{2\pi}\int_{-\infty}^{\infty} S_Y(\alpha)\int_{-\infty}^{\infty} R_X(\tau)\alpha e^{-j(\omega-\alpha)\tau}d\tau d\alpha$$

Then, using (8.48) again,

$$S_Z(\omega) = \frac{1}{2\pi}\int_{-\infty}^{\infty} S_Y(\alpha)S_X(\omega - \alpha)d\alpha \qquad (8.54)$$

This convolution relation is important for applications in signal modulation and demodulation.

Cross-Spectral Densities

The power spectral density is defined only with the autocorrelation function as shown in the Wiener-Khinchin relations (8.48) and (8.49). We also define a **cross-spectral density** as the Fourier transform of a crosscorrelation function:

$$S_{XY}(\omega) = \int_{-\infty}^{\infty} R_{XY}(\tau)e^{-j\omega\tau}d\tau \qquad (8.55)$$

$$R_{XY}(\tau) = \frac{1}{2\pi}\int_{-\infty}^{\infty} S_{XY}(\omega)e^{j\tau\omega}d\omega \qquad (8.56)$$

The salient properties of the PSD do not apply to the cross-spectral density

(CSD). The CSD, however, does have the following properties,

$$S_{XY}^*(\omega) = S_{YX}(\omega) \tag{8.57}$$

$$S_{XY}(-\omega) = S_{YX}(\omega) \tag{8.58}$$

The first statement follows because the crosscorrelation function is real, and the second follows because of the symmetry relation (8.19). We will return to the CSD when we discuss random processes in linear systems.

Section 8.3   ERGODIC RANDOM PROCESSES

◆ ◆ ◆ ◆ ◆

The essential assumption of a WSS random process is that it is independent of where we place the origin of the time axis. This means that sample functions in the ensemble extend in time from $-\infty$ to $+\infty$; stationarity will not let us begin or end sample functions at any observable time. Therefore, two difficulties appear when we apply the theory of WSS random processes to practical problems:

1. Each sample function we observe is finite in duration.

2. We can only see a small number of all possible sample functions.

These practical limitations lead us to ask: What can we learn about an ensemble from only one sample function? We use the window in (8.37); a sample function $x(t)$ extends between $t = \pm\infty$, but our observation $x_T(t)$ is limited to the width of a window. Because the origin of the time axis cannot affect a WSS random process, the window can be placed anywhere we want; only the width of the window interests us.

Expectations cannot be applied to one sample function. Therefore, expectations such as the mean or the correlation function must be approximated with averages over time. The notation $\langle x(t) \rangle$ is defined to represent an average with respect to time:

$$\langle x(t) \rangle = \lim_{t \to \infty} \frac{1}{T} \int_{-T/2}^{T/2} x(t) dt \tag{8.59}$$

Autocorrelation and crosscorrelation written as time averages are

$$\langle x(t)x(t + \tau) \rangle = \lim_{t \to \infty} \frac{1}{T} \int_{-T/2}^{T/2} x(t)x(t + \tau) dt \tag{8.60}$$

$$\langle x(t)y(t + \tau) \rangle = \lim_{T \to \infty} \frac{1}{T} \int_{-T/2}^{T/2} x(t)y(t + \tau) dt \tag{8.61}$$

What we have done with these time averages is to create **estimators** for the mean, autocorrelation, and crosscorrelation:

$$\hat{\mu}_X = \langle X(t) \rangle = \lim_{T \to \infty} \frac{1}{T} \int_{-T/2}^{T/2} X(t)\,dt \tag{8.62}$$

$$\hat{R}_X(\tau) = \langle X(t)X(t + \tau) \rangle = \lim_{T \to \infty} \frac{1}{T} \int_{-T/2}^{T/2} X(t)X(t + \tau)\,dt \tag{8.63}$$

$$\hat{R}_{XY}(\tau) = \langle X(t)Y(t + \tau) \rangle = \lim_{T \to \infty} \frac{1}{T} \int_{-T/2}^{T/2} X(t)Y(t + \tau)\,dt \tag{8.64}$$

The expressions (8.62) through (8.64) are estimators using the random processes $X(t)$ and $Y(t)$ whereas (8.59) through (8.61) use sample functions $x(t)$ and $y(t)$.

The bias of each estimator is (assuming the operations of expectation and averaging with respect to time are interchangeable):

$$E[\hat{\mu}_X] = E[\langle X(t) \rangle] = \langle E[X(t)] \rangle = \langle \mu_X \rangle = \mu_X \tag{8.65}$$

$$\begin{aligned} E[\hat{R}_X(\tau)] &= E[\langle X(t)X(t + \tau) \rangle] \\ &= \langle E[X(t)X(t + \tau)] \rangle \\ &= \langle R_X(\tau) \rangle \\ &= R_X(\tau) \end{aligned} \tag{8.66}$$

A similar relation holds for crosscorrelation:

$$E[\hat{R}_{XY}(\tau)] = R_{XY}(\tau) \tag{8.67}$$

These results indicate that averages over long intervals of time will, **on the average,** be the same as their respective expected values. In other words, the estimators in (8.62) through (8.64) are unbiased; see (6.3) and the introduction to Chapter 6.

Experience tells us there are some WSS random processes in which one sample function contains all random variations needed to characterize an entire random process, meaning that time averages can replace expectations in these special cases:

$$\langle x(t) \rangle = \mu_X \tag{8.68}$$

$$\langle x(t)x(t + \tau) \rangle = R_X(\tau) \tag{8.69}$$

$$\langle x(t)y(t + \tau) \rangle = R_{XY}(\tau) \tag{8.70}$$

Note carefully that the last three equations differ from (8.65) through (8.67) in a very important respect: The last three equations use the sample functions $x(t)$ and $y(t)$ and, therefore, do not use the expectation operator.

Ergodic random processes are random processes for which time averages may be substituted for ensemble averages (expectations). Therefore, (8.68) through (8.70) apply when a random process is ergodic. Any ergodic random process is also WSS, but the reverse is not necessarily true.

Example 8.7   The classical work on thermal noise by Johnson and Nyquist[8] gives the power in a resistor, caused by thermally agitated charge carriers, as:

$$\langle v^2(t) \rangle = 4kTRB \ V^2$$

where

k is the 1.38×10^{-23} joules/K, Boltzmann's constant,

T, in Kelvin, is the temperature of the resistor,

R, in ohms, is the resistance,

B, in Hertz, is the bandwidth of the instrument measuring the noise power.

This equation is an approximation, but it is useful in our engineering applications for frequencies of less than ~ 1000 GHz.

Thermal noise is very close to an ideal: Its correlation function, whether computed as a time average or as an expectation, is approximately zero when $|\tau| > 0$. Also, thermal noise has a mean of zero, and this too is the same whether measured as a time average or as an expectation. Therefore, thermal noise is an example of an ergodic random process. In addition, the amplitude characteristics of thermal noise are described well by the Gaussian random variable.

Average power is given by (8.43):

$$E[V^2(t)] = \langle v^2(t) \rangle = \frac{1}{2\pi} \int_{-2\pi B}^{2\pi B} S_V(\omega) d\omega$$

With this, the average noise from Johnson and Nyquist leads to

$$S_V(\omega) = 2kTR \quad V^2/\text{radians/s} \qquad\qquad \textbf{(8.71)}$$

where $S_V(\omega)$ applies for both positive and negative radian frequencies, but B applies only for positive frequencies in Hertz. This accounts for the constants and units of this PSD.

PSD for thermal noise is a constant—at least for frequencies less than ~ 1000 GHz. This is why thermal noise can be called white noise; see Example 8.5.

As a numerical example, let a 10-kΩ resistor be at a temperature of 300 K. Therefore, there is a voltage across the resistor that is caused by the thermal agitation of the charge carriers within the resistor; this noise voltage is a sample function from an ergodic random process. Its PSD has the constant amplitude of

$$S_V(\omega) = 8.28 \times 10^{-17} \ V^2/\text{radians/s}$$

If this white noise is observed with an instrument having a bandwidth of

1 MHz, its rms voltage is

$$\sqrt{\langle v^2(t) \rangle} = 12.9 \ \mu V$$

• • • • •

Example 8.8 The periodic random process in Figure 8.2 is an ergodic random process, which can be verified as follows. From (8.3), a sample function is

$$y(t) = A \cos(\omega_0 t + \phi)$$

The time average of a sinusoidal sample function is zero. Therefore,

$$\langle y(t) \rangle = E[Y(t)] = 0$$

The correlation function over one period where $T = \dfrac{2\pi}{\omega_0}$ is

$$\frac{A^2}{T} \int_{-T/2}^{T/2} \cos(\omega_0 t + \phi)\cos(\omega_0 t + \omega_0 \tau + \phi)dt$$

$$= \frac{A^2}{2T} \int_{-T/2}^{T/2} [\cos(2\omega_0 t + \omega_0 \tau + 2\phi) + \cos(\omega_0 \tau)]dt$$

$$= \frac{A^2}{2} \cos \omega_0 \tau$$

This result is independent of T. Therefore, as $T \to \infty$

$$\langle y(t)y(t + \tau) \rangle = R_Y(\tau) = \frac{A^2}{2} \cos \omega_0 \tau$$

This establishes the ergodicity of the ensemble illustrated in Figure 8.2.

• • • • •

Assume $X(t)$ is an ergodic random process and that, within a window of width t, we measure a sample function $x(t)$ every Δt seconds. There are then N data:

$$[k, x_T(k\Delta t)]$$

where $0 \leq k \leq N - 1$, where $N = [T/\Delta t]$, and where $[\cdot]$ denotes the integer function. These data are used to calculate an estimated value of μ_X:

$$\mu_X = E[X(t)] = \langle x(t) \rangle \approx \frac{1}{N\Delta t} \sum_{k=0}^{N-1} x_T(k\Delta t) \, \Delta t$$

or

$$\mu_X \approx \frac{1}{N} \sum_{k=0}^{N-1} x_T(k\Delta t)$$

A limit as $N \to \infty$ cannot be performed; we can only use data within the given window. However, given the nature of these data, we must satisfy ourselves that the window T is wide enough to include all the statistical information contained in $x(t)$.

Similarly, an estimation of the autocorrelation function using sampled data is

$$\begin{aligned}
R_X(\tau) &= E[X(t)X(t + \tau)] \\
&= \langle x(t)x(t + \tau) \rangle \\
&\approx \frac{1}{N} \sum_{k=0}^{k_M} x_T(k\Delta t)x_T(k\Delta t + \tau)
\end{aligned} \tag{8.72}$$

where $k_M = M - 1 - \left[\dfrac{|\tau|}{\Delta t}\right]$. Note that the finite length of the data, and the shifted sample function in (8.72) require the upper limit of the sum in (8.72) to decrease as $|\tau|$ increases. This limits the accuracy of (8.72) for large $|\tau|$, so we usually limit $|\tau|$ to $\sim 10\%$ of T, the window width. Also, note that it is usually convenient to select values of τ that are integer multiples of the sampling interval Δt.

Example 8.9   A noise voltage is selected from an ergodic noise random process. It is similar to one of the sample functions in Figure 8.1. The sample function is sampled (measured) at a rate of 1 kHz ($\Delta t = 1$ ms) for 1 s ($N = 1000$). These data are stored in the memory of a computer in an array called $x_T(t)$ and are processed with the autocorrelation algorithm in (8.72). The results are plotted in Figure 8.11 for $\tau = 0$ to $\tau = 100$ ms.

This figure illustrates the characteristics of zero-mean white noise: The autocorrelation function is approximately zero for values of $\tau > 0$. Because the autocorrelation function is even, we plot only the part for $\tau \geq 0$. The variance of the noise is the value of the autocorrelation function when $\tau = 0$; $R(0) = 0.517$. The noise voltage of this sample function is therefore 0.719 Vrms.

◆ ◆ ◆ ◆ ◆

Example 8.10   A sample function obtained from the ergodic random process in Figure 8.2 is

$$y(t) = A \cos(\omega_0 t + 117.3°)$$

Let the amplitude $A = 1$ V, and the frequency $f_0 = 45$ Hz. These are constants for this example, but the phase ($\phi = 117.3$ degrees) is the result of

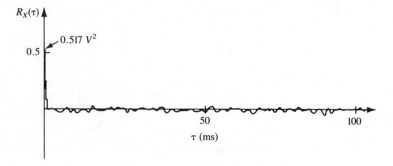

Figure 8.11   An autocorrelation function for the ergodic white noise discussed in Example 8.9.

selecting a phase randomly from within the interval of ± 180 degrees. This sample function is measured every millisecond within a window that is 1-s wide ($\Delta t = 1$ ms and $N = 1000$). The results of the sampling process are placed in a computer array named $y_T(t)$ and then processed with the auto-correlation algorithm (8.72). The results are plotted in Figure 8.12.

This figure clearly shows the periodicity ($T = 22.2$ ms) as well as the average power of the signal (1/2 V^2). It is also very interesting to observe that the value of the phase does not appear in the autocorrelation function. Any value of the phase between ± 180 would produce the same result as is shown in Figure 8.12.

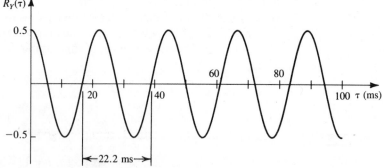

Figure 8.12   An autocorrelation function for the ergodic periodic random process discussed in Example 8.10.

An estimator for crosscorrelation similar to (8.72) is

$$\hat{R}_{XY}(\tau) = \frac{1}{N} \sum_{k=0}^{k_M} x_T(k\Delta t) y_T(k\Delta t + \tau) \tag{8.73}$$

where $k_M = M - 1 - \left[\dfrac{|\tau|}{\Delta t}\right]$. Recall, in calculating values from this, that the crosscorrelation function is not even and therefore needs to be evaluated for positive and negative values of τ — autocorrelation is even but crosscorrelation follows the symmetry relation in (8.19).

Section 8.4   LINEAR SYSTEMS

◆ ◆ ◆ ◆ ◆

Engineers use PSDs not only to characterize random processes, but also to design systems (filters) with desired frequency characteristics. Cross-spectral densities are used to display relationships between two different random signals. They too are used to describe systems by comparing a random process at a system's input with the random process at its output. To illustrate how this is done, we will use systems that are linear, time-invariant, causal, and passive. Linearity means that we can use superposition. Time-invariance means that we can use a system's transfer function $H(j\omega)$, or equivalently, its inverse Fourier transform: the impulse response $h(t)$. The causal nature of a system means that the impulse response is zero for all $t < 0$, while the passive nature of a system means that its impulse response contains a finite amount of energy.

Example 8.11   The simplest low-pass RC filter is shown in Figure 8.13. Using the techniques of circuit theory, the transfer function for this filter is

$$H(j\omega) = \frac{1}{1 + j\omega RC}$$

◆ ◆

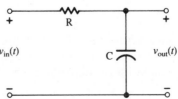

Figure 8.13   The low-pass RC filter discussed in Example 8.11

and its response to a unit impulse is

$$h(t) = \frac{1}{RC} e^{-t/RC} u(t)$$

The value of RC is called the circuit's **time constant.**

◆ ◆ ◆ ◆ ◆

Systems of interest to us contain the lumped elements of resistance, capacitance, and inductance (either self or mutual). They may also contain dependent voltage or current sources and time-delay elements such as transmission lines.

While the spectral nature of a random process is a major interest of ours, we cannot use a transfer function $H(j\omega)$ in the classical way. That is, we cannot relate an output sample function $y(t)$ with an input sample function $x(t)$ by using the transform relation $Y(\omega) = H(j\omega)X(\omega)$. The Fourier transform of a WSS random process does not exist, and therefore the input and output transforms $X(\omega)$ and $Y(\omega)$ do not exist. We discussed this when we developed the PSD. Fortunately, we are rarely interested in the spectrum of a specific sample function taken from a random process. We are very interested, however, in the average effects of a random process. This averaging is, of course, illustrated explicitly with the expectation operator in (8.44). Also, it is implicit with any specific PSD such as those illustrated in Figures 8.7 and 8.10(b).

When discussing the response of a system to a specific input signal, even an input signal that is a sample function of a WSS random process, we use the superposition, or convolution, integral from circuit theory

$$y(t) = \int_{-\infty}^{t} x(\alpha)h(t - \alpha)d\alpha \tag{8.74}$$

The integrand of this integral uses the impulse response $h(t)$, which weights all previous values of the input signal in proportion to their effect on the present output. This weighting of prior inputs is shown in the plot in Figure 8.14(a). The sample functions $x(t)$ and $y(t)$ are the input and output functions of a system $h(t)$, as shown in Figure 8.14(b). When we replace the sample functions $x(t)$ and $y(t)$ with the WSS random processes $X(t)$ and $Y(t)$, the superposition integral (8.74) is

$$Y(t) = \int_{-\infty}^{t} X(\alpha)h(t - \alpha)d\alpha \tag{8.75}$$

How we use this superposition integral, and how we relate it to the spectral descriptions we seek, is the substance of the work in this section.

An equivalent form of the superposition integral (8.75), which is more convenient for the derivations to follow, is

$$Y(t) = \int_{0}^{\infty} h(z)X(t - z)dz \tag{8.76}$$

This is obtained directly from (8.75) using the change of variables $z = t - \alpha$.

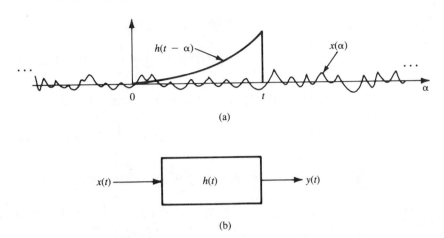

Figure 8.14   (a) The integrand of the superposition integral (8.74) showing how the impulse response $h(t)$ is interpreted as weighting values of $x(t)$ occurring prior to time t. (b) The filter is described by the $h(t)$ with $x(t)$ as the input and $y(t)$ as the output.

● ● ◆ ● ● ● ● ◆ ● ● ◆ ● ● ◆ ● ● ● ● ● ◆ ● ● ● ● ● ● ● ◆ ◆

The Mean of Y(t)

The expected value of $Y(t)$ is, using (8.76),

$$E[Y(t)] = \int_0^\infty h(z)E[X(t-z)]dz$$

The impulse response $h(t)$ describes a time-invariant system, and is moved outside the expectation operator. Then, using (8.13),

$$\mu_Y = E[Y(t)] = \mu_X \int_0^\infty h(z)dz \qquad (8.77)$$

Since $h(t)$ has finite energy, we see from (8.77) that the expected value of $Y(t)$ is a constant; it is merely proportional to the expected value of $X(t)$. Another way of writing (8.77) is

$$\mu_Y = \mu_X H(0) \qquad (8.78)$$

where $H(\omega)$ is the system transfer function and the Fourier transform of $h(t)$. Further, (8.77) and (8.78) show that if $X(t)$ is a zero-mean random process, then $Y(t)$ is also a zero-mean random process.

Relations Between X(t) and Y(t)

To find the crosscorrelation between the WSS random processes $X(t)$ and $Y(t)$, we use (8.17a) and (8.76), and we assume that the operations of integration and expectation can be interchanged:

$$E[X(t)Y(t + \tau)] = \int_0^\infty h(z)E[X(t)X(t + \tau - z)]dz$$

Using (8.14), this reduces to the convolution integral

$$R_{XY}(\tau) = \int_0^\infty h(z)R_X(\tau - z)dz \tag{8.79}$$

The Fourier transform of the crosscorrelation in (8.79) is, using (8.51),

$$S_{XY}(\omega) = \int_0^\infty h(z) \int_{-\infty}^\infty R_X(\tau - z)e^{-j\omega\tau}d\tau dz$$

Using the change of variables $\beta = \tau - z$

$$S_{XY}(\omega) = \int_0^\infty h(z) \int_{-\infty}^\infty R_X(\beta)e^{-j\omega(\beta+z)}d\beta dz$$

$$S_{XY}(\omega) = \int_0^\infty h(z)e^{-j\omega z}dz \int_{-\infty}^\infty R_X(\beta)e^{-j\omega\beta}d\beta$$

$$S_{XY}(\omega) = H(j\omega)S_X(\omega) \tag{8.80}$$

If $X(t)$ is zero-mean white noise, then the input PSD is a constant:

$$S_X(\omega) = \sigma_X^2$$

and (8.80) becomes

$$S_{XY}(\omega) = \sigma_X^2 H(j\omega) \tag{8.81}$$

This means that an unknown transfer function of a system can be measured using a cross-spectral density when the input to the system is zero-mean white noise. A similar relation is obtained using correlation functions: The autocorrelation function of (idealized) zero-mean white noise is

$$R_X(\tau) = \sigma_X^2 \delta(\tau)$$

Using this in (8.79) leads directly to

$$R_{XY}(\tau) = \int_0^\infty h(z)\sigma_X^2 \delta(\tau - z)dz$$

$$R_{XY}(\tau) = \sigma_X^2 h(\tau) \tag{8.82}$$

When the input to a system is white noise, the crosscorrelation is proportional to the system's impulse response.

Example 8.12   Let a zero-mean white noise $X(t)$ be applied to the input of the low-pass filter in Example 8.11. Then, using (8.81), the cross-spectral density is

$$S_{XY}(\omega) = \sigma_X^2 \frac{1}{1 + j\omega RC}$$

Using (8.82), the crosscorrelation in this example is

$$R_{XY}(\tau) = \frac{\sigma_X^2}{RC} e^{-\tau/RC} u(\tau)$$

◆ ◆ ◆ ◆ ◆

Autocorrelation and PSD for the Output Y(t)

The autocorrelation function for the WSS random process $Y(t)$ is, using (8.14) and (8.76) and assuming that the operations of integration and expectation can be interchanged:

$$E[Y(t)Y(t + \tau)] = \int_0^\infty h(\beta) \int_0^\infty h(z)E[X(t - \beta)X(t + \tau - z)]dzd\beta$$

$$E[Y(t)Y(t + \tau)] = \int_0^\infty h(\beta) \int_0^\infty h(z)R_X(\tau + \beta - z)dzd\beta$$

Therefore, the autocorrelation function of the output random process is expressed as a double integral

$$R_Y(\tau) = \int_0^\infty h(\beta) \int_0^\infty h(z)R_X(\tau + \beta - z)dzd\beta \tag{8.83a}$$

Or, using (8.79),

$$R_Y(\tau) = \int_0^\infty h(\beta)R_{XY}(\tau + \beta)d\beta \tag{8.83b}$$

Using the Wiener-Khinchin relation (8.48) in (8.83a),

$$S_Y(\omega) = \int_0^\infty h(\beta) \int_0^\infty h(z) \int_{-\infty}^\infty R_X(\tau + \beta - z)e^{-j\omega\tau}d\tau dzd\beta$$

Then, using the change of variables $\alpha = \tau + \beta - z$,

$$S_Y(\omega) = \int_{\infty}^\infty h(\beta)e^{j\omega\beta}d\beta \int_0^\infty h(z)e^{-j\omega z} dz \int_{-\infty}^\infty R_X(\alpha)e^{-j\omega\alpha}d\alpha$$

$$S_Y(\omega) = H(-j\omega)H(j\omega)S_X(\omega)$$

$$S_Y(\omega) = |H(j\omega)|^2 S_X(\omega) \tag{8.84}$$

This relation is very important because it shows how filters can be designed to control the frequency characteristics of a PSD. In particular, if the input $X(t)$ to a system is zero-mean white noise, then the output PSD is

$$S_Y(\omega) = \sigma_X^2 |H(j\omega)|^2 \qquad (8.85)$$

The output variance σ^2_Y may be obtained from (8.85) by combining (8.20) and (8.43).

Example 8.13   A white noise is applied to the input of the low-pass filter in Example 8.11. Therefore, using (8.85), the PSD of the output random process $Y(t)$ is

$$S_Y(\omega) = \sigma_X^2 \left| \frac{1}{1 + j\omega RC} \right|^2$$

$$S_Y(\omega) = \sigma_X^2 \frac{1}{1 + (\omega RC)^2}$$

A Fourier transform pair of interest in this example is

$$f(t) = e^{-a|t|}, \quad F(\omega) = \frac{2a}{\omega^2 + a^2}$$

We can use this, and the Wiener-Khinchin relation (8.49), to find the autocorrelation function for the output random process $Y(t)$ in this example.

$$R_Y(\tau) = \frac{1}{2\pi} \int_{-\infty}^{\infty} \sigma_X^2 \frac{1}{1 + (\omega RC)^2} e^{j\omega\tau} d\omega$$

$$R_Y(\tau) = \frac{\sigma_X^2}{2RC} \frac{1}{2\pi} \int_{-\infty}^{\infty} \frac{2/RC}{\omega^2 + (1/RC)^2} e^{j\omega\tau} d\omega$$

$$R_Y(\tau) = \frac{1}{2RC} \sigma_X^2 e^{-|\tau|/RC}$$

Plots of $R_Y(\tau)$ and $S_Y(\omega)$ for this example are shown in Figure 8.15. The WSS random process $Y(t)$ in this example is called **pink noise**[g]. Because $X(t)$ is zero-mean, $Y(t)$ also has a mean of zero. Then, the output variance is

$$\sigma_Y^2 = R_Y(0) = \frac{1}{2RC} \sigma_X^2$$

• • • • •

---

[g] The first-order RC network discussed in this example is a low-pass filter. If white noise is the input to the filter, then the lower frequencies (longer wavelengths) tend to be transmitted, and the higher frequencies (shorter wavelengths) tend to be suppressed. This observation leads to the name "pink" being applied to the noise at this filter's output.

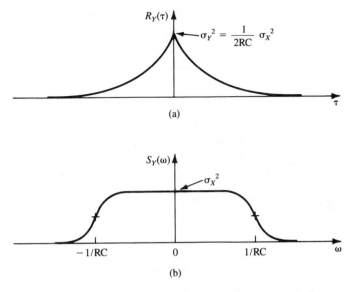

Figure 8.15   (a) The autocorrelation function of zero-mean pink noise. (b) The PSD for zero-mean pink noise. When $\omega = \pm 1/RC$, the magnitude of the PSD is one-half of its maximum. These results were obtained from Example 8.13.

◆ ◆ ◆ ◆ ◆ ◆ ◆   ◆

Note that the probabilistic nature of the white noise at a time t is not specified. The white noise could be Gaussian, or uniform, or any number of other possibilities. Yet their autocorrelation functions are all the same. This is an example of the non-uniqueness of autocorrelation functions; and this happens because all random phase information is lost in the process of performing autocorrelation.

Section 8.5   THE NARROWBAND RANDOM PROCESS

◆ ◆ ◆ ◆ ◆

Electrical communication systems flourish because narrowband filters are readily available. Without these filters, and the selectivity they provide, the limited electromagnetic frequency spectrum would be an overcrowded tangle of interfering messages. With them, however, messages can be transmitted on carrier frequencies confined to their own discrete channel. This is true whether, for example, we are discussing radio and television broadcasting or telephone messages carried within fiber optics. While narrowband filters select desired communication messages, and reject all others, they also pass a fraction of any wideband noise present at their input. The way the filtered noise can affect ordinary amplitude modulation (AM) or frequency modulation (FM) is an interesting example of a WSS random process.

A carrier used with broadcasting AM or FM is

$$v_C(t) = A \cos \omega_0 t \qquad (8.86)$$

In AM, the magnitude becomes $A[1 + k_{AM}f(t)]$, so that

$$v_{AM}(t) = A[1 + k_{AM}f(t)]\cos \omega_0 t$$

Here, the message $f(t)$ is amplitude modulating the carrier. In FM, A is a constant, but a phase is introduced:

$$v_{FM}(t) = A \cos[\omega_0 t + \theta(t)]$$

The phase term is

$$\theta(t) = k_{FM} \int_{t_0}^{t} f(\tau)d\tau$$

so that the **instantaneous frequency**[h] modulated by a message is

$$\frac{d}{dt}\theta(t) = k_{FM}f(t)$$

Therefore, if the noise transmitted through a narrowband filter changes A in (8.86), it then appears as noise in an AM message. However, if a narrowband noise changes the phase of the cosine in (8.86), it appears as noise in an FM message.

Figure 8.16 shows a segment of white Gaussian noise after it was filtered by a narrowband filter. The signal is strongly sinusoidal in its general appearance. However, deviations from an ideal sine wave are readily seen. The amplitude varies randomly, and this is an AM noise. Also, the time between zero crossings varies randomly, and this is the same as a random phase that results in an FM noise.

In the usual communication system, noise variations in amplitude and phase are very slow with respect to the carrier frequency ω_0. This leads to the following model for the narrowband noise:

$$N(t) = N_C(t)\cos \omega_0 t - N_S(t)\sin \omega_0 t \qquad (8.87)$$

---

[h] The angle of the cosine in $v_{FM}(t)$ is $[\omega_0 + \theta(t)]$, and its units are radians. The frequency, in radians per second, is therefore

$$\frac{d}{dt}[\omega_0 t + \theta(t)] = \omega_0 + \frac{d}{dt}\theta(t)$$

where ω_0 is called the carrier frequency. Changes in frequency centered about the carrier frequency are in the term $\frac{d}{dt}\theta(t)$ and are called instantaneous frequency.

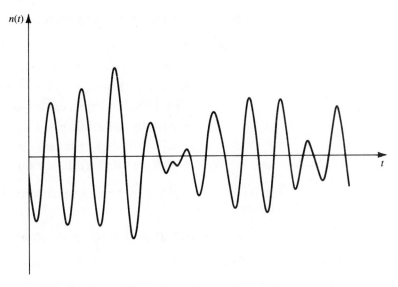

Figure 8.16   Illustrating a sample function from a narrowband random process.

The cosine and sine terms are in-phase and in-quadrature-phase respectively, with the carrier in (8.86). $N_C(t)$ and $N_S(t)$ are random processes, and a sample function of $N(t)$ is written as

$$n(t) = n_C(t)\cos \omega_0 t - n_S(t)\sin \omega_0 t$$

The sample function in Figure 8.16 is a portion of $n(t)$.

We require the narrowband random process $N(t)$ in (8.87) to be WSS. Given this, we can investigate the nature of the in-phase and quadrature random processes $N_C(t)$ and $N_S(t)$. WSS in (8.13) requires that the expected value of $N(t)$ be a constant,

$$E[N(t)] = E[N_C(t)]\cos \omega_0 t - E[N_S(t)]\sin \omega_0 t$$

Because the cosine and sine factors in this expression vary with time, we must choose

$$E[N_C(t)] = E[N_S(t)] = 0 \qquad\qquad\qquad \textbf{(8.88)}$$

Then,

$$E[N(t)] = 0 \qquad\qquad\qquad \textbf{(8.89)}$$

Wide-sense stationarity also requires the autocorrelation function of the narrowband random process to be independent of the time origin. Therefore,

$$
\begin{aligned}
R_N(\tau) &= E[N(t)N(t+\tau)] \\
&= E[(N_C(t)\cos \omega_0 t - N_S(t)\sin \omega_0 t) \\
&\quad \times (N_C(t+\tau)\cos \omega_0(t+\tau) - N_S(t+\tau)\sin \omega_0(t+\tau))] \\
&= E[N_C(t)N_C(t+\tau)]\cos \omega_0 t \cos \omega_0(t+\tau) \\
&\quad - E[N_C(t)N_S(t+\tau)]\cos \omega_0 t \sin \omega_0(t+\tau) \\
&\quad - E[N_S(t)N_C(t+\tau)]\sin \omega_0 t \cos \omega_0(t+\tau) \\
&\quad + E[N_S(t)N_S(t+\tau)]\sin \omega_0 t \sin \omega_0(t+\tau)
\end{aligned}
$$

This relation is simplified by defining the following auto- and crosscorrelation functions,

$$
R_C(\tau) = E[N_C(t)N_C(t+\tau)] \quad \text{and} \quad R_S(\tau) = E[N_S(t)N_S(t+\tau)]
$$

$$
R_{CS}(\tau) = E[N_C(t)N_S(t+\tau)] \quad \text{and} \quad R_{SC}(\tau) = E[N_S(t)N_C(t+\tau)]
$$

For the autocorrelation function $R_N(\tau)$ to be independent of the time-origin, we will require

$$
R_C(\tau) = R_S(\tau) \tag{8.90}
$$

$$
R_{CS}(\tau) = -R_{SC}(\tau) \tag{8.91}
$$

We can see this because, using (8.90) and (8.91), the autocorrelation function becomes

$$
\begin{aligned}
R_N(\tau) &= R_C(\tau)[\cos \omega_0 t \cos \omega_0(t+\tau) + \sin \omega_0 t \sin \omega_0(t+\tau)] \\
&\quad - R_{SC}(\tau)[\sin \omega_0 t \cos \omega_0(t+\tau) - \cos \omega_0 t \sin \omega_0(t+\tau)]
\end{aligned}
$$

Then, using addition theorems from trigonometry,

$$
R_N(\tau) = R_C(\tau)\cos \omega_0 \tau + R_{SC}(\tau)\sin \omega_0 \tau \tag{8.92}
$$

Combining (8.91) with (8.19) leads to the conclusion that the crosscorrelation functions are odd

$$
R_{SC}(-\tau) = -R_{SC}(\tau) \tag{8.93}
$$

This verifies that the autocorrelation function $R_N(\tau)$ in (8.92) is an even function of τ.

The PSD for the narrowband random process is obtained using the Wiener-Khinchin relation (8.48). Obtaining this PSD is very important in communication engineering, but to derive it here will take us too far from the central task of this book.

When $\tau = 0$, we have the curious yet important results:

1. Using (8.90) and (8.92),

$$
R_N(0) = R_C(0) = R_S(0) \tag{8.94}
$$

The average power of the in-phase noise is equal to the average power of the quadrature noise, and each of these is equal to the **total average power.**

2. Using (8.93),

$$R_{SC}(0) = 0 = R_{CS}(0) \tag{8.95}$$

The in-phase noise and the quadrature noise are orthogonal when $\tau = 0$.

Both $N_C(t)$ and $N_S(t)$ are zero-mean random processes (8.88). Therefore, when they are evaluated at the same time (i.e., $\tau = 0$), they are uncorrelated (4.22). We assume that $N_C(t)$ and $N_S(t)$ are Gaussian random processes. Since uncorrelated Gaussian random variables are also independent, $N_C(t)$ and $N_S(t)$ are independent at any time t. It then follows that $N(t)$ itself is a Gaussian random process, because at any time t, using (8.87), $N(t)$ is a linear combination of two independent Gaussian random processes (see (4.35)).

An alternative expression for the narrowband noise in (8.87) is

$$N(t) = R(t)\cos[\omega_0 t + \Gamma(t)] \tag{8.96}$$

where

$$N_C(t) = R(t)\cos \Gamma(t)$$
$$N_S(t) = R(t)\sin \Gamma(t)$$

where $R(t)$ and $\Gamma(t)$ are random processes. A sample function in this representation is

$$n(t) = r(t)\cos[\omega_0 t + \lambda(t)]$$

Another equation relating (8.87) and (8.96) is

$$R(t) = \sqrt{N_C^2(t) + N_S^2(t)} \tag{8.97}$$

where $R(t)$ is called an **envelope random process;** it describes the envelope on the noise shown in Figure 8.16. The relation in (8.97) is the same as that used in Example 4.9. In fact, the similarities between these two cases lead us to say that, at any fixed time t, the envelope random process is a Rayleigh random variable:

$$f_{R(t)}(r) = \frac{r}{R_N(0)} \exp[-r^2/2R_N(0)], \quad r \geq 0$$

It then follows from Example 4.9, where the mean and the variance of the Rayleigh random variable are discussed,

$$E[R(t)] = \sqrt{\frac{\pi}{2} R_N(0)} \tag{8.98}$$

$$\text{Var}[R(t)] = \left(2 - \frac{\pi}{2}\right) R_N(0) \tag{8.99}$$

Example 8.14   The rms value of a narrowband Gaussian noise that is in phase with a carrier is 2.35 μV.

$$R_S(0) = R_C(0) = R_N(0) = (2.35 \times 10^{-6})^2$$

With specific reference to the envelope of the narrowband noise—which is a Rayleigh random process—its mean value is, using (8.98),

$$E[R(t)] = 2.95 \ \mu V$$

Its variance is, using (8.99),

$$\mathrm{Var}[R(t)] = 2.37 \times 10^{-12} \ V^2$$

Therefore, the mean square value of the envelope is

$$E[R^2(t)] = \mathrm{Var}[R(t)] + E^2[R(t)]$$
$$E[R^2(t)] = 2R_N(0) = 11.05 \times 10^{-12} \ V^2$$

and, its rms value is $v_{\mathrm{rms}} = 3.32 \ \mu V$.

• • • • •

The narrowband noise in (8.87) and (8.96) is only the noise without the carrier (8.86) present. If these two are added, corresponding to the case of additive signal and noise,

$$v(t) = v_C(t) + N(t)$$
$$= [A + N_C(t)]\cos \omega_0 t - N_S(t)\sin \omega_0 t \qquad \textbf{(8.100)}$$

Figure 8.17 plots (8.100) as a phasor diagram and shows the noise variations when they are small with respect to A, the amplitude of the carrier. From this figure, we see that $N_C(t)$, which is in phase with A, is the major contributor to an AM noise, and that $N_S(t)$, which is in quadrature phase with A, is the major contributor to an FM noise.

• •

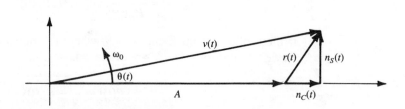

Figure 8.17   A phasor diagram showing the effect of the narrowband noise components $n_c(t)$ and $n_s(t)$ on a carrier with phasor amplitude A.

Example 8.15   The noise power coming through a narrowband filter is

$$v_N^2 = 2.7 \times 10^{-7} \text{ V}^2$$

What value should the amplitude of an unmodulated AM carrier have —A in (8.86)—if the ratio of carrier power to the power in $N_C(t)$ is to be 60 dB?

$$R_C(0) = R_N(0) = 2.7 \times 10^{-7}$$

The carrier power is

$$\langle v_C^2(t) \rangle = A^2/2$$

Then,

$$10 \log \left[\frac{A^2}{2R_N(0)} \right] = 60 \text{ dB}$$

leads to $A = 0.73$. Because of the results in (8.94), the same answer is obtained if we ask for the amplitude of an unmodulated FM carrier.

♦ ♦ ♦ ♦ ♦

Exercises

♦   ♦   ♦   ♦   ♦

1. $X(t)$ is a WSS random process with the autocorrelation function $R_X(\tau)$ and $C(t)$ is the carrier random process

$$C(t) = A \cos(\omega_0 t + \theta)$$

where A and ω_0 are constants and θ is uniformly distributed between $\pm \pi$. The $X(t)$ and $C(t)$ are uncorrelated. The random process $W(t)$ is

$$W(t) = X(t)C(t)$$

a. Find the mean of $W(t)$ at any time t.

b. Find the autocorrelation function for $W(t)$.

c. Is $W(t)$ a WSS random process?

2. The random process $Y(t)$ is

$$Y(t) = A \cos(\omega_0 t + \theta)$$

where A and ω_0 are constants and θ is a random variable uniformly distributed between $\pm \pi$. The random process $U(t)$ is

$$U(t) = Y^2(t)$$

a. Find the mean of $U(t)$ at any time t.

b. Find the autocorrelation function for $U(t)$.

c. Is $U(t)$ a WSS random process?

d. Find the crosscorrelation $E[Y(t)U(t + \tau)]$.

3. $X(t)$ and $C(t)$ are two uncorrelated WSS random processes with the autocorrelation functions

$$R_C(\tau) = \frac{A}{2} \cos \omega_0\tau \quad \text{and} \quad R_X(\tau) = P\frac{\sin W\tau}{W\tau}$$

where $\omega_0 = 5W$. Let $Y(t) = X(t)C(t)$.

a. Find the autocorrelation $R_Y(\tau)$

b. Plot $R_Y(\tau)$ for $W\tau$ from 0 to 5π in steps of $\pi/20$. Let $AP = 2$.

4. A zero-mean periodic signal $x(t)$ with a period of T may be described using a Fourier series

$$x(t) = \sum_{k=1}^{\infty} A_k \cos(k\omega_0 t + \phi_k)$$

where $\omega_0 = 2\pi f_0 = 2\pi/T$. Suppose that $x(t)$ can be time-shifted randomly within an interval of $\pm T/2$. This gives rise to the WSS random process $X(t)$

$$X(t) = \sum_{k=1}^{\infty} A_k \cos(k\omega_0 t + \phi_k + k\theta)$$

where θ is uniformly distributed between $\pm \pi$. Show that the autocorrelation function for $X(t)$ is

$$R_X(\tau) = \sum_{k=1}^{\infty} \frac{A_k^2}{2} \cos (k\omega_0\tau)$$

5. When $R_Z(\tau)$ in (8.16) was derived, it was assumed that the random pulses in Figure 8.3 are equally likely $\pm V$, and that the width of each pulse is a constant T. This led to $P(\mathbf{A})$, the probability that two values, one at t_1 and the other at t_2, are on the same pulse to be

$$P(\mathbf{A}) = 1 - \frac{|t_2 - t_1|}{T}$$

Assume now that pulse widths are not constant; assume that pulse widths are distributed exponentially with parameter λ. We still assume that each pulse is equally likely $\pm V$. Then

$$P(\mathbf{A}) = \exp(-\lambda|t_2 - t_1|)$$

Find the autocorrelation $R_Z(\tau)$ for this case.

6. The autocorrelation function in (8.16) is for the WSS random process $Z(t)$ illustrated in Figure 8.3. A random process $X(t)$ is the sum of $Z(t)$ and the random variable U:

$$X(t) = Z(t) + U$$

where $E[U] = 0$, $\text{Var}[U] = A^2$, and U and $Z(t)$ are uncorrelated. Find the autocorrelation function $R_X(\tau)$ and determine if it is WSS.

7. The random process $X(t)$ has the autocorrelation function

$$R_X(\tau) = 15 \, e^{-2|\tau|}$$

The random process $Y(t)$ is

$$Y(t) = X(t) - 3$$

a. What is the mean of $Y(t)$?

b. What is the autocorrelation function for $Y(t)$?

c. What is the variance of $Y(t)$?

d. What is the crosscorrelation $R_{XY}(\tau)$?

8. $X(t)$ and $Y(t)$ are zero-mean uncorrelated WSS random processes. The random processes $U(t)$ and $V(t)$ are

$$U(t) = X(t) + Y(t)$$
$$V(t) = X(t) - Y(t)$$

What are the correlation functions $R_U(\tau)$, $R_V(\tau)$, $R_{VY}(\tau)$, $R_{UX}(\tau)$, and $R_{UV}(\tau)$?

9. $X(t)$ and $Y(t)$ are uncorrelated, zero-mean, WSS random processes. Their PSDs are $S_X(\omega)$ and $S_Y(\omega)$. A new random process $Z(t)$ is formed by the relation

$$Z(t) = aX(t) + bY(t)$$

where a and b are real constants. Find an expression for the PSD of $Z(t)$ in terms of the PSDs for $X(t)$ and $Y(t)$.

10. A random process $Z(t)$ is formed by the sum of two uncorrelated, zero-mean WSS random processes:

$$Z(t) = X(t) + Y(t)$$

The following relations are known:

$$S_X(\omega) = (VT)^2 \frac{\sin^2(\omega T/2)}{(\omega T/2)^2} \quad \text{and} \quad R_Y(\tau) = \frac{AW}{\pi} \frac{\sin W\tau}{W\tau}$$

Parameters used in these relations are $T = 3$ ms, $V = 10$ V, $A = 5$ (units), $f_0 = W/2\pi = 150$ Hz.

a. What are the units of the parameter A?

b. What is the value of $R_Z(0)$?

11. The WSS random process $X(t)$ has the PSD $S_X(\omega)$, which is the constant K when $|\omega| < W$, and is zero otherwise. Find an expression for the variance of $X(t)$.

12. A WSS random process has the discrete spectrum

$$S_X(\omega) = 7\delta(\omega \pm \omega_0) + 3\delta[\omega \pm (\omega_0 + \omega_S)] + 3\delta[\omega \pm (\omega_0 - \omega_S)]$$

where $\omega_S \ll \omega_0$.

a. Sketch a plot of the PSD.

b. What is the average power of $X(t)$?

13. The PSD of a WSS random process $X(t)$ is shown in Figure 8.18. What is σ_X^2?

14. A PSD is given as

$$S_X(\omega) = \frac{10\omega^2}{\omega^4 + 10}$$

Find the average power of $X(t)$.

15. An autocorrelation function for the WSS random process $X(t)$ is

$$R_X(\tau) = 15e^{-2|\tau|} + 9$$

Find the PSD $S_X(\omega)$.

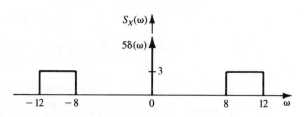

Figure 8.18   The PSD for Exercise 13.

16. An autocorrelation function for the WSS random process $Y(t)$ is

$$R_Y(\tau) = 9 + 15 \left(1 - \frac{|\tau|}{T}\right), \quad |\tau| < T$$
$$= 9, \qquad\qquad\qquad \text{otherwise}$$

Find the PSD $S_Y(\omega)$.

17. A band-limited WSS random process $X(t)$ has the PSD

$$S_X(\omega) = 5 \cos\left(\frac{\pi\omega}{2\omega_M}\right) \quad |\omega| < \omega$$
$$= 0, \qquad\qquad \text{otherwise}$$

A carrier random process $C(t)$, which is uncorrelated with $X(t)$, has the PSD

$$S_C(\omega) = 100\pi[\delta(\omega + \omega_0) + \delta(\omega - \omega_0)]$$

where $\omega_0 = 10\omega_M$.

a. What is the average power of $X(t)$?

b. Let $Y(t) = X(t)C(t)$. What is the PSD of the random process $Y(t)$? What is its average power?

18. The random processes $X(t)$ and $Y(t)$ have the autocorrelation functions

$$R_X(\tau) = 15e^{-10|\tau|} \quad \text{and} \quad R_Y(\tau) = 4.5\cos(100\tau)$$

If $Z(t) = X(t)Y(t)$, and if $X(t)$ and $Y(t)$ are uncorrelated, what is the PSD for $Z(t)$?

19. The PSD of the random process $X(t)$ is

$$S_X(\omega) = 50\pi\delta(\omega + 1000) + 50\pi\delta(\omega - 1000)$$

The PSD for the random process $Y(t)$, which is not correlated with $X(t)$, is the constant value 30π as long as $|\omega| < 100$, but is zero otherwise. If $Z(t) = X(t)Y(t)$, what is the PSD for the random process $Z(t)$?

20. A WSS random process $X(t)$ has the PSD shown in Figure 8.19, where $W \ll \omega_0$. The random process $Y(t)$ is obtained from

$$Y(t) = X(t)\cos(\omega_0 t + \theta)$$

where θ is uniformly distributed between $\pm\pi$. Find the PSD for $Y(t)$.

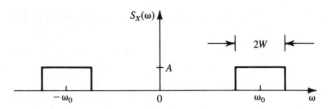

Figure 8.19   The PSD for Exercise 20.

• •

21. A measurement system, which has a bandwidth of $\Delta f = 100,000$ Hz, measures the average noise voltage across a device that has an effective noise temperature of 450 K, and an effective resistance of 52 Ω.

    a. What is the two-sided PSD of this noise source?

    b. What rms noise voltage is measured?

22. Assume that the following data are obtained from a windowed sample function obtained from an ergodic random process. Use (8.72) to estimate the autocorrelation function for $\tau = 0, 2,$ and 4 ms, where $\Delta t = 2$ ms.

$x(t)$	1.5	2.2	1.0	−3.0	−1.6	1.7	−2.5	2.0	1.6	−1.8
k	0	1	2	3	4	5	6	7	8	9

23. Assume that the following data are obtained from a windowed sample function obtained from an ergodic random process. Use (8.72) to estimate the autocorrelation functon for $\tau = 0, 3,$ and 6 ms, where $\Delta t = 3$ ms.

$x(t)$	1.0	2.1	1.5	2.2	−0.5	−2.0	−3.5	−1.5	2.0	−1.3
k	0	1	2	3	4	5	6	7	8	9

24. Assume that the following data are obtained from a windowed sample function obtained from an ergodic random process. Use (8.72) to estimate the autocorrelation functon for $\tau = 0, 7$ and 14 ms, where $\Delta t = 7$ ms.

$x(t)$	0.4	1.1	0.8	−0.4	0.3	−1.7	−2.0	−1.2	−0.2	0.8
k	0	1	2	3	4	5	6	7	8	9

25. Use the computer to construct a data file called $v(k)$ for $0 \leq k \leq 999$

measurements. The data to be put into this file are independent realizations of a Gaussian random variable with a mean of zero and a variance of 7. The data $v(k)$ therefore make up a windowed sample of Gaussian white noise. Write (8.72) as an algorithm, let $\Delta t = 1$, and apply it to the data $v(k)$ at times $\tau = 0, 1, 2, \ldots, 100$. Show that the plot of the resultant data is an approximation to Figure 8.4(a).

26. Use the computer to construct a data file called $s(k)$ for $0 \le k \le 999$ measurements. The data to be put into this file are a sinusoid with random phase

$$s(t) = 4 \cos[2\pi(k/20) + \theta]$$

where θ is arbitrary, say, $\theta = 0.7\pi$, or any other value selected randomly between $\pm \pi$. The data $s(k)$ are therefore a windowed sample of a sinusoid with random phase. Write (8.72) as an algorithm, let $\Delta t = 1$, and apply it to the data $s(k)$ at times $\tau = 0, 1, 2, \ldots, 100$. Show that the plot of the resultant data is an approximation to Figure 8.4(b).

27. Use the computer to construct a data file called $s(k)$ for $0 \le k \le 999$ measurements. The data to be put into this file are to be constructed by you and should be similar to the sample functions in Figure 8.3. Let each pulse have a length $T = 20$ s, and have an amplitude randomly (equally likely) selected to be $+3$ or -3. The data $s(k)$ are therefore a windowed sample of a sequence of random pulses related to the pdf in (8.6). Write (8.27) as an algorithm, let $\Delta t = 1$, and apply it to the data $s(k)$ in intervals of time $\tau = 0, 1, 2, \ldots, 100$. Show that the plot of the resultant data is an approximation to Figure 8.4(c).

28. Verify the Fourier transform pair given in Example 8.13.

29. Calculate the crosscorrelation $R_{YX}(\tau) = E[Y(t)X(T + \tau)]$ for the low-pass filter in Example 8.11. The input to the filter is zero-mean white noise $X(t)$. This calculation should verify (8.19) using $R_{XY}(\tau)$ as shown in Example 8.12.

30. Verify the result for $R_Y(\tau)$ in Example 8.13 by using (8.83b).

31. A linear system has the impulse response $h(t) = 5e^{-t/3} u(t)$. The input to the system is a WSS random process with the autocorrelation function

$$R_X(\tau) = 2e^{-|\tau|/2}$$

Calculate the value of $R_{XY}(\tau)$ when $\tau = 1$.

32. The input to the circuit in Figure 8.20 is a zero-mean wide-sense

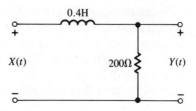

Figure 8.20   The circuit for Exercise 32.

stationary random process with the PSD

$$S_X(\omega) = \frac{35{,}000}{\omega^2 + (700)^2}$$

What is $S_Y(\omega)$ when $\omega = 400$ radians/s?

33. The input signal to the network in Figure 8.21 is a zero-mean white noise with a variance of 7. What is the PSD of the output random process $Y(t)$?

34. The transfer function of a linear system is

$$H(s) = \frac{4(s + 1)}{s^2 + 3s + 1} e^{-0.2s}$$

The input to this system is a zero-mean white Gaussian noise with a variance of 5. What is the PSD of the output Y from this system when $\omega = 3$ radians/s?

35. The transfer functon of a system is

$$H(s) = \frac{s + 1}{s^2 + 3s + 2}$$

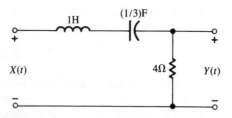

Figure 8.21   The circuit for Exercise 33.

The input to this system is a WSS random process that has the PSD

$$S_X(\omega) = \frac{6}{\omega^2 + 9}$$

Find the PSD of the output random process.

References

• • • • •

1. Cooper, George R., and Clare D. McGillem. *Probabilistic Methods of Signal and System Analysis.* 2d ed. New York: Holt, Rinehart and Winston, 1986.

2. Peebles, Peyton Z., Jr. *Probability, Random Variables, and Random Signal Principles.* 2d ed. New York: McGraw-Hill Book Company, 1987.

3. Helstrom, Carl W. *Probability and Stochastic Processes for Engineers.* New York: Macmillan Publishing Company, 1984.

4. Larson, Harold J., and Bruno O. Shubert. *Probabilistic Models in Engineering Sciences, Volume I: Random Variables and Stochastic Processes.* New York: John Wiley and Sons, 1979.

5. Leon-Garcia, Alberto. *Probability and Random Processes for Electrical Engineering.* Reading, Mass.: Addison-Wesley Publishing Company, 1989.

6. Shanmugan, K. Sam, and Arthur M. Breipohl. *Random Signals— Detection, Estimation and Data Analysis.* New York: John Wiley and Sons, 1988.

7. Papoulis, Athanasios. *Probability, Random Variables, and Stochastic Processes.* New York: McGraw-Hill Book Company, 1965.

8. Carlson, A. B. *Communication Systems.* 3d ed. New York: McGraw-Hill Book Company, 1986.

Algorithms for Random Number Generators

> *Random numbers are too important to be left to chance.*
>
> S. Paul Williams

This appendix presents specific algorithms for modeling a variety of random variables. Crucial to the operation of these algorithms is the availability of a random number generator whose output is uniformly distributed in the interval between zero and one. Most computer systems have this uniform random number generator available as a function.

Use of a uniform random number generator typically requires proper management of an integer called a **seed,** which is used to initialize the URNG algorithm. If the reader is familiar with a URNG algorithm and the management of its seed, then he or she may refer directly to any of the algorithms in this appendix. If not, the reader is advised to read the following.

This is an outline of how an algorithm for the uniform random number generator can be devised. However, let the reader be cautioned: A large body of work exists on this topic, and the algorithm design is not as facile a task as this brief introduction may imply.

To begin, m is some constant integer called a **modulus,** while n is some variable integer generally large with respect to m. As different values of n are selected, the **remainder** of n/m is an integer that gives the appearance of being random. We designate the remainder as $n(\mod m)$. Besides being an integer, the remainder is limited in its range of possible values to

$$0 \le n(\mod m) \le m - 1 \tag{A.1}$$

Assume all generated values of $n(\mod m)$ occur uniformly within the interval from zero to $m - 1$. It then follows that the ratio

$$x = n(\mod m)/m \tag{A.2}$$

is a number occurring uniformly in the interval $0 \le x < 1$. This observation illustrates the fundamental idea behind an algorithm that generates random numbers that are uniformly distributed between zero and one.

The algorithm is also recursive: A sequence of integers is constructed using

$$I_k = aI_{k-1}(\mod m) \tag{A.3}$$

This recursion formula may be coded using

$$I_k = a*I_{k-1} - \text{INTEGER}(a*I_{k-1}/m)*m \tag{A.4}$$

The integer function gives the largest integer less than or equal to its argument. Each integer I_k in the recursion process satisfies the limits in (A.1) and, using (A.2), is used to calculate a random number x_k:

$$x_k = I_k/m \tag{A.5}$$

The seed I_0 is used to start the recursion process. This type of algorithm is called a **multiplicative linear congruential** uniform random number generator.

The introductory book on simulations by Law and Kelton is convenient for further study about uniform random number generators.[1] Law and Kelton recommend some values for m and a that experience and theory have shown to be better than others. One of their recommendations is

$$m = 2^{31} - 1 = 2,147,483,647$$
$$a = 7^5 = 16,807$$

These choices for m and a are based on the work of Lewis, Goodman, and Miller.[2] From (A.3), if I_k is zero, then the algorithm ceases to be useful since all values of I_k following will also be zero. However, it has been reported[1] that, with these specific values for m and a, the values for I_k are limited to the

$$2^{31} - 2$$

integers in the interval $0 < I_k \le m - 1$. That is, the algorithm will use

$$2^{31} - 2 = 2,147,483,646$$

integers between 0 and m only once before the algorithm repeats itself. We assume that since the entire sequence is uniform between 0 and m that all smaller subsequences will also be uniform. That may not be true. Further, since I_k in this algorithm can never be exactly 0 or m per Ref. 1, the random number x_k in (A.5) can never be exactly 0 or 1. We consider this restriction to be a virtue because there will be situations in which we will want to calculate $\ln(x_k)$ or $\ln(1 - x_k)$.

This appendix contains not only an algorithm for URNG, but several other random number generators also: Bernoulli, binomial, exponential, Gaussian (normal), and Poisson.

How these other algorithms work is described at various places in the body of the text. All we want for the reader to observe now is that URNG is used for each of them. Algorithms are written as subroutines in FORTRAN. Sufficient comments are introduced so that the reader may translate the FORTRAN coding into another computer language if that is necessary.

The output from the URNG algorithm is the first ten values of x_k and I_k when the seed $I_0 = 1$. As another aid in checking the accuracy of computer code, the value of $I_{1000} = 522,329,230$.

References

♦   ♦   ♦   ♦   ♦

1. Law, A. M., and W. D. Kelton. *Simulation Modeling and Analysis.* New York: McGraw-Hall Book Company, 1982.

2. Lewis, P. A. W., A. S. Goodman, and J. J. Miller, "A Pseudo-Random Number Generator for the System/360," *IBM Syst. J.,* Vol. 8, pp. 136–146, 1969.

Section A.1   Code: URNG—Uniform Random Number Generator

♦   ♦   ♦   ♦   ♦

```
C    URNG - Uniform Random Number Generator
C
C    URNG is a function whose output is a real number uniformly
C    distributed between zero and one, exclusive of zero and one.
C    The algorithm will operate 2**31 - 2 = 2,147,483,646 times
C    before the random number ouput sequence will repeat itself.
C    Within these limits, each number in the output sequence is
C    assumed to be uncorrelated with all others.  The integer
C    DSEED is global.  It is to be initialized once in the calling
C    program, and then never altered by the calling program.
```

```
C23456789
      FUNCTION URNG(DSEED)
C
      DOUBLE PRECISION DSEED
C
C  A recursion formula is started for DSEED.
C
      DSEED = 16807 * DSEED
C
C  Calculate the next seed.
C
      DSEED = DSEED - DINT(DSEED / 2147483647) * 2147483647
C
C  Calculate the random number: 0 < URNG < 1, and then return.
C
      URNG = DSEED / 2147483647
      RETURN
      END
```

The following program illustrates the use of the URNG function. Output data are shown in the listing below.

```
C23456789
      DOUBLE PRECISION DSEED
      DSEED = 1
      DO 2 I=1, 10
          X = URNG(DSEED)
          WRITE(6,900)I, X, DSEED
    2 CONTINUE
  900 FORMAT(I5,F12.6,F13.1)
      STOP
      END

    1    0.000008         16807.0
    2    0.131538     282475249.0
    3    0.755605    1622650073.0
    4    0.458650     984943658.0
    5    0.532767    1144108930.0
    6    0.218959     470211272.0
    7    0.047045     101027544.0
    8    0.678865    1457850878.0
    9    0.679296    1458777923.0
   10    0.934693    2007237709.0
```

Section A.2   Code: BRNRNG—Bernoulli Random Number Generator

◆ ◆ ◆ ◆ ◆

```
C    BRNRNG - Bernoulli Random Number Generator
C
C    BRNRNG is a subroutine which uses a uniform random number
C    generator URNG to produce random numbers with Bernoulli
C    statistics.  The Bernoulli random variable is either a one,
C    which occurs with probability p, or a zero, which occurs
C    with probability q.  p + q = 1.  The input parameters to the
C    subroutine are P and DSEED.  The Bernoulli random number
C    returned by the subroutine is the integer KX.
C    Mean = p, Variance = pq.
C
      SUBROUTINE BRNRNG(P, DSEED, KX)
C23456789
C
C    Initialize the Bernoulli random variable to zero, and get a
C    random number Y which is uniformly likely between 0 and 1.
C
      KX = 0
      Y = URNG(DSEED)
C
C    If 0 < Y < P then set KX to one.  Otherwise leave KX as zero.
C    Then return to the calling program.
C
      IF(Y .LT. P) KX = 1
      RETURN
      END
```

The following program illustrates the use of the subroutine BRNRNG. If this program is run with the URNG function (from this appendix) the output data are as shown in the listing below.

```
C23456789
      DOUBLE PRECISION DSEED
      DSEED = 1
      DO 2 I = 1,10
          CALL BRNRNG(0.6, DSEED, KBRN)
          WRITE(6,900)I, KBRN
    2 CONTINUE
  900 FORMAT(2I5)
      STOP
      END
```

```
 1  1
 2  1
 3  0
 4  1
 5  1
 6  1
 7  1
 8  0
 9  0
10  0
```

Section A.3   Code: BINRNG — Binomial Random Number Generator

◆ ◆ ◆ ◆ ◆

```
C    BINRNG - Binomial Random Number Generator
C
C    BINRNG is a subroutine which uses a uniform random number
C    generator URNG to produce random numbers with Binomial
C    statistics.  The Binomial random variable is an integer
C    having the value 0, 1, 2, . . . , or N.  (p + q)**N = 1.
C    The input parameters to the subroutine are P, N, and
C    DSEED. The Binomial random number returned by the
C    subroutine is the integer KY.  Mean = Np, Variance = Npq.
C
     SUBROUTINE BINRNG(P, N, DSEED, KY)
C23456789
C    Add N Bernoulli random numbers, then return to the
C    calling program.
C
     KY = 0
     DO 2 I=1,N
C
C    Generate a Bernoulli random number.
C
        KX = 0
        Y = URNG(DSEED)
        IF(Y .LT. P) KX = 1
C
        KY = KY + KX
   2 CONTINUE
     RETURN
     END
```

The following program illustrates the use of the subroutine BINRNG. If this program is run with the URNG function (from this appendix) the output data are as shown in the listing below.

```
C23456789
      DOUBLE PRECISION DSEED
      DSEED = 1
      DO 2 I=1,10
          CALL BINRNG(0.5, 10, DSEED, KBIN)
          WRITE(6,900)I, KBIN
    2 CONTINUE
  900 FORMAT(2I5)
      STOP
      END

      1    5
      2    6
      3    3
      4    4
      5    4
      6    7
      7    5
      8    4
      9    2
     10    6
```

Section A.4   Code: EXPRNG—Exponential Random Number Generator

♦ ♦ ♦ ♦ ♦

```
C    EXPRNG - Exponential Random Number Generator
C
C    EXPRNG is a subroutine which uses a uniform random number
C    generator URNG to produce random numbers with Exponential
C    statistics.  The Exponential random variable is obtained from
C    the density function f(x) = a exp(-ax) where x is non-negative.
C    The input parameters to the subroutine are A and DSEED.  The
C    Exponential random number returned by the subroutine is Y, a
C    real number.  Mean = 1/a, Variance = 1/a**2.
C
```

```
      SUBROUTINE EXPRNG(A, DSEED, Y)
C23456789
C
C  Use URNG as an input for the inverse function of f(x) to
C  calculate an Exponential random number.
C  Then return to the calling program.
C
      X = URNG(DSEED)
      Y = (-1.0 / A) * ALOG(X)
      RETURN
      END
```

The following program illustrates the use of the subroutine EXPRNG. If this program is run with the URNG function (from this appendix) the output data are shown in the listing below.

```
C23456789
      DOUBLE PRECISION DSEED
      DSEED = 1
      DO 2 I=1,10
          CALL EXPRNG(2.0, DSEED, Y)
          WRITE(6,900)I, Y
    2 CONTINUE
  900 FORMAT(I5,F10.5)
      STOP
      END

    1    5.87901
    2    1.01423
    3    0.14012
    4    0.38973
    5    0.31484
    6    0.75943
    7    1.52833
    8    0.19367
    9    0.19335
   10    0.03377
```

Section A.5   Code: GRNG — Gaussian Random Number Generator

◆ ◆ ◆ ◆ ◆

```
C    GRNG - Gaussian Random Number Generator
C
C    GRNG is a subroutine which uses a uniform random number
C    generator URNG to produce random numbers with Gaussian
C    (Normal) statistics.  The Gaussian random variable has a mean
C    of XAV, and a standard deviation of XSD. The input parameters
C    to the subroutine are XAV, XSD, and DSEED.  The Gaussian
C    random variable returned by the subroutine is X, a real number.
C
      SUBROUTINE GRNG(XAV, XSD, DSEED, X)
C23456789
C
C    Add twelve values obtained from the uniform random number
C    generator URNG.
C
      X = 0.0
      DO 2 I=1,12
          X = X + URNG(DSEED)
    2 CONTINUE
C
C    Scale the result by XSD, and adjust the mean to XAV.
C    Then return to the calling program.
C
      X = XSD * (X - 6.0) + XAV
      RETURN
      END
```

The following program illustrates the use of the subroutine GRNG. If this program is run with the URNG function (from this appendix) the output data are as shown in the listing below.

```
C23456789
      DOUBLE PRECISION DSEED
      DSEED = 1
      DO 2 I=1,10
          CALL GRNG(1.5, 3.2, DSEED, Z)
          WRITE(6,900)I, Z
    2 CONTINUE
  900 FORMAT(I5,F10.5)
      STOP
      END
```

```
 1   -0.61090
 2   -1.05528
 3    2.40535
 4    6.91305
 5   -0.59361
 6    1.46275
 7    2.66922
 8    6.90274
 9   -1.79632
10    4.27264
```

Section A.6 Code: POIRNG — Poisson Random Number Generator

◆ ◆ ◆ ◆ ◆

```
C   POIRNG - Poisson Random Number Generator
C
C   POIRNG is a subroutine which uses a uniform random number
C   generator URNG to produce random numbers with Poisson
C   statistics.  The Poisson random variable is the integer k:
C   P(k) = (b**k) * exp(-b) / (k!), b = a*t, k = 0, 1, 2, ... .
C   a is the parameter from the Exponential random variable.
C   The input parameters to the subroutine are A, T, DSEED.
C   The Poisson random number returned by the subroutine is the
C   integer K.  Mean = b, Variance = b, b = a*t.
C
      SUBROUTINE POIRNG(A, T, DSEED, K)
C23456789
C   Set the counter K to zero.
C
      K = 0
C
C   K is the number of times exponential random numbers can be
C   added without having the sum exceed T.
C
      YSUM = 0.0
    2 X = URNG(DSEED)
      Y = (-1.0 / A) * ALOG(1.0 - X)
      YSUM = YSUM + Y
      IF(YSUM .LE. T) THEN
          K = K + 1
          GO TO 2
      ENDIF
```

```
C
C   K is a Poisson random number; return to the calling
C   program.
C
    RETURN
    END
```

The following program illustrates the use of the subroutine POIRNG. If this program is run with the URNG function (from this appendix) the output data are as shown in the listing below.

```
C23456789
      DOUBLE PRECISION DSEED
      DSEED = 1
      DO 2 I=1,10
          CALL POIRNG(2.0, 1.0, DSEED, KPOI)
          WRITE(6,900)I, KPOI
    2 CONTINUE
  900 FORMAT(2I5)
      STOP
      END

      1    0
      2    0
      3    3
      4    0
      5    4
      6    1
      7    0
      8    2
      9    1
     10    4
```

Appendix

B A Brief Review of Some Counting Techniques

◆ ◆

Section B.1 The Fundamental Principle of Counting

◆ ◆ ◆ ◆ ◆

Suppose that we have a collection of n_1 items, each distinguishable from the others. Further, suppose that there is a second collection containing n_2 items, each distinguishable from the others. Then, the number of ways these two collections can be combined by first choosing an item from n_1 and then from n_2 is

$$n_1 n_2$$

Example B.1 The number of ways a letter of the alphabet can be combined with a single digit, with the letter first, is

$$26 \cdot 10 = 260$$

◆ ◆ ◆ ◆ ◆

This process of counting can be continued if other collections are combined:

$$n_1 n_2 n_3 \ldots$$

Note that a specific order of the collections is specified.

Section B.2   Permutations

♦ ♦ ♦ ♦ ♦

A **permutation** is an arrangement of distinguishable items in a specific order.

Example B.2 Suppose we have five distinguishable items a,b,c,d,e. Then, abcde, abced, and edcba are three different permutations of five items taken five at a time. Also, abc, abd, and eca are permutations of five items taken three at a time.

♦ ♦ ♦ ♦ ♦

We use the notation $P(n,k)$ to designate the number of permutations that can be counted if n items are taken k at a time.

$$P(n,n) = n(n-1)(n-2) \ldots \cdot 3 \cdot 2 \cdot 1 = n!$$

$$P(n,k) = \frac{n!}{(n-k)!} \tag{B.1}$$

Example B.3 $P(5,5) = 5! = 120$ and $P(5,2) = 5!/3! = 120/6 = 20.$

♦ ♦ ♦ ♦ ♦

Section B.3   Combinations

♦ ♦ ♦ ♦ ♦

A **combination** is a collection of items without regard to the order of the items in the collection.

Example B.4 Each of the following permutations is the same combination.

abc, acb, bca, cba.

♦ ♦ ♦ ♦ ♦

The number of combinations of n items taken k at a time is denoted $\binom{n}{k}$. We use the fundamental principle of counting to verify

$$P(n,k) = \binom{n}{k}k!$$

Therefore, using (B.1),

$$\binom{n}{k} = \frac{n!}{k!(n-k)!} \tag{B.2}$$

Several useful relations involving combinations are:

$$\binom{n}{k} = \binom{n}{n-k} \tag{B.3}$$

$$\binom{n}{0} = 1 \tag{B.4}$$

$$\binom{n}{1} = n \tag{B.5}$$

$$\binom{n}{k} = \binom{n-1}{k} + \binom{n-1}{k-1} \tag{B.6}$$

The bionomial theorem is:

$$(a+b)^n = \sum_{k=0}^{n} \binom{n}{k} a^k b^{n-k} \tag{B.7}$$

The Vandermonde convolution relation is:

$$\sum_{k=0}^{n} \binom{r}{k}\binom{N-r}{n-k} = \binom{N}{n} \tag{B.8}$$

where n is the smaller of r or $N-r$.

Appendix

C

The Gaussian Random Variable

The cumulative distribution function (cdf) for a Gaussian random variable with arbitrary mean μ_X and standard deviation σ_X is

$$F_X(x) = \frac{1}{\sqrt{2\pi\sigma_X^2}} \int_{-\infty}^{x} \exp[-(\alpha - \mu_X)^2/2\sigma_X^2]d\alpha$$

Using the change of variables $\beta = (\alpha - \mu_X)/\sigma_X$:

$$F_X(x) = \frac{1}{\sqrt{2\pi}} \int_{-\infty}^{(x-\mu_X)/\sigma_X} \exp(-\beta^2/2)d\beta \qquad \text{(C.1)}$$

the **normalized** Gaussian cdf (3.55) is denoted by $\psi(z)$:

$$\psi(x) = \frac{1}{\sqrt{2\pi}} \int_{-\infty}^{z} \exp(-\beta^2/2)d\beta \qquad \text{(C.2)}$$

The following relations may be obtained from (C.1) and (C.2):

$$\psi(-z) = 1 - \psi(z) \qquad \text{(C.3)}$$

$$F_X(x) = \psi\left(\frac{x - \mu_X}{\sigma_X}\right) \qquad \text{(C.4)}$$

Table C.1 Values of $\psi(z)$, the Normalized Gaussian Cumulative Distribution Function

z	0.00	0.01	0.02	0.03	0.04	0.05	0.06	0.07	0.08	0.09	z
0.0	0.5000	0.5040	0.5080	0.5120	0.5160	0.5199	0.5239	0.5279	0.5319	0.5359	0.0
0.1	0.5398	0.5438	0.5478	0.5517	0.5557	0.5596	0.5636	0.5675	0.5714	0.5753	0.1
0.2	0.5793	0.5832	0.5871	0.5910	0.5948	0.5987	0.6026	0.6064	0.6103	0.6141	0.2
0.3	0.6179	0.6217	0.6255	0.6293	0.6331	0.6368	0.6406	0.6443	0.6480	0.6517	0.3
0.4	0.6554	0.6591	0.6628	0.6664	0.6700	0.6736	0.6772	0.6808	0.6844	0.6879	0.4
0.5	0.6915	0.6950	0.6985	0.7019	0.7054	0.7088	0.7123	0.7157	0.7190	0.7224	0.5
0.6	0.7257	0.7291	0.7324	0.7357	0.7389	0.7422	0.7454	0.7486	0.7517	0.7549	0.6
0.7	0.7580	0.7611	0.7642	0.7673	0.7704	0.7734	0.7764	0.7794	0.7823	0.7852	0.7
0.8	0.7881	0.7910	0.7939	0.7967	0.7995	0.8023	0.8051	0.8078	0.8106	0.8133	0.8
0.9	0.8159	0.8186	0.8212	0.8238	0.8264	0.8289	0.8315	0.8340	0.8365	0.8389	0.9
1.0	0.8413	0.8438	0.8461	0.8485	0.8508	0.8531	0.8554	0.8577	0.8599	0.8621	1.0
1.1	0.8643	0.8665	0.8686	0.8708	0.8729	0.8749	0.8770	0.8790	0.8810	0.8830	1.1
1.2	0.8849	0.8869	0.8888	0.8907	0.8925	0.8944	0.8962	0.8980	0.8997	0.9015	1.2
1.3	0.9032	0.9049	0.9066	0.9082	0.9099	0.9115	0.9131	0.9147	0.9162	0.9177	1.3
1.4	0.9192	0.9207	0.9222	0.9236	0.9251	0.9265	0.9279	0.9292	0.9306	0.9319	1.4
1.5	0.9332	0.9345	0.9357	0.9370	0.9382	0.9394	0.9406	0.9418	0.9429	0.9441	1.5
1.6	0.9452	0.9463	0.9474	0.9484	0.9495	0.9505	0.9515	0.9525	0.9535	0.9545	1.6
1.7	0.9554	0.9564	0.9573	0.9582	0.9591	0.9599	0.9608	0.9616	0.9625	0.9633	1.7
1.8	0.9641	0.9649	0.9656	0.9664	0.9671	0.9678	0.9686	0.9693	0.9699	0.9706	1.8
1.9	0.9713	0.9719	0.9726	0.9732	0.9738	0.9744	0.9750	0.9756	0.9761	0.9767	1.9

Table C.1 Values of $\psi(z)$, the Normalized Gaussian Cumulative Distribution Function (continued)

z	0.00	0.01	0.02	0.03	0.04	0.05	0.06	0.07	0.08	0.09	z
2.0	0.9773	0.9778	0.9783	0.9788	0.9793	0.9798	0.9803	0.9808	0.9812	0.9817	2.0
2.1	0.9821	0.9826	0.9830	0.9834	0.9838	0.9842	0.9846	0.9850	0.9854	0.9857	2.1
2.2	0.9861	0.9864	0.9868	0.9871	0.9875	0.9878	0.9881	0.9884	0.9887	0.9890	2.2
2.3	0.9893	0.9896	0.9898	0.9901	0.9904	0.9906	0.9909	0.9911	0.9913	0.9916	2.3
2.4	0.9918	0.9920	0.9922	0.9925	0.9927	0.9929	0.9931	0.9932	0.9934	0.9936	2.4
2.5	0.9938	0.9940	0.9941	0.9943	0.9945	0.9946	0.9948	0.9949	0.9951	0.9952	2.5
2.6	0.9953	0.9955	0.9956	0.9957	0.9959	0.9960	0.9961	0.9962	0.9963	0.9964	2.6
2.7	0.9965	0.9966	0.9967	0.9968	0.9969	0.9970	0.9971	0.9972	0.9973	0.9974	2.7
2.8	0.9974	0.9975	0.9976	0.9977	0.9977	0.9978	0.9979	0.9979	0.9980	0.9981	2.8
2.9	0.9981	0.9982	0.9982	0.9983	0.9984	0.9984	0.9985	0.9985	0.9986	0.9986	2.9
3.0	0.9987	0.9987	0.9987	0.9988	0.9988	0.9989	0.9989	0.9989	0.9990	0.9990	3.0
3.1	0.9990	0.9991	0.9991	0.9991	0.9992	0.9992	0.9992	0.9992	0.9993	0.9993	3.1
3.2	0.9993	0.9993	0.9994	0.9994	0.9994	0.9994	0.9994	0.9995	0.9995	0.9995	3.2
3.3	0.9995	0.9995	0.9995	0.9996	0.9996	0.9996	0.9996	0.9996	0.9996	0.9997	3.3
3.4	0.9997	0.9997	0.9997	0.9997	0.9997	0.9997	0.9997	0.9997	0.9997	0.9998	3.4
3.5	0.9998	0.9998	0.9998	0.9998	0.9998	0.9998	0.9998	0.9998	0.9998	0.9998	3.5
3.6	0.9998	0.9998	0.9999	0.9999	0.9999	0.9999	0.9999	0.9999	0.9999	0.9999	3.6
3.7	0.9999	0.9999	0.9999	0.9999	0.9999	0.9999	0.9999	0.9999	0.9999	0.9999	3.7
3.8	0.9999	0.9999	0.9999	0.9999	0.9999	0.9999	0.9999	0.9999	0.9999	0.9999	3.8
3.9	1.0000	1.0000	1.0000	1.0000	1.0000	1.0000	1.0000	1.0000	1.0000	1.0000	3.9
4.0	1.0000	1.0000	1.0000	1.0000	1.0000	1.0000	1.0000	1.0000	1.0000	1.0000	4.0

$$P(x < X) = 1 - F_X(x) = 1 - \psi\left(\frac{x - \mu_X}{\sigma_X}\right) \tag{C.5}$$

$$P(a < X \leq b) = F_X(b) - F_X(a) = \psi\left(\frac{b - \mu_X}{\sigma_X}\right) - \psi\left(\frac{a - \mu_X}{\sigma_X}\right) \tag{C.6}$$

The following algorithm (from Ref. 1, Item 26.2.17 on p. 932) calculates values of $\psi(z)$ in (C.2) for values of z that are non-negative:

$$c_1 = 0.127414796 \qquad c_2 = -0.142248368$$
$$c_3 = 0.710706871 \qquad c_4 = -0.726576013$$
$$c_5 = 0.530702714 \qquad p = 0.2316419$$

$$t = \frac{1}{1 + pz}$$
$$r = t(c_1 + t\{c_2 + t[c_3 + t(c_4 + tc_5)]\})$$
$$\psi(z) = 1 - r \exp(-z^2/2)$$

Values of $\psi(z)$ for z from 0.00 to 4.00 are given in Table C.1 on pages 352–51.

Reference

◆ ◆ ◆ ◆ ◆

1. *Handbook of Mathematical Functions.* ed. M. Abramowitz and I. Stegun. Chapter 26. "Probability Functions." M. Zelen and N. Severo. NBS Applied Math Series, No. 55, Washington D.C. USGPO 1964. (This publication is also available with an "Errata Notice" from New York: Dover Publications, 1972.)

Appendix

D A Derivation of the Gaussian and Rayleigh Probability Models

• •

There are many situations in which an attempt is made to place something at a specific point in a plane: An electron beam is focused on a phosphor screen, a robot positions a chip on a PC board, or an astronomer measures the location of a star. Let the origin in Figure D.1 represent a point to be located. If there are no errors, the point (0,0) is found every time. However, errors occur randomly, and the location at (x,y) is selected. This point is separated from (0,0) by

$$\rho = \sqrt{x^2 + y^2}$$

We are interested in describing the probability that observations occur within the circle of radius r shown in Figure D.1. The random variable of the radial distance is denoted by Z. Therefore, using (4.13),

$$P(Z < r) = F_Z(r) = \int_R f_{XY}(x,y)dxdy$$

where the region R is bounded by the circle of radius r centered at the origin.

We assume that there is no preferred direction in the x,y plane, and that random variations in the x and y directions are independent. Then (4.17) applies. These assumptions require that $f_X(x)$ and $f_Y(y)$ be the same pdf; the

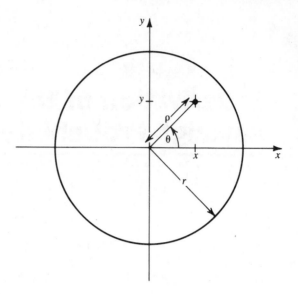

Figure D.1   Illustrating the location of a random observation in the x,y plane. The point may be located in rectangular coordinates (x,y) or in cylindrical coordinates (ρ,θ). The circle encloses all observations such that $0 \le \rho \le r$.

• •

choice of how the rectangular coordinate system is oriented is arbitrary. Thus,

$$F_Z(r) = \int_R f_X(x)\, f_Y(y)dxdy = \int_R f_X(x)\, f_X(y)dxdy$$

Changing from rectangular to cylindrical coordinates, the differential area $dxdy$ becomes $\rho d\theta d\rho$. Further, because we have assumed that there is no preferred direction in the x,y plane, the integrand in cylindrical coordinates must be independent of θ and only be a function of ρ;

$$F_Z(r) = 2\pi \int_0^r f_X(x)\, f_X(y)\rho d\rho$$

where x and y are related by

$$r = \sqrt{x^2 + y^2} \tag{D.1}$$

Using (3.11),

$$f_Z(r) = 2\pi r f_X(x)\, f_X(y) \tag{D.2}$$

Using the natural logarithm,

$$\ln\left(\frac{f_Z(r)}{2\pi r}\right) = \ln f_X(x) + \ln f_X(y)$$

Differentiating both sides with respect to x,

$$\frac{dr}{dx}\frac{d}{dr}\ln\left(\frac{f_Z(r)}{2\pi r}\right) = \frac{d}{dx}\ln f_X(x) \tag{D.3}$$

Using (D.1) we find

$$\frac{dr}{dx} = \frac{x}{r}$$

It then follows that the differential equation (D.3) can be written with functions of r only on the left of the equals sign, and functions of x only on the right. For this to be true for all possible values of r and x requires that each side of the equation be equal to the same constant. We call this constant a **constant of separation,** and denote it with $-a^2$, where a is real but otherwise arbitrary. This leads to

$$\frac{1}{r}\frac{d}{dr}\ln\left(\frac{f_Z(r)}{2\pi r}\right) = \frac{1}{x}\frac{d}{dx}\ln f_X(x) = -a^2 \tag{D.4}$$

Using only the equation involving x in (D.4), we solve for the pdf $f_X(x)$:

$$\frac{1}{x}\frac{d}{dx}\ln f_X(x) = -a^2$$

$$\frac{d}{dx}\ln f_X(x) = -a^2 x$$

$$\ln f_X(x) = -a^2 x^2/2 + b$$

$$f_X(x) = c\,\exp(-a^2 x^2/2) \tag{D.5}$$

where $c = e^b$. Application of (3.14) to (D.5) leads to

$$a = c\sqrt{2\pi}$$

The random variable X has, by assumption, a mean of zero. Therefore, its variance (3.38), applied to (D.5), leads to another relation involving the constants a and c:

$$a^3 \sigma_X^2 = c\sqrt{2\pi}$$

Combining the above two relations involving a and c results in:

$$a^2 = \frac{1}{\sigma_X^2}$$

$$c = \frac{1}{\sqrt{2\pi\sigma_X^2}}$$

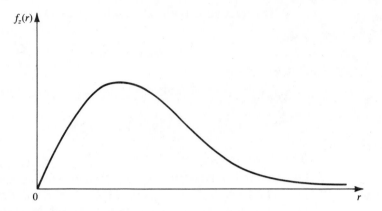

$f_z(r)$

0 r

Figure D.2   A plot of a Rayleigh pdf.

• •

Substitution of these two constants into (D.5) shows that the random variable X is Gaussian (3.60) with a mean of zero:

$$f_X(x) = \frac{1}{\sqrt{2\pi\sigma_X^2}} \exp(-x^2/2\sigma_X^2) \qquad \textbf{(D.6)}$$

Now that the pdf $f_X(x)$ is known, we can substitute it into (D.2) to find the pdf for the random radial distance Z:

$$f_Z(r) = \frac{2\pi r}{2\pi\sigma_X^2} \exp[-(x^2 + y^2)/2\sigma_X^2]$$

Using (D.1),

$$f_Z(r) = \frac{r}{\sigma_X^2} \exp[-r^2/2\sigma_X^2) \qquad \textbf{(D.7)}$$

This is a Rayleigh pdf, and is illustrated with the plot in Figure D.2. (The Rayleigh pdf is also discussed in Example 3.4.)

This appendix demonstrates that the Gaussian pdf (D.6) and the Rayleigh pdf (D.7) may be derived using a practical situation: locating a point in an isotropic plane when random errors are present.

Appendix

Chi-Square and Student's *t* Random Variables

Statistical work frequently uses data from chi-square and Student's *t* probability density functions. The usual process in statistical applications is first to relate a probability to an area under a pdf, and then to determine abscissa values that specify the area. We illustrate this in Figure E.1 for both the chi-square and Student's *t* pdfs. Abscissa values as a function of selected probabilities for these two pdfs are listed in Tables E.1 and E.2.

For the chi-square random variable, an abscissa value is called v, and the area under the pdf to the right of v is called $Q(v|n)$, where n is the number of degrees of freedom. An algorithm for $Q(v|n)$ when n is odd is obtained from the *Handbook of Mathematical Functions*[1] from which their equations 26.2.1, 26.2.5, 26.2.17, and 26.4.4 are used:

$$Q(v|n) = 0.7978846 \ e^{-v/2} \left[\sum_{m=1}^{5} b_m t^m + \sum_{r=1}^{(n-1)/2} \frac{v^{(2r-1)/2}}{1 \cdot 3 \cdot 5 \cdot \ \ldots \ \cdot (2r-1)} \right] \quad \text{(E.1)}$$

where $t = \dfrac{1}{1 + p\sqrt{v}}$, $v \geq 0$ and

$$b_1 = 0.319381530 \qquad b_4 = -1.821255978$$
$$b_2 = -0.356563782 \qquad b_5 = 1.330274429$$
$$b_3 = 1.781477937 \qquad p = 0.2316419$$

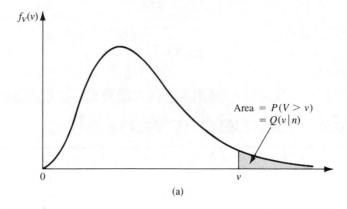

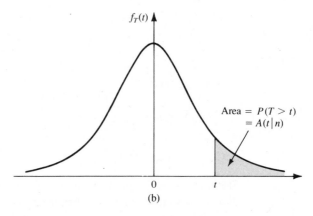

Figure E.1 Illustrating specific areas for (a) a chi-square pdf and (b) a Student's t pdf.

• •

When $n = 1$, (E.1) becomes

$$Q(v|1) = 2[1 - \psi(\sqrt{v})], \quad v \geq 0$$

where $\psi(x)$ is the normalized Gaussian random variable.

When n is even, the following algorithm for $Q(v|n)$ is obtained from the *Handbook of Mathematical Functions*[1]:

$$Q(v|n) = e^{-v/2}\left[1 + \sum_{r=1}^{(n-2)/2}\frac{(v/2)^r}{r!}\right] \tag{E.2}$$

where $v \geq 0$. This algorithm uses their equations 26.2.1, 26.2.5, and 26.4.5.

When $n = 2$,

$$Q(v|2) = e^{-v/2}, \quad v \geq 0$$

Table E.1 Values of the Abscissa v Versus the Probability $P(V > v)$ for the Chi-Square Random Variable*

n	0.995	0.990	0.975	0.950	0.900	0.750	0.500	0.250	0.100	0.050	0.025	0.010	0.005	0.001
1	0.000	0.000	0.001	0.004	0.016	0.102	0.455	1.323	2.706	3.841	5.024	6.635	7.879	10.828
2	0.010	0.020	0.051	0.103	0.211	0.575	1.386	2.773	4.605	5.991	7.378	9.210	10.597	13.816
3	0.072	0.115	0.216	0.352	0.584	1.213	2.366	4.108	6.251	7.815	9.348	11.345	12.838	16.266
4	0.207	0.297	0.484	0.711	1.064	1.923	3.357	5.385	7.779	9.488	11.143	13.277	14.860	18.467
5	0.412	0.554	0.831	1.145	1.610	2.675	4.351	6.626	9.236	11.071	12.833	15.086	16.750	20.515
6	0.676	0.872	1.237	1.635	2.204	3.455	5.348	7.841	10.645	12.592	14.449	16.812	18.548	22.458
7	0.989	1.239	1.690	2.167	2.833	4.255	6.346	9.037	12.017	14.067	16.013	18.475	20.278	24.322
8	1.344	1.646	2.180	2.733	3.490	5.071	7.344	10.219	13.362	15.507	17.535	20.090	21.955	26.124
9	1.735	2.088	2.700	3.325	4.168	5.899	8.343	11.389	14.684	16.919	19.023	21.666	23.589	27.877
10	2.156	2.558	3.247	3.940	4.865	6.737	9.342	12.549	15.987	18.307	20.483	23.209	25.188	29.588
11	2.603	3.053	3.816	4.575	5.578	7.584	10.341	13.701	17.275	19.675	21.920	24.725	26.757	31.264
12	3.073	3.570	4.404	5.226	6.304	8.438	11.340	14.845	18.549	21.026	23.337	26.217	28.300	32.910
13	3.565	4.107	5.009	5.892	7.041	9.299	12.340	15.984	19.812	22.362	24.736	27.688	29.820	34.528
14	4.074	4.660	5.629	6.571	7.789	10.165	13.339	17.117	21.064	23.685	26.119	29.141	31.319	36.123
15	4.601	5.229	6.262	7.261	8.547	11.037	14.339	18.245	22.307	24.996	27.488	30.578	32.801	37.697
16	5.142	5.812	6.908	7.962	9.312	11.912	15.339	19.369	23.542	26.296	28.845	32.000	34.267	39.252
17	5.697	6.408	7.564	8.671	10.085	12.792	16.338	20.489	24.769	27.587	30.191	33.409	35.719	40.790
18	6.265	7.015	8.231	9.390	10.865	13.675	17.338	21.605	25.989	28.869	31.526	34.805	37.156	42.312
19	6.843	7.632	8.906	10.117	11.651	14.562	18.338	22.718	27.204	30.144	32.853	36.191	38.582	43.820
20	7.434	8.260	9.591	10.851	12.443	15.452	19.337	23.828	28.412	31.410	34.170	37.566	39.997	45.315
21	8.033	8.897	10.283	11.591	13.239	16.344	20.337	24.935	29.615	32.671	35.479	38.932	41.401	46.797
22	8.642	9.542	10.982	12.338	14.041	17.240	21.337	26.039	30.813	33.925	36.781	40.289	42.796	48.268
23	9.260	10.196	11.688	13.090	14.848	18.137	22.337	27.141	32.007	35.173	38.076	41.639	44.181	49.729
24	9.886	10.856	12.401	13.848	15.658	19.037	23.337	28.241	33.196	36.415	39.364	42.980	45.559	51.179
25	10.519	11.524	13.119	14.611	16.473	19.939	24.337	29.339	34.382	37.653	40.647	44.314	46.928	52.620
26	11.160	12.198	13.843	15.379	17.292	20.843	25.336	30.435	35.563	38.885	41.923	45.642	48.290	54.052
27	11.807	12.878	14.573	16.151	18.114	21.749	26.336	31.528	36.741	40.113	43.195	46.963	49.645	55.476
28	12.461	13.564	15.308	16.928	18.939	22.657	27.336	32.621	37.916	41.337	44.461	48.278	50.993	56.892
29	13.121	14.256	16.047	17.708	19.768	23.566	28.336	33.711	39.088	42.557	45.722	49.588	52.336	58.301
30	13.787	14.953	16.791	18.493	20.599	24.478	29.336	34.800	40.256	43.773	46.979	50.892	53.672	59.703

Example: If a chi-square random variable with $n = 17$ degrees of freedom is selected, and if it is given that $P(V > v) = 0.250$, then the value of the abscissa is $v = 20.489$.

* The parameter n represents the degrees of freedom.

Table E.2   Values of the Abscissa *t* Versus the Probability $P(T > t)$ for Student's *t* Random Variables*

n	0.1	0.05	0.025	0.01	0.005
1	3.078	6.314	12.706	31.821	63.657
2	1.886	2.920	4.303	6.965	9.925
3	1.638	2.353	3.180	4.525	5.797
4	1.533	2.132	2.777	3.744	4.596
5	1.476	2.016	2.571	3.365	4.030
6	1.440	1.944	2.448	3.143	3.707
7	1.415	1.895	2.365	2.999	3.500
8	1.397	1.860	2.307	2.897	3.356
9	1.383	1.834	2.263	2.822	3.250
10	1.372	1.813	2.229	2.764	3.170
11	1.364	1.796	2.202	2.719	3.106
12	1.356	1.783	2.179	2.682	3.055
13	1.350	1.771	2.161	2.651	3.013
14	1.345	1.762	2.145	2.625	2.977
15	1.341	1.753	2.132	2.603	2.947
16	1.337	1.746	2.120	2.584	2.921
17	1.334	1.740	2.110	2.567	2.899
18	1.331	1.734	2.101	2.553	2.879
19	1.328	1.730	2.094	2.540	2.861
20	1.326	1.725	2.086	2.529	2.846
21	1.323	1.721	2.080	2.518	2.832
22	1.321	1.718	2.074	2.509	2.819
23	1.320	1.714	2.069	2.500	2.808
24	1.318	1.711	2.064	2.493	2.797
25	1.317	1.709	2.060	2.486	2.788
26	1.315	1.706	2.056	2.479	2.779
27	1.314	1.704	2.052	2.473	2.771
28	1.313	1.702	2.049	2.468	2.764
29	1.312	1.700	2.046	2.463	2.757
INF	1.282	1.645	1.960	2.327	2.576

Example: If Student's *t* random variable with $n = 13$ degrees of freedom is selected, and if it is given that $P(T > t) = 0.05$, then the abscissa value is $t = 1.771$.

♦ ♦ ♦ ♦ ♦

Example: A pdf for Student's *t* random variable is symmetric about the origin. Therefore, if Student's *t* random variable with $n = 13$ degrees of freedom is selected, and if it is given that $P(T > t) = 0.95$, then the abscissa value is $t = -1.771$.

* The parameter *n* represents the degrees of freedom.

Table E.1 was constructed by first calculating values of $Q(v|n)$ as a function of v, and then interpolating these data to find v for selected values of $Q(v|n)$.

For Student's t random variable, an abscissa value is called t, and the area under the pdf to the right of t is called $A(t|n)$, where n is the number of degrees of freedom.

When $n = 1$, Student's t random variable becomes the Cauchy random variable, and its pdf and cdf are

$$f_T(t) = \frac{1}{\pi(t^2 + 1)}$$

$$F_T(t) = 1 - A(t|n) = \frac{1}{2} + \frac{1}{\pi}\tan^{-1}(t)$$

When $n = 2$, Student's t pdf is

$$f_T(t) = \frac{1}{(t^2 + 2)^{3/2}}$$

This leads directly to the cdf

$$F_T(t) = 1 - A(t|n) = \frac{1}{2}\left(1 + \frac{t}{\sqrt{t^2 + 2}}\right)$$

As $n \to \infty$, Student's t random variable is related to the normalized Gaussian random variable:

$$\psi(t) = 1 - A(t|\infty)$$

For degrees of freedom $3 \le n < \infty$, the *Handbook of Mathematical Functions*[1] gives an algorithm for calculating t as a function of $A(t|n)$. Using their equations 26.7.5 and 26.2.23,

$$p = A(t|n)$$
$$y = \sqrt{-2\ln(p)}$$
$$x = y - \frac{c_0 + c_1 t + c_2 t^2}{1 + d_1 t + d_2 t^2 + d_3 t^3}$$
$$g_1 = (x^3 + x)/4$$
$$g_2 = (5x^5 + 16x^3 + 3x)/96$$
$$g_3 = (3x^7 + 19x^5 + 17x^3 - 15x)/384$$
$$g_4 = (79x^9 + 776x^7 + 1482x^5 - 1920x^3 - 945x)/92160$$
$$t = x + g_1/n + g_2/n^2 + g_3/n^3 + g_4/n^4$$

where

$$\begin{aligned} c_0 &= 2.515517 & d_1 &= 1.432788 \\ c_1 &= 0.802853 & d_2 &= 0.189269 \\ c_2 &= 0.010328 & d_3 &= 0.001308 \end{aligned}$$

Reference

◆   ◆   ◆   ◆   ◆

1. *Handbook of Mathematical Functions.* ed. M. Abramowitz and I. Stegun. Chapter 26. "Probability Functions." M. Zelen and N. Severo. NBS Applied Math Series, No. 55, Washington D.C. USGPO 1964. (This publication is also available with an "Errata Notice" from New York: Dover Publications, 1972.)

Appendix

The Wiener-Khinchin Relations

Here we show that the autocorrelation function $R_X(\tau)$ and the power spectral density $S_X(\omega)$ are Fourier transforms of each other. We begin with the defining relation for the power spectral density (8.44) in the case of the wide-sense stationary random process:

$$S_X(\omega) = \lim_{T \to \infty} \frac{1}{T} E[\, |X_T(\omega)|^2]$$

Next, we use the integral forms of the Fourier transforms. These contain $X_T(t)$, the windowed portion of the random process $X(t)$,

$$S_X(\omega) = \lim_{T \to \infty} \frac{1}{T} E \left[\int_{-\infty}^{\infty} X_T(t_2) \exp(-j\omega t_2) dt_2 \int_{-\infty}^{\infty} X_T(t_1) \exp(+j\omega t_1) dt_1 \right]$$

$$S_X(\omega) = \lim_{T \to \infty} \frac{1}{T} E \left[\int_{-T/2}^{T/2} X(t_2) \exp(-j\omega t_2) dt_2 \int_{-T/2}^{T/2} X(t_1) \exp(+j\omega t_1) dt_1 \right]$$

The autocorrelation function (8.14) of a wide-sense stationary random process is even (8.18),

$$E[X(t_2)X(t_1)] = R_X(t_1 - t_2) = R_X(t_2 - t_1)$$

365

Therefore,

$$S_X(\omega) = \lim_{T \to \infty} \frac{1}{T} \int_{-T/2}^{T/2} \int_{-T/2}^{T/2} R_X(t_2 - t_1) \exp[-j\omega(t_2 - t_1)] dt_1 dt_2$$

The region over which this integral is evaluated is shown in Figure. F.1. The entire t_1, t_2-plane is covered as $T \to \infty$.

Now we introduce the change of variables:

$$t_1 = t \quad \text{and} \quad \tau = t_2 - t_1$$

The integral for the power spectral density then becomes

$$S_X(\omega) = \lim_{T \to \infty} \frac{1}{T} \int_{-T/2}^{T/2} \int_{-T/2-t}^{T/2-t} R_X(\tau) e^{-j\omega\tau} d\tau dt$$

Figure F.2 shows region of integration in the t, τ-plane. The entire t, τ-plane is covered as $T \to \infty$.

For convenience in the following derivation, we define the integral $I(T)$ by

$$I(T) = \int_{-T/2}^{T/2} \int_{-T/2-t}^{T/2-t} R_X(\tau) e^{-j\omega\tau} d\tau dt$$

so the the power spectral density is

$$S_X(\omega) = \lim_{T \to \infty} \frac{1}{T} I(T) \qquad \textbf{(F.1)}$$

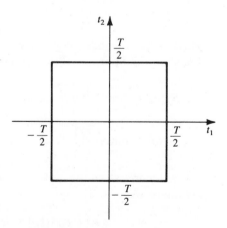

Figure F.1   A rectangular region of integration.

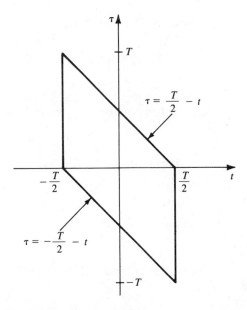

Figure F.2 A region of integration obtained when the region in Figure F.1 is transformed by $t = t_1$ and $\tau = t_2 - t_1$.

• •

Then, we separate the integral $I(T)$ into two parts: $I^+(T)$ is for the region where $\tau > 0$, and $I^-(T)$ is for the region where $\tau < 0$:

$$I(T) = I^+(T) + I^-(T)$$

First, we find

$$I^+(T) = \int_0^T \int_{-T/2}^{T/2-\tau} R_X(\tau)e^{-j\omega\tau}dt\,d\tau$$

Integrating we find,

$$I^+(T) = \int_0^T (T-\tau)R_X(\tau)e^{-j\omega\tau}d\tau$$

Similarly,

$$I^-(T) = \int_{-T}^0 (T+\tau)R_X(\tau)e^{-j\omega\tau}d\tau$$

Combining these two integrals, we obtain

$$I(T) = T\int_{-T}^T R_X(\tau)e^{-j\omega\tau}d\tau - 2\int_0^T \tau\cos(\omega\tau)R_X(\tau)d\tau$$

Then, returning to (F.1),

$$S_X(\omega) = \lim_{T \to \infty} \frac{1}{T} \left[T \int_{-T}^{T} R_X(\tau) e^{-j\omega\tau} d\tau - 2 \int_{0}^{T} \tau \cos(\omega\tau) R_X(\tau) d\tau \right]$$

Finally, we let $T \to \infty$, and find that $S_X(\omega)$ and $R_X(\tau)$ are Fourier transforms of each other provided $\tau R_X(\tau)$ is absolutely integrable:

$$\int_{0}^{\infty} |\tau R_X(\tau)| \, d\tau < \infty \tag{F.2}$$

$$S_X(\omega) = \int_{-\infty}^{\infty} R_X(\tau) e^{-j\omega\tau} d\tau \tag{F.3}$$

$$R_X(\tau) = \frac{1}{2\pi} \int_{-\infty}^{\infty} S_X(\omega) e^{+j\omega\tau} d\omega \tag{F.4}$$

This transform pair, (F.3) and (F.4), is called the **Wiener-Khinchin relations.**

Appendix

A Summary of Selected Probability Models

Section G.1   Discrete Random Variables

Reference: $\delta(x)$ is the Dirac-delta function and $u(x)$ is the unit step function.

Bernoulli: $p,q \geq 0$, $p + q = 1$. (See pages 186, 187.)

$$f_X(x) = q\delta(x) + p\delta(x - 1)$$

$$F_X(x) = qu(x) + pu(x - 1)$$

$$\mu_X = p, \quad \sigma_X^2 = pq$$

$$\Phi_X(j\omega) = q + pe^{j\omega}$$

The Bernoulli random variable is a special case of the binomial random variable when $n = 1$.

Binomial: $p,q \geq 0$, $p + q = 1$, $n \geq 1$. (See pages 65, 187, 223.)

$$P_n(k) = \binom{n}{k} p^k q^{n-k}, \quad 0 \leq k \leq n$$

$$f_X(x) = \sum_{k=0}^{n} P_n(k)\delta(x - k)$$

$$F_X(x) = \sum_{k=0}^{n} P_n(k)u(x-k)$$

$$\mu_X = np, \quad \sigma_X^2 = npq$$

$$\Phi_X(j\omega) = (q + pe^{j\omega})^n$$

Geometric: $p,q \geq 0$, $p + q = 1$. (See page 190.)

$$P(k,1) = pq^{k-1}, \quad 1 \leq k < \infty$$

$$f_X(x) = \sum_{k=0}^{\infty} P(k,1)\delta(x-k)$$

$$F_X(x) = \sum_{k=0}^{\infty} P(k,1)u(x-k)$$

$$\mu_X = \frac{1}{p}, \quad \sigma_X^2 = \frac{q}{p^2}$$

$$\Phi_X(j\omega) = pe^{j\omega}(1 - qe^{j\omega})^{-1}$$

The geometric random variable is a special case of the Pascal random variable when $m = 1$.

Hypergeometric: $r,b \geq 0$, $r + b = N$, $0 \leq n \leq N$. (See pages 192, 193.)

$$P(X = k) = \frac{\binom{r}{k}\binom{b}{n-k}}{\binom{N}{n}}, \quad 0 \leq k \leq \min(n,r)$$

$$f_X(x) = \sum_{k=0}^{\min(n,r)} P(X = k)\delta(x-k)$$

$$F_X(x) = \sum_{k=0}^{\min(n,r)} P(X = k)u(x-k)$$

$$\mu_X = n\frac{r}{N}, \quad \sigma_X^2 = n\frac{r}{N}\left(1 - \frac{r}{N}\right)\frac{N-n}{N-1}$$

Pascal: $p,q \geq 0$, $p + q = 1$, $m \geq 1$. (See pages 189, 190.)

$$P(k,m) = \binom{k-1}{m-1} p^m q^{k-m}, \quad k = m, m+1, m+2, \ldots$$

$$f_X(x) = \sum_{k=m}^{\infty} P(k,m)\delta(x-k)$$

$$F_X(x) = \sum_{k=m}^{\infty} P(k,m)u(x-k)$$

$$\mu_X = \frac{m}{p}, \quad \sigma_X^2 = \frac{mq}{p^2}$$

$$\Phi_X(j\omega) = (pe^{j\omega})^m(1 - qe^{j\omega})^{-m}$$

Another common name for the Pascal random variable is the **negative binomial** random variable.

Poisson: b > 0. (See pages 196-200, 225.)

$$P_k = \frac{b^k}{k!} e^{-b}, \quad k = 0,1,2, \ldots$$

$$f_X(x) = \sum_{k=0}^{\infty} P_k \delta(x - k)$$

$$F_X(x) = \sum_{k=0}^{\infty} P_k u(x - k)$$

$$\mu_X = b, \quad \sigma_X^2 = b$$

$$\Phi_X(j\omega) = \exp[b(e^{j\omega} - 1)]$$

Section G.2   Continuous Random Variables

• • • • •

Reference: $\Gamma(x)$ is the gamma function and $\psi(x)$ is the cdf for the normalized Gaussian random variable. (See Appendix C.)

Beta: a,b > 0. (See page 128.)

$$f_X(x) = \frac{\Gamma(a + b)}{\Gamma(a)\Gamma(b)} x^{a-1}(1 - x)^{b-1}, \quad 0 < x < 1$$

$$= 0, \text{ otherwise}$$

$$\mu_X = \frac{a}{a + b}, \quad \sigma_X^2 = \frac{ab}{(a + b)^2(a + b + 1)}$$

Cauchy: a > 0. (See pages 128, 173.)

$$f_X(x) = \frac{a}{\pi(x^2 + a^2)}, \quad |x| < \infty$$

$$F_X(x) = \frac{1}{\pi} \tan^{-1}\left(\frac{x}{a}\right) + \frac{1}{2}, \quad |x| < \infty$$

The mean and the variance for the Cauchy random variable are undefined.

$$\Phi_X(j\omega) = \exp(-a|\omega|)$$

Chi-square: n is a positive integer called the **degrees of freedom.** (See pages 159, 164, and Appendix E.)

$$f_X(x) = \frac{1}{\Gamma\left(\dfrac{n}{s}\right) 2^{n/2}} x^{(n/2)-1} e^{-x/2}, \quad x > 0$$

$$= 0, \text{ otherwise}$$

$$\mu_X = n, \quad \sigma_X^2 = 2n$$

$$\Phi_X(j\omega) = (1 - 2j\omega)^{-n/2}$$

The chi-square random variable is a special case of the gamma random variable when $b = 2$ and $a = n/2$.

Erlang: k is a positive integer, $\lambda > 0$. (See pages 157, 158, 162, 163, 204–206.)

$$f_X(x) = \frac{\lambda^k x^{k-1} e^{-\lambda x}}{(k-1)!}, \quad x > 0$$

$$= 0, \text{ otherwise}$$

$$\mu_X = \frac{k}{\lambda}, \quad \sigma_X^2 = \frac{k}{\lambda^2}$$

$$\Phi_X(j\omega) = \left(1 - \frac{j\omega}{\lambda}\right)^{-k}$$

The Erlang random variable is a special case of the gamma random variable when $a = k$, and when $b = 1/\lambda$.

Exponential: $\lambda > 0$. (See pages 118, 127, 157.)

$$f_X(x) = \lambda e^{-\lambda x}, \quad x \geq 0$$

$$= 0, \text{ otherwise}$$

$$F_X(x) = 1 - e^{-\lambda x}, \quad x \geq 0$$

$$= 0, \text{ otherwise}$$

$$\mu_X = \frac{1}{\lambda}, \quad \sigma_X^2 = \frac{1}{\lambda^2}$$

$$\Phi_X(j\omega) = \frac{\lambda}{\lambda - j\omega}$$

The exponential random variable is a special case of the Erlang random variable when $k = 1$.

Gamma: $a,b > 0$. (See pages 127, 128, 207, 208.)

$$f_X(x) = \frac{1}{b^a \Gamma(a)} x^{a-1} e^{-x/b}, \quad x > 0$$
$$= 0, \text{ otherwise}$$
$$\mu_X = ab, \quad \sigma_X^2 = ab^2$$
$$\Phi_X(j\omega) = (1 - j\omega b)^{-a}$$

Gaussian: (See pages 94, 95, 358, and Appendix C.)

$$f_X(x) = \frac{1}{\sqrt{2\pi}\sigma_X} \exp\left(\frac{-(x - \mu_X)^2}{2\sigma_X^2}\right), \quad |x| < \infty$$
$$F_X(x) = \psi\left(\frac{x - \mu_X}{\sigma_X}\right), \quad |x| < \infty$$
$$\mu_X = E[X], \quad \sigma_X^2 = \text{Var}[X]$$
$$\Phi_X(j\omega) = \exp\left(j\omega\mu_X - \frac{\omega^2\sigma_X^2}{2}\right)$$

Another common name for the Gaussian random variable is the **normal** random variable.

Laplace: $b > 0$. (See page 127.)

$$f_x(x) = \frac{b}{2} \exp(-b|x|), \quad |x| < \infty$$
$$F_X(x) = \frac{1}{2} e^{bx}, \quad -\infty < x < 0$$
$$= 1 - \frac{1}{2} e^{-bx}, \quad 0 \leq x < \infty$$
$$\mu_X = 0, \quad \sigma_X^2 = \frac{2}{b^2}$$
$$\Phi_X(j\omega) = \frac{b^2}{\omega^2 + b^2}$$

Lognormal: $Y = e^X$ where X is Gaussian: μ_X, σ_X^2. (See pages 110, 133, 270.)

$$f_Y(y) = \frac{1}{y\sigma_X\sqrt{2\pi}} \exp[-(\ln y - \mu_X)^2/2\sigma_X^2], \quad y > 0$$
$$= 0, \text{ otherwise}$$

$$F_Y(y) = \psi[(\ln y - \mu_X)/\sigma_X], \quad y > 0$$
$$= 0, \text{ otherwise}$$

$$\mu_Y = \exp\left(\mu_X + \frac{\sigma_X^2}{2}\right)$$

$$\sigma_Y^2 = \exp(2\mu_X + \sigma_X^2)[\exp(\sigma_X^2) - 1]$$

Rayleigh: $b > 0$. (See pages 89, 160, 325, 358.)

$$f_X(x) = \frac{2x}{b} \exp\left(\frac{-x^2}{b}\right), \quad x \ge 0$$
$$= 0, \text{ otherwise}$$

$$F_X(x) = 1 - \exp\left(\frac{-x^2}{b}\right), \quad x \ge 0$$
$$= 0, \text{ otherwise}$$

$$\mu_X = \sqrt{\frac{\pi b}{4}}, \quad \sigma_X^2 = (4 - \pi)\frac{b}{4}$$

If the Rayleigh random variable X is obtained from

$$X = \sqrt{Z_1^2 + Z_2^2}$$

where Z_1^2 and Z_2^2 are independent Gaussian random variables with means of zero and variances of σ_Z^2, then $b = 2\sigma_Z^2$.

Student's t: $r > 2$. (See pages 174–76, and Appendix E.)

$$f_X(x) = \frac{\Gamma\left(\dfrac{r+1}{2}\right)}{\sqrt{\pi r}\, \Gamma\left(\dfrac{r}{2}\right)\left(1 + \dfrac{x}{r}\right)^{(r+1)/2}}, \quad |x| < \infty$$

$$\mu_X = 0, \quad \sigma_X^2 = \frac{r}{r-2}$$

Uniform: (See pages 80, 91, 92.)

$$f_X(x) = \frac{1}{b-a}, \quad a < x < b$$
$$= 0, \text{ otherwise}$$

$$\mu_X = \frac{a+b}{2}, \quad \sigma_X^2 = \frac{(b-a)^2}{12}$$

$$\Phi_X(j\omega) = \frac{e^{j\omega b} - e^{j\omega a}}{j\omega(b-a)}$$

Weibull: m,c > 0. (See pages 265, 266.)

$$f_X(x) = \left(\frac{m}{c}\right)\left(\frac{x}{c}\right)^{m-1} \exp\left[-\left(\frac{x}{c}\right)^m\right], \quad x > 0$$
$$= 0, \text{ otherwise}$$

$$F_X(x) = 1 - \exp\left[-\left(\frac{x}{c}\right)^m\right], \quad x > 0$$
$$= 0, \text{ otherwise}$$

$$\mu_X = c\Gamma\left(1 + \frac{1}{m}\right)$$

$$\sigma_X^2 = c^2\left[\Gamma\left(1 + \frac{2}{m}\right) - \Gamma^2\left(1 + \frac{1}{m}\right)\right]$$

Appendix

Answers to Selected Exercises

• •

Chapter 1

2. 2240.0, 939.3
4. -0.227, 10.87, -0.945
6. 0.153, -8.67, 0.801
8. $x = \text{URNG(seed)}$; (a) $y = [13x]$; (b) $y = 1280x + 5760$; (c) IF $x < 0.40$ THEN $y = 1$ ELSE $y = 0$
11. $k = [(x_i - 279.76)/5.010] + 1$
13. $n = 963$, $\Sigma x_i = 12{,}886.36$, $\Sigma x_i^2 = 172{,}710.76$, 13.38, 0.283
15. $n = 959$, $\Sigma x_i = 759{,}548.55$, $\Sigma x_i^2 = 607{,}132{,}818.4$, 792.0, 5797.6
17. (0.071, 0.909), (0.121, 1.818), . . . , (0.836, 9.091)
19. (1.4, 0.909), (6.4, 1.818), . . . , (94.0, 9.091)
21. $k = [(R_i - 448.21)/12.45] + 1$
23. 1399.8 Ω, 1564.5 Ω, 1729.2 Ω

Chapter 2

1. e, g, f, b, c, a, d
3. 4/12, 5/12, 4/12, 2/12, 7/12, 2/12, 7/12, 0, 8/12
5. 7/12, 1/12, 6/12, 0, 8/12, 1/12, 6/12, 1/12, 1
7. 0.0508, 0.1791, 0.2748, 0.4031, 0.6325, 0, 0.1914, 0.3264

9. 0.4191, 0.3470, 0.6491, 0.8499, 0, 0.2203, 0.4211

11. 0.1170, 0.6491, 0.3371, 0.2791

13. 0.0930, 0.5903, 0.2657

15. 0.9843

17. 0.3333

19. 0.98

21. 0.2319, 0.9313, 0.3732

23. 0.3164, 0.4219, 0.7383

Chapter 3

1. 1.5, 0.6875

3. 0.5303, 0.4648

5. 0.1619

7. 0.375, 0.2, 0.0594

9. 1.1999, 1.7142, 0.2744

15. $-2/c, 2/c^2$

17. 10, 4

19. 0.8413, 0.8159, 0.6572

20. 0.6731

22. 0.1574

24. 76.86%

27. 1086 Ω, 40 Ω

29. 0.34, 0.53, 3.79

31. 0.40, 4.0630, 4.8217

32. 3.7150, 3.25

35. Gaussian, $\mu_Y = 900$, $\sigma_Y^2 = 40{,}000$, both part a) and part b)

39. -1, 20, Gaussian

41. $1/(\pi\sqrt{V^2 - y^2})$, $|y| < V$

45. $y = \quad 3\ln(2x), \qquad 0 < x < 1/2$
$\qquad = -3\ln[2(1-x)], \qquad 1/2 < x < 1$

47. $F_X(x) = 0.3 + 0.4667x - 0.0778x^2$, $\quad 0 < x < 3$

49. $(2/7)\delta(y) + 6/7$ between $y = 0$ and $y = 5/6$

51. 3.035, 7.676

53. 17.19, 43.40

55. 0.5483, 0.6688

57. 0.0668, 0.0808, 0.0738

59. $0.38 \exp(-y/4) \, u(y - 4)$

61. using (3.89), 0.141

Chapter 4

1. 1/3, no, $F_{XY}(x, y) = (1/3)(xy + x^2y^2/4)$, 5/12

3. no, 1/3

5. $-0.207, -6.8$

7. 59, 13

9. 2/3, 2/3, 1/3

11. 136.30, 8.95, 30.53

17. $z/4$ where $0 < x < 1$, 1/4 where $1 < z < 4$, $(5 - z)/4$ where $4 < z < 5$, 2.5, 1.417

19. $\{1 - \exp[-7(w + 3)]\}$ where $-3 < w < 3$, $(e^{21} - e^{-21})e^{-7w}/6$ where $3 < w$, 0.143, 3.0204

21. $0.09\delta(w + 2) + 0.42\delta(w - 1) + 0.49\delta(w - 4)$

23. $f_Z(z) = f_X(x) * f_Y(-y)$

25. 5, 3.317

27. 1/3, 0.0283, 17.67, 79.5

29. 21

31. 165

32. 0.772

34. 0.4115

36. 0.6103

Chapter 5

1. $F(k) = 0.0090, 0.0796, 0.3003, 0.6455, 0.9155, 1$; 0.355

3. 1830

5. $F(5) = 0.927$

9. 0.4242, 0.4848, 0.0909

11. 0.192

12. $F(k) = 0.0067, 0.0404, 0.1246, 0.2650, 0.4405, 0.6160, 0.7622, 0.8666, 0.9319, \ldots$; 0.742

15. 0.121

17. 3973, 2081, 728, 190

19. $P(8760 < Y) = 0.893$ if $n = 13$; $= 0.938$ if $n = 14$

21. 0.463

25. 0.435

27. 0.648

29. 12.5, 3.2, 19.2 (min), 24 (min)

31. 83 (s), 15.5

33. (0.34, 0), 0.103

Chapter 6

3. 1056.15, 1054.62, 1049.85, 949.56

5. $\dfrac{1}{2n} \sum_{i=1}^{n} x_i^2$, unbiased

   7. 53.76 μs, 53.75 μs, 0.685 μs

   9. 1000.54; 964.50, 1036.58; 949.58, 1051.50

  11. 100, 1

  13. $63.47 < \sigma_X < 158.9$

  14. 10, 20

  15. (1.95, 30.08), (2.89, 10.66)

  17. 982.49, 82.77; (923.26, 1041.72); (56.93, 151.12)

Chapter 7   **1.** 693.1 h

   3. $\dfrac{\lambda^2 t}{1 + \lambda t}$, $\lambda/2$

  11. 0.941

  13. MTTF $= 5/(6\lambda)$, $1/(2\lambda)$

  15. 7

  19. 0.793, 823, 0.00066, 0.0019

  20. 6.06, 1.45, 0.000069, 0.0017

Chapter 8   **1.** 0, $R_X(\tau)(\text{A}^2/2)\cos \omega_0 \tau$, yes

   3. $AP \cos(5W\tau) \sin(W\tau)/2W\tau$

   5. $V^2 e^{-\lambda|\tau|}$ where $\tau = t_2 - t_1$

   7. -3, $R_X(\tau) + 9$, 15, $R_X(\tau)$

   9. $a^2 S_X(\omega) + b^2 S_Y(\omega)$

  11. kW/π

  13. 3.82

  14. 1.988

  15. $\dfrac{60}{\omega^2 + 4} + 18\pi\delta(\omega)$

  17. $1.013\omega_M$, $250 \cos\left(\dfrac{\pi(\omega \pm \omega_0)}{2\omega_M}\right)$, $10.13\omega_M$

  19. 750π, $900 < |\omega| < 1100$, otherwise zero

  21. 6.46×10^{-19} V^2/radians per second, 3.59×10^{-7} V

  23. 3.69, 1.51, 0.067

  31. 15.20

  33. $\dfrac{112\omega^2}{\omega^4 + 10\omega^2 + 9}$

  35. $\dfrac{6}{\omega^4 + 13\omega^2 + 36}$

INDEX

◆ ◆